ELECTRICAL MACHINERY

ELECTRICAL MACHINERY

PRINCIPLES, OPERATION AND MANAGEMENT

BY

TERRELL CROFT

CONSULTING ELECTRICAL ENGINEER

AUTHOR OF AMERICAN ELECTRICIANS' HANDBOOK, WIRING OF
FINISHED BUILDINGS, WIRING FOR LIGHT AND POWER, ETC.,

FIRST EDITION

NINTH IMPRESSION

McGRAW-HILL BOOK COMPANY, Inc.

239 WEST 39TH STREET. NEW YORK

LONDON: HILL PUBLISHING CO., Ltd.

6 & 8 BOUVERIE ST., E. C.

1917

THE MAPLE PRESS YORK PA

PREFACE

It has been the author's experience that there are certain things which it is necessary and desirable for the average man to know about electrical machinery—and it is entirely possible to transmit this essential information without the use of difficult mathematics. Furthermore, there are a great many more things about electrical machines which (though they may be interesting) it is not necessary that the average man should know.

In preparing this "Electrical Machinery" book we have endeavored to include the essential and desirable things and to omit the non-essentials. We have tried to explain the theoretical principles and outline the operating facts, relating to alternating-current and direct-current generators and motors, and similar electrical machines, on this basis. Control apparatus has been given due attention. Furthermore, we believe that any individual who can read English will be able to get the meat from this volume without the expenditure of excessive effort.

Following out the general idea above disclosed, much of the material has to do with installation and operation—trouble location, its correction and the like. There is practically nothing in here on design because of two splendid reasons: (1) The manufacturers in this United States design, build and sell perfectly good electrical apparatus much more effectively and economically than can any one who is not regularly engaged in the business. Hence, when the average man wants electrical equipment he buys it on the market. (2) It requires a lot of special knowledge and mathematics to design electrical machinery.

Summarizing: "Electrical Machinery" is a manual of explanation of basic theoretical principles, operation and management prepared particularly to assist the average man who is now, or who expects sometime to be, engaged in practical electrical work.

We want to make this a better and more helpful book each time it is revised in the future. Therefore, if any reader finds in it anything which he cannot understand, will he please write the author about it? Also, if you find any errors—some errors always, regardless of how carefully the checking has been done, creep into every technical book—please advise us; they will be corrected in the next edition. Finally, we will be most grateful for all suggestions for the future enlargement or improvement of the book, in any manner whatsoever.

TERRELL CROFT.

33 AMHERST AVENUE, UNIVERSITY CITY,
    SAINT LOUIS, MISSOURI,
        June, 1917.

ACKNOWLEDGMENTS

The author desires to acknowledge the assistance which has been rendered by a number of concerns and individuals in the preparation of this book.

Considerable of the material appeared originally as articles in certain trade and technical periodicals among which are: *Practical Engineer, The National Electrical Contractor, Power, Southern Engineer, Electrical Review and Western Electrician, Railway Electrical Engineer, Electrical Age and The Power Plant.* Credit for this prior publication is hereby accorded.

Among the concerns which coöperated in supplying text data and material for illustrations are: *The Ridgway Dynamo & Engine Company, The Lincoln Electric Company, The Westinghouse Electric & Manufacturing Company, The Triumph Electric Company, The Electric Machinery Company, The General Electric Company, The Reliance Electric & Engineering Company, The Gurney Ball Bearing Company.* Special acknowledgment is accorded to the *Wagner Electric & Manufacturing Company* for permission to incorporate in this book the substance of the material, relating to generator and motor testing, from its publication, *A Manual of Electrical Testing.*

Mr. H. Weichsel, Chief Designer, Wagner Electric and Manufacturing Company, collaborated with the author in the preparation of the information about single-phase motors. This material originally appeared as two articles in *Electrical Review and Western Electrician* for May 12th and 19th, 1917. Mr. A. C. Lanier, Chairman, Department of Electrical Engineering, University of Missouri, Columbia, Mo., furnished some data concerning the compensated direct-current generator. S. C. Wagner, Superintendent of Distribution, Electric

Company of Missouri, read the galley and page proofs, called attention to a number of errors and suggested numerous improvements.

Other acknowledgments have been made throughout the book. If any has been omitted it has been through oversight and if brought to the author's attention it will be incorporated in the next edition.

CONTENTS

PAGE

PREFACE   v

SECTION 1

Principles, Construction and Characteristics of Direct-Current Generators and Motors   1

SECTION 2

Management of Direct-Current Generators 50

SECTION 3

Management of and Starting and Controlling Devices for Direct-Current Motors 70

SECTION 4

Troubles of Direct-Current Generators and Motors 105

SECTION 5

Testing of Direct-Current Generators and Motors 148

SECTION 6

Principles, Construction and Characteristics of Alternating-Current Generators 157

SECTION 7

Management of Alternating-Current Generators. 178

SECTION 8

Principles, Construction and Characteristics of Induction and Repulsion Motors 190

SECTION 9

PAGE

Synchronous Motors and Condensers. 229

SECTION 10

Management of, and Starting and Controlling Devices for Alternating-
Current Motors 239

SECTION 11

Troubles of Alternating-Current Generators and Motors 263

SECTION 12

Testing of Alternating-Current Generators and Motors 276

SECTION 13

Test Determination of Motor-Drive Power Requirements. 288

SECTION 14

Motor Generators and Frequency Changes 301

INDEX 305

ELECTRICAL MACHINERY

SECTION 1

PRINCIPLES, CONSTRUCTION AND CHARACTERISTICS OF DIRECT-CURRENT GENERATORS AND MOTORS

1. An Electrical Generator or Dynamo* is a machine for converting mechanical power into electrical power. A generator develops an e.m.f. by cutting lines of force and this e.m.f. forces a current to flow provided the external circuit is closed.

2. Performance Specifications are furnished by the manufacturers of generators to prospective customers which indicate the efficiencies, temperature rise, etc., of any generator that may be under consideration. These specifications show what may be expected of the machine in service and should be thoroughly studied by the buyer.

3. Voltage Regulation (do not confuse with speed regulation) is the ratio of the *change* of voltage, between *"no load"* and *"full load,"* to the *full-load voltage.* It is usually expressed as a percentage. Thus, the speed of the machine remaining constant:

$$(1) \ \ Voltage \ regulation = \frac{no\text{-}load \ voltage \ - \ full\text{-}load \ voltage}{full\text{-}load \ voltage}.$$

By regulation is always meant some change which a machine makes of its own accord when the load is changed. This change is inherent in the machine and is determined by its construction.

4. Control always means some change which an attendant brings about in a machine, as, for instance, the raising of the voltage by cutting resistance out of the field circuit.

* A. I. E. E. STANDARDIZATION RULE No. 101, June 28, 1916.

5. Direct-current Generators develop a direct or continuous
e.m.f., that is, one that is always in the same direction.   Commercial direct-current generators have commutators and may
thereby be distinguished from modern alternating-current
machines.   Additional information in regard to commutation
as applied to direct-current motors, which is in general true for
direct-current generators, is given hereinafter.

6. Excitation of Generator Fields.—To generate an e.m.f.,
conductors must cut a magnetic field which in commercial
machines must be relatively strong.   A permanent magnet
can be used for producing such a field in a generator of small
output, such as a telephone magneto or a generator for sparking for an automobile; but for generators for light and power
the field is produced by electromagnets, which may be excited
by the machine itself or "separately excited" from another
source.

7. Series-wound or Constant-current Generators have
their armature coils, field coils and external circuits in series

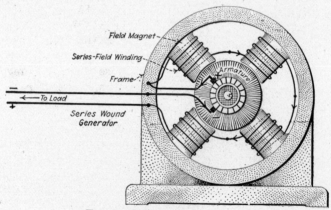

Fig. 1.—Series-wound generator.

with one another.   See Fig. 1.   Series generators are now used
commercially only for series arc-lighting circuits and are
equipped with automatic regulators (Fig. 2) to maintain the
current constant, irrespective of the resistance of the external
circuit, or the number of lamps in service.   The same current

passes through each lamp in the series and through the generator.   The voltage at the brushes of a series machine is equal to (neglecting a small line loss) the voltage per lamp times the number of lamps.   Thus on a circuit of 100 lamps each requiring 50 volts the brush pressure would be $100 \times 50 = 5,000$ *volts*.   As shown by the graph of Fig. 3, II, up to a certain maximum value

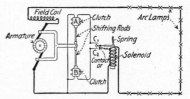

Fig. 2.—Essentials of brush-shifting mechanism for a constant-current generator.

with an increase in load—resistance in this case—the voltage of the generator increases, tending to maintain the current

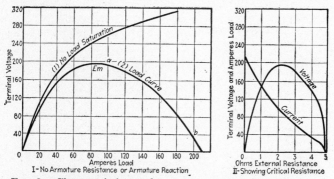

I-No Armature Resistance or Armature Reaction.

II-Showing Critical Resistance

Fig. 3.—Characteristic graphs or curves of a series generator.

(The graph No. 1 of I indicates the relation between voltage and current if there is no armature resistance or armature reaction.   Hence, this is actually a no-load saturation graph of the machine.   It is determined by separately exciting the field coils so that no current flows in the armature.   Graph No. 2 shows the actual relation between terminal voltage and load current.   The total voltage drop consists of that portion due to the decrease in flux caused by armature reaction and that required to send the current through the armature, brushes and series coils.

In the graph of II the values of current in a series generator and the resistance of the external circuit are plotted.   The critical resistance of this particular machine is 4.9 ohms.   With an external resistance greater than 4.9 ohms, the machine will not excite itself or "build up".)

constant.   Automatic regulation to maintain constant current is usually effected, commercially, by either shifting the brushes or by cutting in and out portions of the field winding or by a combination of the two methods.

NOTE.—A graph is a line representing graphically the relation between two quantities which vary simultaneously. Graphs were formerly called *curves*.

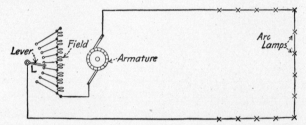

FIG 4.—Regulation of an arc-lamp machine by field variation.

8. The Essentials of an Arrangement for Regulation by Brush Shifting are shown in Fig. 2. (By regulation in this case is meant the maintenance of a constant current.) The course of the main current is indicated by the heavy line.

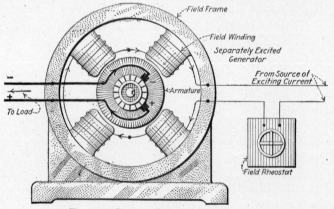

FIG. 5.—Separately-excited generator.

When the current is at normal value the *contactor* is held midway between the contacts C_1 and C_2 by the spring. If the current increases slightly, the core is pulled down into the *solenoid* and brings the *contactor* with it, which makes contact with C_2. This permits a small current in shunt with the solenoid to flow through the *clutch B*, the mechanical details of which are not shown.   This *clutch* pulls the *shifting rod* down and so shifts the brushes as to tend to maintain the current at a constant value.   A decrease in current allows the

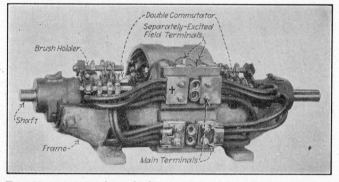

FIG. 6.—A separately-excited generator with a double commutator for electrolytic work.   (General Electric Co., 5 kw., 6 or 12 volts, 835 or 415 amp., 1150 r.p.m.)

spring to pull the *contactor* against C_1; *clutch A* operates and the brushes are shifted in the opposite direction.

9. The Principle of an Arc-light (Constant-current) Machine That is Regulated by Field Variation is illustrated in Fig. 4. The *lever L* is shifted automatically and cuts in or out turns of the field magnet so as to maintain a constant current in the external circuit.

10. Separately Excited Generators are used for electroplating and for other electrolytic work where it is essential that the polarity of a machine be not reversed.   Self-excited machines may change their polarities.   The essential diagrams are shown in Fig. 5.   The fields may be excited from any direct-current, constant-potential source, such as a storage battery or lighting circuit.

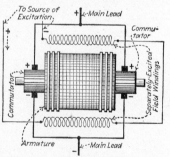

FIG. 7.—Showing connections for a double-commutator on a separately-excited generator.

The field magnets can be wound for any voltage because they have no electrical connection with the armature. With a constant field excitation, the voltage will drop slightly from no-load to full-load because of armature drop and armature

FIG. 8.—A double-commutator armature for a low-voltage "electrolytic" generator.

reaction. Inasmuch as the machines of this type (Fig. 6) used in electrolytic and electroplating work may carry exceedingly large currents, they are frequently provided with two commutators as shown in Figs. 7 and 8 so that the current may

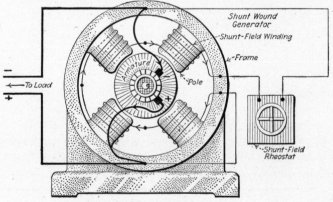

FIG. 9.—Shunt-wound generator.

be carried jointly by the two commutators. That is, each commutator should carry one-half of the total current output of the machine.

11. The Shunt-wound Generator is shown diagrammatically in Fig. 9. Shunt generators are now seldom used. They

have been largely superseded by compound-wound machines.
The exciting current, a small part of the total current, is
shunted through the fields. The exciting current varies from
possibly 5 per cent. of the total current in small machines to
1 per cent. in large ones. The exciting current is determined
by the voltage at the brushes and the resistance of the field
winding. Residual magnetism in the field cores permits a
shunt generator to "build up." This small amount of magnetism that is retained in the field cores induces a voltage in
the armature.* This voltage sends a slight current through
the field coils which increases the magnetization. Thus, the
induced voltage in the armature is increased. This in turn
increases the current in the fields, which still further increases

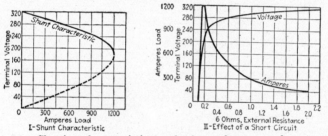

FIG. 10.—Showing characteristic graphs for a shunt-wound generator.

the magnetization, and so on, until the saturation point and
normal voltage of the machine are reached. This "building
up" action is the same for any self-excited generator and
often requires 20 to 30 seconds.

12. When a Shunt Generator Runs at Constant Speed,
as more and more current is drawn from the generator, the
voltage across the brushes falls slightly. This fall is due to
the fact that it requires more and more of the generated
voltage to force this increasing current through the windings
of the armature. That is, the armature IR drop increases.
This leaves a smaller part of the total e.m.f. for brush e.m.f.
Then when the brush pressure falls there is a slight decrease
in the field current, which is determined by the brush pressure.
This causes the total e.m.f. to drop a little, which still further

* ELEMENTS OF ELECTRICITY, W. H. Timbie.

lowers the brush potential. These two causes combine to gradually lower the brush pressure (voltage) especially at heavy overloads. The curve in Fig. 10 shows these characteristics. For small loads the curve is nearly horizontal, but at heavy overloads it shows a decided drop. The point where the output of a commercial machine drops off is beyond the operating range and is only of theoretical interest.

13. The Voltage of a Shunt Machine May be Kept Fairly Constant by providing extra resistance, R, in the field circuit, see Fig. 11, which may be cut out as the brush potential falls. This will allow more current to flow through the field coils and increase the number of magnetic lines set up in the magnetic circuit. If the speed is maintained constant, the armature conductors cut through the stronger magnetic field at the same speed, and thus induce a greater e.m.f. and restore the brush potential to its former value. This resistance may be cut out either automatically or by hand.

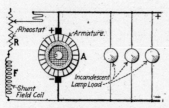

Fig. 11.—Elementary circuit of a shunt-wound generator and load.

14. A Shunt-wound Generator Normally Gives a Fairly Constant Voltage even with varying loads, and can be used for incandescent lighting and other constant-potential loads. These generators do not operate well in parallel, partially because the voltage of one machine may rise above that of the others and it will run them as motors. Shunt generators running in parallel do not "divide the load" satisfactorily between themselves. They are seldom installed now, as compound-wound generators are more satisfactory for most purposes. Shunt generators may be bipolar (two poles) or multipolar (more than two poles) as may compound-wound generators. See the following Arts.

15. The Compound-wound Generator is shown diagrammatically in Fig. 12. If a series winding be added to a shunt generator (Fig. 9) the two windings will tend to maintain a constant voltage as the load increases. The magnetization due to the series windings increases as the line current increases, which will cause the voltage generated by the armature to rise. The drop of voltage at the brushes that occurs in a

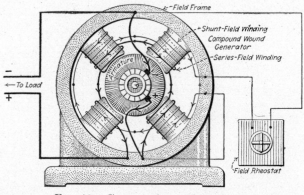

Fig. 12.—Compound-wound generator.

shunt generator is thus compensated for. See also Fig. 13 and Art. 76.

16. A Flat-compounded Compound-wound Generator is one having its series coils so proportioned that the voltage (**Fig. 15**) remains practically constant at all loads within its range.

17. An Over-compounded Generator has its series windings so proportioned that its full-load voltage (Fig. 14) is greater than its no-load voltage. Over-compounding is necessary where it is desirable to maintain a practically-constant voltage at some point out on the line distant from

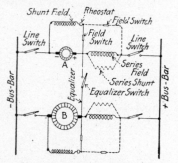

Fig. 13.—Elementary connections for parallel operation of compound-wound generator.

the generator. It compensates for line drop.

18. The Characteristic Curve of a Compound-wound Machine (Fig. 15) indicates how the terminal voltage is due to the action of both shunt and series windings. The voltage of the compound generator at any load (AD) is equal to the sum of the voltage due to shunt winding (AC) plus that due to the series winding (AB). Generators are usually over-compounded so that the full-load voltage is from 5 to 10 per cent. greater than the no-load voltage. See Fig. 14.

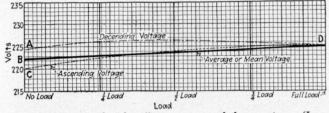

Fig. 14.—Voltage graphs of an "over-compounded generator. (In practice most compound-wound generators are thus over-compounded.)

Although compound-wound generators are usually provided with a field rheostat, it is not intended for regulating voltage as the rheostat of a shunt-wound machine is. It is provided to permit of initial adjustment of voltage and to compensate for changes of the resistance of the shunt winding caused by

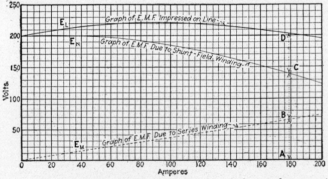

Fig. 15.—Characteristic graph for a compound-wound generator. (This graph is from a flat compound machine.)

heating. With a compound-wound generator, the voltage having been once adjusted, the series coils automatically strengthen the magnetic field as the load increases. For direct-current power and lighting work, compound-wound generators are used almost universally.

19. If a Compound-wound Generator is Short-circuited the field strength due to the series windings will be greatly increased, but the field due to the shunt winding will lose its strength.   For the instant or so, that the shunt magnetization is diminishing, a heavy current will flow.   If the shunt magnetization is a considerable proportion of the total magnetization, the current will decrease after the heavy rush and little harm will be done if the armature has successfully withstood the heavy rush.   However, if the series magnetization is quite strong in proportion to the shunt, their combined effect may so magnetize the fields that the armature will be burnt out.

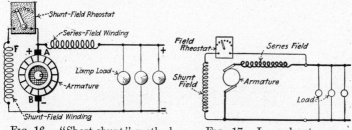

FIG. 16.—"Short-shunt" method of connecting a compound-wound generator.

FIG. 17.—Long-shunt compound-wound generator.

20. A Short-shunt Compound-wound Generator (Fig. 16) has its shunt field, F, connected directly across the brushes, A and B.   Generators are usually connected in this way because it tends to maintain the shunt-field current more nearly constant on variable loads, as the drop in the series winding does not directly affect the voltage impressed on the shunt field.

21. A Long-shunt Generator has its shunt-field winding connected across the terminals of the generator.   See Fig. 17.

22. The Compounding of a Direct-current Generator Will Change with Its Speed* because the location of the no-load, normal-voltage point (A, Fig. 18) on the magnetization graph is determined by the speed.   Thus consider the following example:

---

* Gordon Fox in ELECTRICAL REVIEW AND WESTERN ELECTRICIAN.

EXAMPLE.—Point *A* (Fig. 18) represents the magnetization corresponding to an e.m.f. of 230 volts without load at 250 r.p.m. The series ampere-turn magnetization is represented by *AB*. The full-load voltage is higher than the no-load voltage by an increment or increase *BC*, which represents the amount of overcompounding. Assume that the generator speed is increased to 275 r.p.m. The no-load e.m.f. corresponding to 230 volts at the terminals would now be about 10 per cent. lower because the speed has been increased 10 per cent. This point is at *D*. The number of series ampere-turns at full-load is the same shown as before, the distance *DE* (equal to *AB*) representing this magnetizing influence.

The over-compounding is here shown by the increment *EF*. It will be noted that the distance *EF* is considerably greater than *BC*. This means that the generator will over-compound to a greater degree when

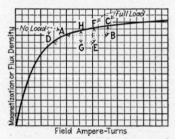

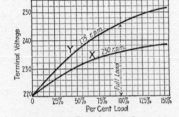

FIG. 18.—Magnetization graph of a 220-volt direct-current generator normally operating at 250 r.p.m.

FIG. 19.—Graphs for the same generator showing voltage regulation at different speeds.

operated at 275 r.p.m. than when driven at 250 r.p.m., other conditions being unchanged. The distance *EF* does not represent the voltage rise accurately. It represents the increase in magnetic density from no-load to full-load. An equal increase in magnetic density will cause a greater increase in voltage at 275 r.p.m. than at 250 r.p.m. Hence, the rise in voltage at the increased speed is, in reality, greater than is indicated on the graph.

23. The Voltage Regulation for the Same Generator Operating at Two Different Speeds* is shown by the graphs of Fig. 19. The curve, *X*, for the generator operating at 250 r.p.m. is here similar to *AC* of Fig. 18. This curve is not strictly accurate, as engine regulation, armature reaction and internal resistance tend to cause the voltage to decrease with

* Gordon Fox in ELECTRICAL REVIEW AND WESTERN ELECTRICIAN.

load.   The increase in terminal voltage due to over-compounding, renders the shunt-field influence greater under full-load conditions.   This latter factor about offsets those first mentioned, leaving the curve, as shown, nearly unchanged. The curve, *Y*, showing the voltage regulation of the generator when driven at 275 r.p.m., is obtained from the portion *DF* in Fig. 18.   The values have been modified, however, by increasing the magnetic density increments, such as *EF*, by the ratio 275 : 250 to correct for increase in speed.

24. The Portion of the Magnetization Curve Over Which a Generator Operates Determines the Contour of its Voltage-regulation Curve,[*] and this may materially affect parallel

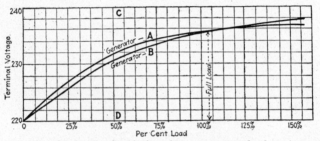

Fig. 20.—Graphs showing regulation of two generators both compounded to impress the same voltage at full load.

operation.   In Fig. 20 are shown two voltage-regulation curves of two generators having equal voltage rise from no-load to full-load.   They are both equally over-compounded.   But, at fractional loads, for instance at half-load, *CD*, there is considerable difference in terminal voltage.   If these two generators were connected in parallel, machine *A* would take a greater share of the load at half-load.   To secure correct load division over the entire operating range, two or more generators must have compounding curves which are similar.   From what has preceded it is evident that by adjustments of prime-mover speed it is possible to modify the compounding curves so as to improve the load division.

[*] Gordon Fox in ELECTRICAL REVIEW AND WESTERN ELECTRICIAN.

25. Speed Changes Have an Effect on the Temperature of a Generator.* When operating at increased speeds the iron is worked lightly, hence core losses are low. The increase in

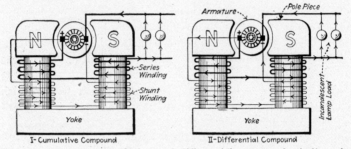

Fig. 21.—Showing cumulative and differential-compound windings for direct-current generators and motors.

windage and ventilation also tends toward cooler operation. When the machine is operated below normal speed, it will tend to run warmer. The shunt-field coils in particular will

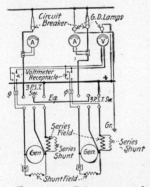

Fig. 22.—Diagram of connections of two compound-wound generators to switch-board (Westinghouse).

be affected, since more shunt ampere-turns are required to secure the desired no-load voltage.

26. Differential and Cumulative-compound Windings for direct-current motors and generators are illustrated diagrammatically in Fig. 21. With a machine which is wound differentially the shunt and series fields oppose each other (*II*), and as the load increases, the electromagnetic field due to the series winding would increase correspondingly and "overcome" the field due to the shunt winding. This would tend to change the direction of the magnetic field in the air gap and reverse the direction of the e.m.f. of a generator or the direction of rotation of a motor. Where machines are "cumulative-compound" wound, as at *I*, the

---

* Gordon Fox in ELECTRICAL REVIEW AND WESTERN ELECTRICIAN.

series and shunt-field windings "assist" instead of "oppose" each other.

27. A Series Shunt for a Compound-wound Generator consists of a low-resistance conductor arranged across the terminals of the series field (see Figs. 13 and 22) by means of which the compounding effect of the series winding may be regulated by shunting more or less of the armature current past the series coils. The series shunt may be in the form of grids, on large machines, or for smaller generators in the form of ribbon resistors. In the latter case the resistors are usually insulated and folded into small compass.

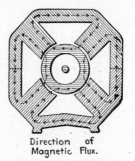

Direction   of
Magnetic Flux.

FIG. 23.—Magnetic circuits of a four-pole generator.

28. Nearly All Commercial Direct-current Generators and Motors Have More Than Two Poles.—In some of the preceding diagrams only two were shown so that the diagrams would be simple. A two-pole machine is a bipolar machine; one having more than two poles is a multipolar machine. Fig. 23 shows the direction of the magnetic flux of a four-pole machine. Dia-

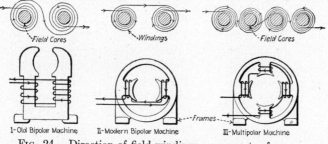

FIG. 24.—Direction of field windings on generator frames.

grams for machines having more poles would be similar. In multipolar machines there is usually one pair of brush sets for each pair of poles, but with series-wound armatures, such as are frequently used for railway, automobile and crane motors, one set of brushes may suffice for a multipolar machine. The connections of different makes of machines vary in detail and the manufacturers will always furnish complete diagrams, so no attempt will be made to give them here. The directions of the field windings on generator frames are given in Fig. 24. The directions of the windings on machines having more than four poles are similar, in general, to those of the four-pole machines.

29. Direct-current Generators May be Classified Into: (1) Non-commutating Pole; (2) Commutating Pole; and (3) Compensated, as regards their commutating characteristics. In non-commutating-pole generators no special provision is made to insure the existence of a flux to produce sparkless

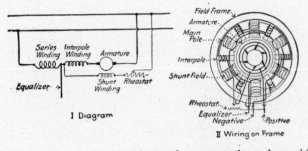

Fig. 25.—Diagram of compound-wound commutating-pole machines.

commutation—except that this condition may be partially realized by shifting the brushes of the machine. With commutating-pole generators the auxiliary poles produce a flux at such a location that it will—as hereinafter described—practically eliminate brush sparking. The compensated generator (Art. 37), in addition to having commutating poles, has conductors to neutralize the effect of armature reaction, imbedded in the main pole faces.

30. Commutating-pole Generators and Motors, Fig. 25.*— The principal advantage of the commutating-pole construction resides in the fact that with it the commutation can be rendered practically perfect under any condition of service.

* STANDARD HANDBOOK.

31. The Object in Using the Commutating Poles* is to
produce within the armature coil under commutation an e.m.f.
of the proper value and sign to reverse the current in the coil
while it is yet under the brush—a result that is essential to
perfect commutation.   The variation in the flux distribution
in the air gap of a commercial direct-current machine of the
ordinary shunt-wound type, at no-load and under full-load,
is shown in Fig. 26.   Consider now the value and position
of the flux in the coil under the brush when the machine is
operating at full-load.   The motion of the armature through
this flux causes the generation within the coil of an e.m.f.,
and the sign of this e.m.f. is such as to tend to cause the
current in the coil to continue
in the direction which it had
before the coil reached the
brush, and hence it opposes
the desired reversal of the current before the coil leaves the
brush.

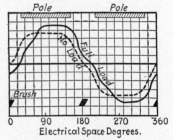
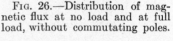

FIG. 26.—Distribution of magnetic flux at no load and at full
load, without commutating poles.

There is an additional detrimental influence which tends to
retard the rapid reversal of the
current even when all other in-
fluences are absent.   This
latter influence is due to the local magnetizing effect of the
current in the coil under the brush.   On account of this, lines
of force surround the conductor, the change in the intensity
of which lines, with the fluctuations of the current as it tends
to be reversed, generates in the coil an e.m.f. which opposes
the change in the intensity of the current.   This reactive
e.m.f. is in the same direction as that due to the cutting of
the flux by the coil under the brush and is likewise proportional to the speed.

It will be apparent that even were the field distortion completely neutralized, the detrimental reactive e.m.f. would yet
remain.   The improved and practically perfect commutation
of a commutating-pole machine is due to the fact that the

* WESTINGHOUSE PUBLICATION.

2

flux, which is locally superposed upon the main field, not only counterbalances the undesirable main flux cut by the coil under the brush, but it causes to be generated within the coil an e.m.f. sufficient to equal and oppose the reactive e.m.f. just referred to. This effect will be appreciated from a study of Fig. 27, which represents the distorted flux of the motor of the usual design, as shown in Fig. 26, and indicates the results to be expected when the flux due to the auxiliary or commutating pole is given the relatively proper value.

The effect of the commutating poles is the more pronounced the weaker the main field; and the commutation voltage thereby induced if correct for a low speed, is correct for a high speed. With increase of load-current and main-field distortion there is a proportional increase of counter-magnetizing field produced in the coil under the brush, up to the point of magnetic saturation of the auxiliary or commutating pole. Sparkless operation is insured for all operating ranges both of speed and load.

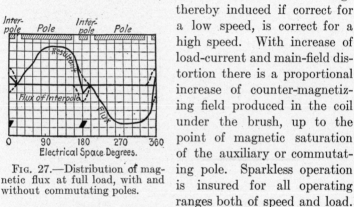

Fig. 27.—Distribution of magnetic flux at full load, with and without commutating poles.

32. Commutating-pole, Direct-current Generators are similar in construction and operation to commutating-pole motors. Ordinary generators* that operate under severe overloads and over a wide speed range are liable to spark under the brushes at the extreme overloads and at higher speeds. This is because the field due to the armature current distorts the main field to such an extent that the coils being commutated under the brush are no longer in a magnetic field of the proper direction and strength. To overcome this, "interpoles" (Figs. 28 and 29) are placed between the main poles. See Fig. 25. These commutating poles introduce a magnetic field of such direction and strength as to maintain the magnetic field, at the point where the coils are commutated, at the proper strength for

* Westinghouse Elec. & Manfg. Co.

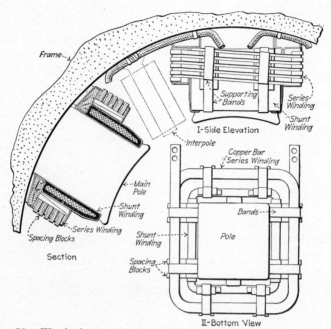

FIG. 28.—Westinghouse method of constructing main poles for medium and large direct-current generators.

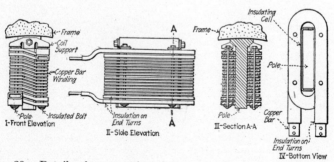

FIG. 29.—Details of construction of a commutating pole on a Westinghouse generator.

perfect commutation. Commutating poles are sometimes called "interpoles" but *"commutating poles"* is the preferable term.

33. The Winding of the Commutating Poles is connected in series with the armature so that the strength of the corrosive commutating-pole field is proportional to the load. The adjustment and operation of commutating-pole generators is not materially different from that of non-commutating-pole machines.

34. When the Brush Position of a Commutating-pole Machine Has Once Been Properly Fixed, No Shifting is Afterward Required or should be made, and most of these gen-

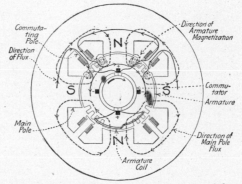

Fig. 30.—Distribution of flux in a commutating-pole generator.

erators are shipped without any shifting device. An arrangement for securely clamping the brush-holder rings to the field frame is provided.

35. In Commutating-pole Apparatus Accurate Initial Adjustment of the Brush Position is Necessary.—The correct brush position is on the no-load neutral point, which is located by the manufacturer. A templet is furnished with each machine, or some other provision is made whereby the correct brush location can be determined by the installer. If the brushes are given a backward lead on a commutating-pole generator, the machine will over-compound and will not commutate properly. With a forward lead of the brushes, a

generator will under-compound and will not commutate
properly.

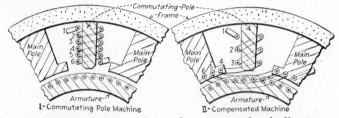

Fig. 31.—Showing commutating and compensated pole direct-current
generators.

**36. The Action of the Magnetic Flux in a Commutating-pole
Generator** is illustrated in Fig. 30.   The direction of the main
field flux is shown by the dashed line.   The direction of the

armature magnetization is
shown by the dotted lines.
The direction of the flux in the
interpole is shown by the full
line. It is evident that the
interpole flux is in a direction
opposite to that of the armature flux, and as the interpole
coil is more powerful in its
magnetizing action than the
armature coils, the flux of the
armature coils is neutralized.
With a less powerful magnetizing force from the interpole
than from the armature, the
armature would overpower the
interpole and reverse the direction of the flux, which would
result in an unsatisfactory
commutating condition.

Fig. 32.—Portion of the stator
of a "compensated." Direct-current generator showing magnetizing conductors embedded in the
main-pole faces.

37. The Compensated Generator* has, by virtue of its compensated winding which is located in the main pole faces

* See article "The Compensated Generator" by David Hall in Practical Engineer
for Sept. 15, 1916.

(Figs. 31 and 32), the property within itself of compensating armature reaction. That is, it neutralizes the magnetizing effect of the armature winding. In the compensated machine, conductors in series with the armature winding are also imbedded in the main pole faces, as suggested in the illustration. With the conductors thus located in the pole faces, the effect of armature magnetization and the distortion of flux incident thereto may be more effectively "neutralized" than with commutating poles alone.

NOTE.—It should be noted* that the commutating-pole machine and the compensated machine are distinct forms. The compensating winding and the commutating poles may or may not be combined in the same machine. That is, a "compensated," direct-current motor or generator may be designed without commutating poles. It is, however, the almost-universal practice in designing modern direct-current machines to provide a commutating pole and winding or to provide a central tooth with heavy excitation to generate commutating flux over the commutation zone regardless of whether or not a compensating winding is used.

The compensating windings are, in general, particularly desirable only for machines in which the voltage between commutator bars is, for some reason or other, relatively great. Hence, they are applied to high-voltage machines or to machines which, due to severe operating conditions, would be subjected to excessive voltage between the commutator bars under the pole tip. Without compensation, the coils connecting to such bars would, at the instant of commutation, be cutting a magnetic field of high density because of armature reaction. Furthermore, the increase in iron losses, in the armature teeth, at full load over their no-load losses, which results from flux distortion is, in non-commutating-pole machines, largely eliminated by the use of the compensating winding. This, in certain cases, may render it possible to dispose the active material in the armature somewhat more economically in compensated machines than would be possible in machines of the non-compensated types.

38. Three-wire Direct-current Generators† are ordinary direct-current generators (Figs. 33, 34 and 35) with the modifications and additions (Fig. 36) described below. They are usually wound for 125–250-volt three-wire circuits. In Westinghouse three-wire generators four equidistant taps

---

* A. C. LANIER.

† Westinghouse Elec. & Manfg. Co.

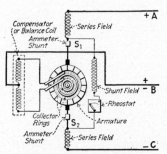

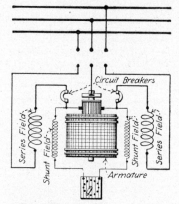

Fig. 33.—Diagram of a three-wire generator showing connections for shunt and series coils and balance coil.

Fig. 34.—Another type of three-wire generator operating independently.

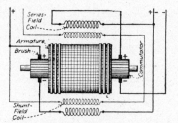

Fig. 35.—A double-commutator, single-armature, three-wire generator (125 volts per commutator).

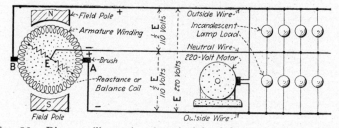

Fig. 36.—Diagram illustrating the principle of the three-wire generator.

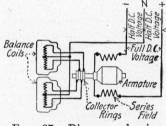

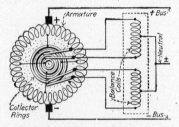

FIG. 37.—Diagram showing connections for three-wire generator.

FIG. 38.—Showing fundamental connections for a Westinghouse three-wire generator.

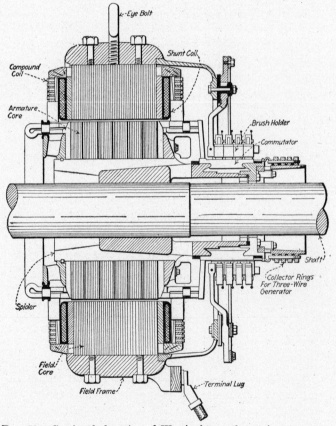

FIG. 39.—Sectional elevation of Westinghouse three-wire generator.

are made in the armature winding, and each pair of taps diametrically opposite each other is connected together through a balance coil. See Figs. 37 and 38. The middle points of the two balance coils are connected together and this junction constitutes the neutral point to which the third or neutral wire of the system is connected. A constant voltage is maintained between the neutral and outside wires which, within narrow limits (Fig. 36) is one-half the generator voltage. The generator shaft is extended at the commutator end for the collector rings (Fig. 39).

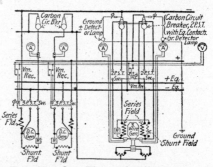

FIG. 40.—One Three-wire direct-current generator, 125–250 volts in parallel with two two-wire generators, 125 volts. Diagram of connections.

Four collector brushes and brush holders are used in addition to the regular direct-current brushes and brush holders.

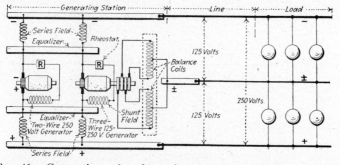

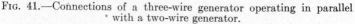

FIG. 41.—Connections of a three-wire generator operating in parallel with a two-wire generator.

39. The Series Coils of Compound-wound Three-wire Generators Are Divided into Halves (see Figs. 40 and 41), one of which is connected to the positive and one to the negative side. This is done to obtain compounding on either side of the system when operating on an unbalanced load. To understand this, consider a generator with the series field in the negative side only and with most of the load on the positive side of the system. The current flows from the positive brush through the load and back through the neutral wire without passing through the series field. The generator is then operating as an ordinary shunt machine. If most of the load be on the negative side, the current flows out the neutral wire and back through the series fields, boosting the voltage on that side only. Such operation is evidently not satisfactory, and so the divided series fields are provided.

40. Wires Connecting the Balance Coils to a Three-wire Generator must be short and of low resistance. Any considerable resistance in these will affect the voltage regulation. The unbalanced current flows along these connections; consequently, if they have much resistance, the resulting drop in voltage reduces the voltage on the heavily loaded side.

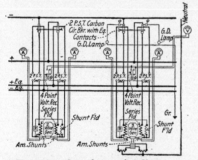

FIG. 42.—One three-wire direct current generator, 125–150 volts, in parallel with one two-wire generator, 250 volts. Diagram of connections.

41. Switches Are Not Ordinarily Placed in the Circuits Connecting the Collector Rings to the Balance Coils.— When necessary, the coils may be disconnected from the generator by raising the brushes from the collector rings. Switching arrangements often make it necessary to run the balance-coil connections to the switchboard and back. This necessitates heavy leads to keep the drop low. If heavy leads are not used, then poor regulation may result. The balance coils are so constructed that there is very little likelihood of anything happening to them that will not be taken care of by the main circuit-breakers. Complete switchboard connection diagrams are given in Figs. 40, 42 and

43.   Fig. 44 shows a simplified diagram of two three-wire generators arranged for parallel operation.

42. Commutating-pole, Three-wire Generator Connections (Fig. 45) are so made that one-half of the commutating-pole winding is in the positive side and the other half is in

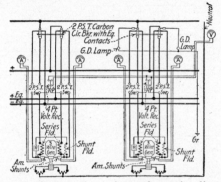

Fig. 43.—Diagram of connections of two three-wire direct-current generators operating in parallel, 125–250 volts.

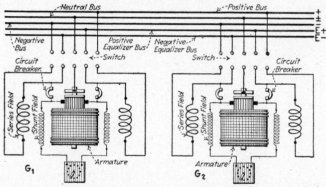

Fig. 44.—Two three-wire generators (of the type having the balance coil mounted in and rotating with the armature) connected for parallel operation.

the negative side.   This insures proper action of the interpoles at unbalanced load.   See Figs. 40, 42 and 43 and the text accompanying them.

43. The Sources of the Losses in Direct-current Motors and Generators are (Fig. 46):   (1) The resistance of cir-

cuits carrying current, including those of the armature,
field coils, interpoles and brush contact; (2) hysteresis and

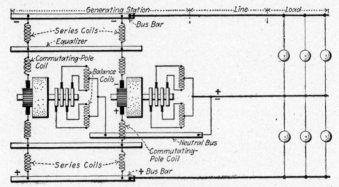

Fig. 45.—Connections for the parallel operation of two commutating-
pole, three-wire generators.

eddy currents in the armature-core structure; (3) friction,

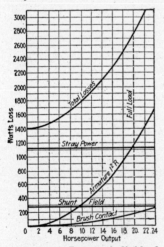

Fig. 46.—Losses, individual
and total, in a 20 h.p., 220-
volt, direct-current motor, or
in an equivalent generator.

including that of the commutator and bearings, and windage,
or the friction produced by the
rotation of the armature in the
air.

**44. Performance Data for
Standard Compound-wound
Direct-current, Commutating-
pole Generators** will be found
tabulated in the author's
American Electrician's Handbook. The efficiencies at various loads, and the current outputs at the different standard
voltages for machines of the
standard capacities are there
given.

**45. The Performance Guar-
antees on Direct-current Gen-
erators** for reciprocating engine drive are still made on the
so-called "normal" basis described hereinunder. It is not

improbable that all direct-current generators will ultimately be rated on the continuous basis (Art. 47*a*). These normally rated direct-current generators are usually guaranteed to operate continuously at their full-rated (nameplate) kilowatt outputs with a temperature rise not to exceed 40 deg. C. and furthermore they will operate at an overload of 25 per cent. above their normal or nominal ratings for two hours with a temperature rise not to exceed 55 deg. C. Direct-current generators for turbine drive are also rated on the normal basis and will deliver continuously their rated kw. outputs with a 45-deg. C. rise and have an overload capacity of 25 per cent. for two hours, with a rise not to exceed 55 deg. These rises are now all based on an ambient (Art 47*b*) temperature of 25 deg. C.*

46. Performance Data for Direct-current Motors will be found tabulated in the author's American Electrician's Handbook. The current inputs and efficiencies of machines of different capacities and voltages are there shown.

47. Performance Guarantees on Direct-current Motors are now usually made on the so-called "normal" basis. However, it is probable that all motors made in this country will shortly be rated on the continuous (Art. 47*a*) basis. The normal rating usually given these motors specifies that they will operate continuously at their rated (nameplate) horse-power outputs with a temperature rise not to exceed 40 deg. C. and that they will operate at a 25 per cent. overload for two hours with a temperature rise not to exceed 55 deg. C. The above rises are now based on an ambient (Art. 47*b*) temperature of 25 deg. C.*

47a. Continuous Rating.†—A machine thus rated shall be able to operate continuously at rated output, without exceeding the limitations referred to in *Std. Rule* No. 260.

NOTE.—*Rule* 260 is: "To insure satisfactory results, electrical machinery should be specified to conform to the *Institute Standardization*

* Note, from Art. 47*b*, that 25 deg. C., though it is now used by practically all manufacturers for d. c. machines is not the standard recommended by the A. I. E. E. It is probable that the standard 40 deg. ambient temperature will ultimately be adopted universally.

† A. I. E. E. Standardization Rules.

Rules, in order that it shall comply, in operation, with approved limitations in the following respects, so far as they are applicable: (*a*) Operating temperature, (*b*) Mechanical strength. (*c*) Commutation. (*d*) Dielectric strength. (*e*) Insulation resistance. (*f*) Efficiency. (*g*) Power factor. (*h*) Wave shape. (*i*) Regulation.

47b. The Ambient Temperature * is the temperature of the air or water which, coming into contact with the heated parts of a machine, carries off its heat. (See Arts. 47 and 256.)

NOTE.—For water-cooled machinery, the standard temperature of reference for incoming cooling water shall be 25° C* (77 deg. F), measured at the intake of the machine. "The standard* ambient temperature of reference for air shall be 40 deg. C (104 deg. F)."

48. To Compute the Kilowatt Output, or the Current, or Voltage of any Direct-current Generator, it is merely necessary to remember that the product of *current* × *voltage* = *watts* and that there are 1,000 watts in a kilowatt. Thus:

$$(2) \qquad kw._0 = \frac{E \times I}{1,000} \qquad \text{(kilowatts)}$$

$$(3) \qquad E = \frac{kw._0 \times 1,000}{I} \qquad \text{(volts)}$$

$$(4) \qquad I = \frac{kw._0 \times 1,000}{E} \qquad \text{(amperes)}$$

Wherein, $kw._0$ = the power output of the generator, in kilowatts. E = the e.m.f., in volts, which the generator impresses at its terminals on the line. I = the current impelled by the generator, in amperes.

EXAMPLE.—What is the kilowatt output of a direct-current generator when it is impressing 500 volts on its external circuit and impelling a current of 124 amp.? SOLUTION.—Substitute in equation (2): $kw._0 = (E \times I) \div 1,000 = (500 \times 124) \div 1,000 = 62$ kw.

EXAMPLE.—A certain 220-volt direct-current generator has a full-load rating of 50 kw. What is the full-load current of this machine? SOLUTION.—Substitute in equation (4): $I = (kw._0 \times 1,000) \div E = (50 \times 1,000) \div 220 = 227$ amp.

49. To Compute, for a Direct-current Generator, Either the Horse-power Input, the Kilowatt Output or the Efficiency when the Values for Any Two of these Quantities are

* A. I. E. E. Standardization Rules, December 1916.

Known (it being remembered that there are 746 watts in a horse-power) the following formulas may be used:

(5) $$h.p._i = \frac{kw._o}{\mathbf{E} \times 0.746}$$ (horse-power)

(6) $$kw._o = h.p._i \times \mathbf{E} \times 0.746$$ (kilowatts)

(7) $$\mathbf{E} = \frac{kw._o}{h.p._i \times 0.746}$$ (efficiency)

Wherein, all of the symbols have the same meanings as in Art. 50 except that $kw._o$ = the output in kilowatts of the generator.

EXAMPLE.—If a direct-current generator delivering 400 kw. has at that load an efficiency of 87 per cent., what horse-power is then required to drive the machine? SOLUTION.—Substitute in equation (5): $h.p._i = kw._o \div (\mathbf{E} \times 0.746) = 400 \div (0.87 \times 0.746) = 400 \div 0.65 = 615.4$ h.p.

50. To Compute, for a Direct-current Generator, Either the Horse-power Required to Drive it, its Voltage, Current or Efficiency when the Value of only One of these Quantities is not Known, one of the following formulas may be used:

(8) $$h.p._i = \frac{E \times I}{\mathbf{E} \times 746}$$ (horse-power)

(9) $$E = \frac{h.p._i \times \mathbf{E} \times 746}{I}$$ (volts)

(10) $$I = \frac{h.p._i \times \mathbf{E} \times 746}{E}$$ (amperes)

(11) $$\mathbf{E} = \frac{E \times I}{h.p._i \times 746}$$ (efficiency)

Wherein, $h.p._i$ = the input of the generator in horse-power. E = the e.m.f., in volts, impressed by the generator on the external circuit. I = the current impelled in the external circuit by the generator. $\mathbf{E}$ = the efficiency of the generator expressed decimally.

EXAMPLE.—What horse-power would be required at the pulley, *P*, of the direct-current, 220-volt generator shown in Fig. 47, when the machine was delivering 300 amp., assuming that its efficiency at this load is 90 per cent.? SOLUTION.—Substitute in equation (8): $h.p._i = (E \times I) \div (\mathbf{E} \times 746) = (220 \times 300) \div (0.90 \times 746) = 66,000 \div 671.4 = 98.3$ h.p. That is, under these conditions, 98.3 h.p. would have to be delivered at the pulley, *P*, to pull the load.

EXAMPLE.—What will be the efficiency of a 220-volt, direct-current generator, if, when it is delivering a current of 108 amp. it requires 37.5 h.p. at the pulley of the generator to drive it? SOLUTION.—Substitute in equation (11): $E = (E \times I) \div (h.p._i \times 746) = 23,760 \div 27,975 = 0.849$ or, say, 85 per cent.

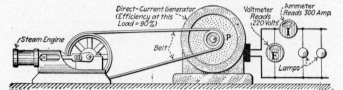
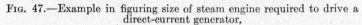

FIG. 47.—Example in figuring size of steam engine required to drive a direct-current generator.

51. To Find the Size Engine Required to Drive a Direct-current Generator first compute the horse-power necessary to drive the machine at full-load by using equation (8). Then, select the engine of such a capacity that it will drive the generator, the overload capacity of the engine and the generator, if there is such, being considered in each case. If the generator is rated on the maximum or continuous basis, due allowance must be made for this in selecting the engine. If the generator is to be belt-driven an allowance for a power loss of from 2 to 5 per cent. in the belt drive should also be made.

NOTE.—For a direct-current generator, $0.746 \times$ *engine brake horse-power = the kilowatt capacity of the engine*, which would be the power input, in kilowatts, to the generator. Multiplying this quantity by the assumed efficiency of the generator will give the kilowatts output of the generator. Where this generator efficiency is not known it may be assumed to be 90 per cent., which is an average value. Thus, for a working approximation: $0.90 \times 0.746 \times$ *brake horse-power = the kilowatt rating of generator*. A complete table of the efficiencies of direct-current generators of various capacities will be found in the author's AMERICAN ELECTRICIAN'S HANDBOOK. In the discussion immediately preceding, it has been assumed that the brake horse-power of the engine in question is known. If it is not, a sufficiently accurate expression for brake horse-power may be obtained by multiplying the indicated horse-power of the engine by its efficiency, an average value for which may be taken as 90 per cent.

EXAMPLE.—What size internal-combustion engine, that is, gas, gasoline or oil engine, should be used to drive the 50-kw. normally rated, direct-current generator shown in Fig. 48? SOLUTION.—Normally rated generators usually have an overload capacity of 25 per cent. for two hours. Hence, the maximum power that this machine could develop for any considerable length of time would be: 50 $kw. \times 1.25$ = 62.5 $kw.$ Now, from equation (5), $h.p._i = kw._o \div (E \times 0.746)$ = $62.5 \div (0.84 \times 0.746) = 99.6$ h.p. That is, 99.6 h.p. would be required in mechanical power at the generator pulley, to produce 62.5 kw. of electrical power at the generator terminals. Assuming a belt

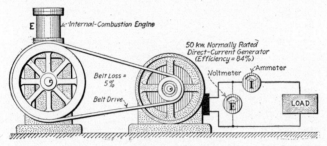

FIG. 48.—Example in computing size of gas-engine required to drive a direct-current generator.

loss of 5 per cent. there would be required at the engine flywheel: 99.6 $h.p. \times 1.05 = 104.6$ $h.p.$ Hence the engine, E, should have a rating of at least 104.6 h.p. if the full capacity of the generator is to be developed. Normally, combustion engines have little, if any, overload capacity. In practice, a 100-h.p. internal-combustion engine would probably be used for the application in this discussion.

EXAMPLE.—If the generator shown in Fig. 47 had a normal full-load rating of 100 kw. and an efficiency of 90 per cent., there would be required to drive it at full-load: 100 $kw. \div 0.90 = 111$ $kw.$ Now, the horse-power equivalent of 111 $kw.$ is: 111 $kw. \div 0.746 = 149$ $h.p.$ Then, if a belt loss of 3 per cent. be assumed, the engine would have to develop, when full-load is on the generator, 149 $h.p. \div 0.97 = 154$ $h.p.$ That is, an engine rated at about 154 brake horse-power should be used to drive this machine. The overload capacity of a steam engine, as engines are usually rated, is about equivalent to the overload capacity of a normally rated, direct-current generator.

52. Direct-current Motors are of the same construction as direct-current generators having the same types of windings. That is, the construction of a shunt-wound motor is the same as that of a shunt-wound generator, a compound wound motor the same as a compound-wound generator, and so on. In fact, the electrical machinery manufacturers frequently use precisely the same direct-current machines for generators as for motors, merely changing the nameplates on them, as occasion requires, before shipping them. Hence, it follows that much of the information relating to direct-current generators given in the preceding pages will apply directly to direct-current motors.

53. Performance Data for Direct-current Motors (standard efficiencies, ratings, speeds and similar information) will be found tabulated in the author's AMERICAN ELECTRICIAN'S HANDBOOK.

54. The Output or Horse-power of a Direct-current Motor, or any other motor for that matter, is proportional to the product of its torque and its speed.

55. The Torque of a Direct-current Motor is proportional to its effective magnetic field, the number of armature conductors, and the current or amperes flowing in the armature.

56. The Speed of a Direct-current Motor is proportional to the following ratio:—[(*voltage impressed on motor terminals*) — (*volts drop due to armature-circuit resistance*)] ÷ [(*number of armature conductors*) × (*effective magnetic field*)].

57. Commutation of Direct-current Motors.—Before commutating-pole motors were manufactured, commutation determined the overload capacity of direct-current motors. A modern commutating-pole motor will carry 100 to 125 per cent. overload, that is, 2 to 2.25 times the normal or full-load without sparking. The heating of the machine under load is now a more important factor than formerly

58. Direct-current Motors of the Series, Shunt and Compound Types Have Different Speed Characteristics. *—That is, as the load on an unloaded motor is increased, its speed may decrease slowly or rapidly or remain practically constant, depending on how the motor is wound (series, shunt or compound) and on its design. Motors of all types should develop

---

* See article, "Speed Characteristics of Direct-current Motors," Alan M. Bennett, POWER, Jan. 26, 1915.

their rated speeds at full-load after they have been in operation for a sufficient period to attain their maximum full-load
temperatures, hence the term "speed of a motor" means the
full-load speed under these conditions. Variations from the
rated speed may be conveniently considered at two periods
in the operation of the motor, namely: (1) at the time the
motor is started cold; and (2) at no-load, but after the motor
has attained its working temperature. The amount by which
the speed under the first condition differs from the rated speed
is known as the *speed variation* of the motor. It is sometimes
referred to as the variation from "cold to hot" at full-load.
The change from rated speed at no-load, but at working temperature, that is, the difference between full-load speed and
no-load speed, is known as the *speed regulation* of the motor.

Speed regulation is usually
expressed as a percentage of
the full-load speed. For each
condition the departure from
rated speed is expressed as a
percentage of the rated speed.
As would be inferred, both the
speed variation and the regulation may differ for motors
of the same general class and
the same rating because these
characteristics are determined
by the designs of the ma-
chines. See Fig. 49. It can
be shown that the speed of a
motor varies *directly as the
impressed voltage minus the I*

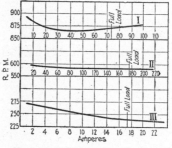

Fig. 49.—Graphs showing speed
characteristics of shunt motors of
different designs. Curve I from a
20-h.p. four pole, 230-volt, 900
r.p.m. Motor. Curve II from a
50-h.p. four-pole, 230-volt, 575
r.p.m. motor. Curve III from a
4-h.p. four-pole, 230-volt, 235
r.p.m. motor. (*Electric Journal.*)

× *R drop in the armature circuit and inversely as the flux.*
In this expression, *I* = the armature current, and *R* = the
resistance of the motor windings and the brush contacts
which are in series with the armature. It follows that any
condition affecting the operation of a motor which tends to
increase either this *I* × *R* drop or the flux, will lower the
speed of the motor. Conversely, a decrease in either flux or

$I \times R$ drop will raise the speed.   How this $I \times R$ drop and
the flux vary in motors with series, shunt and compound wind-

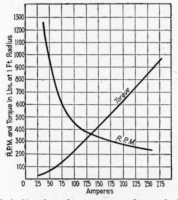

Fig. 50.—Graph indicating the torque and speed characteristics of a
series-wound direct-current motor.   (A 37.5 h.p., 4-pole, 230-volt, 540
r.p.m. machine.)

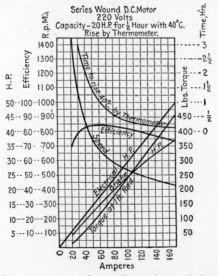

Fig. 51.—Performance curves for a direct-current series-wound motor.

ings, and thereby affect the speed, and why they vary in machines with these different types of windings will be briefly

discussed in following articles. Speed variation and control of series-, shunt-, and compound-wound motors are further treated in Arts. 121, 124, and 125.

59. The Speed-torque Characteristics of a Series-wound Direct-current Motor are shown graphically by the graph of Fig. 50. It will be noted that the speed decreases rapidly as the load on (amperes taken by) the motor increases. Furthermore, the torque developed by the motor increases as the current increases. The significance of these graphs is further explained in the example following Art. 61, which discusses the graphs of Fig. 51; see also the comparative graphs, A, B, C and D, of Fig. 52.

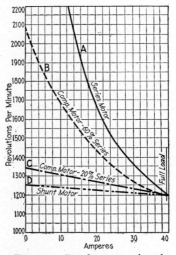

FIG. 52.—Graphs comparing the speed-load characteristics of 10 h.p. shunt, series- and compound-wound, direct-current motors.

Some of the variation in the speed of a series motor is due to the $I \times R$ drop in its brush contacts, armature and series winding. However, most of the variation is due to the fact that the flux—which is generated by the series-field winding which carries line current—increases almost directly with the load. The $I \times R$ drop increases somewhat because R, the resistance of the armature, remains practically constant but I, which with a series motor is the line current, increases directly with the load. The fact that as the motor is loaded its windings become hotter and hence have a higher resistance than at no-load, also has the same effect. Hence, this heat effect would tend to increase the $I \times R$ drop and lower the speed, but in practice it is of little consequence.

Note that with the series motor the increase of temperature has an ultimate effect opposite to that which obtains with a

shunt motor (Art. 63), for which increased temperature results in increased speed.   The speed variation in an average
series motor due to increased temperature is, at full-load,
approximately 2 per cent.   This is almost negligible, especially
as compared with the change in speed of the motor due to
the change in its series-field current—or load.   While the
change in speed produced by the $I \times R$ drop due to a change
of load is greater with a series than with a shunt motor (because as the load increases, the $I \times R$ drop in the series-field
exciting winding is increased), it is small as compared with
the change in speed due to flux variation.   In fact it can be
shown that the speed of a series motor, particularly when it
is operating below the saturation point of the field, will vary
almost exactly inversely with the change of flux.   This proves
that the $I \times R$ drop is of little consequence.   Fig. 52 shows
graphically how much more rapidly the speed of a series motor
changes with the load than does that of a shunt or lightly
compounded motor.

**60. Theoretically, a Series Motor Will Run at an Infinite
Speed when Pulling No-load.**—Practically, one of these machines if connected across a source of constant e.m.f. and
operated without a load will "speed up" until it bursts its
armature band wires and throws the armature winding out
of the slots by centrifugal force.   That is, unloaded series
motors "run away."

**61. The Method of Reading Direct-current, Series-wound,
Motor Performance Graphs*** is illustrated by Fig. 51.   To
determine the nominal full-load characteristics of a motor having the curves illustrated, proceed as follows:

EXAMPLE.—First find the point at which the brake horse-power curve
intersects the 20-h.p. horizontal line (20 h.p. being the nominal rating
of the motor).   This point is on the 80-amp. vertical line.   The characteristics of the motor at nominal full-load will be those denoted by
the curves at the points where the 80-amp. vertical line intersects them.
Thus the motor will take 80 amp.; the torque will be 175 lb. at 1-ft.
radius; the speed will be about 600 r.p.m.; the efficiency 84 per cent.; and
it will take 35 min. continuous operation for the motor temperature
to rise to 40 deg. C.

   * WESTINGHOUSE PUBLICATION.

If the motor is, for example, required to develop 250 lb. torque, its characteristics under this condition are found in a similar manner, the proper ampere vertical line being that which intersects the point where the 250-lb. torque horizontal line and the torque curve intersect—in this case 105 amp.

An inspection of the curves shows that the torque is maximum at starting and decreases as the speed increases. The higher the torque, the greater the current required and the more rapidly the motor temperature will rise. Moreover it is evident that the rating of 20 h.p. for this motor is arbitrary only. This rating is based on the power developed with a temperature rise of 40 deg. C. in one-half hour's continuous operation; if the motor is operated continuously for periods of one hour, it could not be conservatively rated above 15 h.p., while if the periods of operation are very short and intervals of rest long, a rating of higher than 20 h.p. would be satisfactory.

62. The Proper Connections for a Shunt Motor are as shown in Fig. 53. The field B is connected as shown, so that, when the main switch D is closed, it becomes excited before the armature circuit switch at E is closed. Thus, when the motor

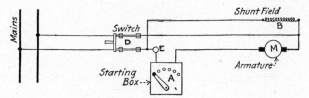

FIG. 53.—Control apparatus connections for a shunt motor.

armature has current admitted to it by the closing of switch at E and by the operation of starting rheostat A, the field is already on, and the full torque of the motor is thereby obtained at starting. The torque of a motor is equal to the product of flux per pole, the ampere-turns on the armature, and the number of poles. Hence, if the full field is not on the motor at the instant of starting, full torque will not be obtained at that instant. See also Figs. 83, 86, and 104 for connections for starting equipment for direct-current shunt motors.

63. The Speed Characteristic for a Shunt Motor is shown in Fig. 54. See also Fig. 55. It will be noted that the speed remains almost constant from no-load to full-load and that the torque increases almost directly with the load. With a shunt motor on a constant-potential circuit, since the shunt-field winding, Fig. 9, is connected directly across the constant-voltage supply source, the main flux remains almost constant at all loads. However, as the motor heats, the resistance of the shunt-field winding will increase, which decreases correspond-

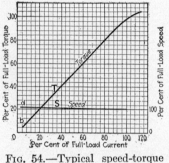

FIG. 54.—Typical speed-torque graph of a shunt-wound motor.

ingly the shunt-field exciting current and the main flux. But this flux is decreased slightly, which tends to make the

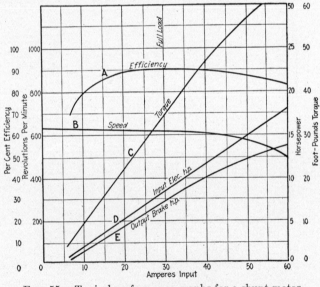

FIG. 55.—Typical performance graphs for a shunt motor.

motor "speed up." Tests show that the speed increase due to increase in temperature of the shunt-field winding is, from "cold to hot" at full-load, from 4 to 8 per cent. for commercial motors.   But this tendency toward an increase in speed, due to increased resistance of the field winding, has little effect in practice because the $I \times R$ drop in the motor armature as the load comes on the motor more than offsets its temperature effect.   Obviously, as the load on the motor increases, the $I \times R$ drop in the armature circuit increases in proportion and it is due to this that the speed of a shunt motor decreases from no-load to full-load as shown in Figs. 54 and 52.   Tests indicate that the speed regulation of shunt motors as they are ordinarily manufactured ranges from about 4 to 6 per cent.

64. By Shifting the Brushes the Tendency of a Shunt Motor to Decrease in Speed as its Load Increases can be Partially Offset in non-commutating pole motors.   The reverse is also true.   To effect this result, the brushes should be shifted "backward."   By this procedure, a portion of the flux due to the armature ampere-turns is caused to oppose the main flux.   This weakens the main flux with the result that the speed of the motor is increased. However, brush shifting can be utilized to increase the speed of a motor only within the limits wherein sparking at the commutator will not be excessive.

65. The Speed Regulation of a Commutating-pole Shunt Motor is affected by the action of the commutating poles. These commutating poles produce a weakening effect on the

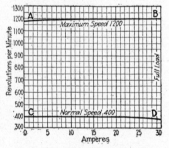

Fig. 56.—Speed graphs for a 7½-h.p., commutating-pole, adjustable-speed shunt motor.

main-field flux similar to that produced by the current in the armature.   The result may be an increase in the speed with the load (Fig. 56).   This effect is particularly noticeable with adjustable-speed motors when they are being operated at high speeds—that is, with weak fields.   Then, due to the action of commutating poles, a motor may rotate at a higher speed at full-load than at no-load, as shown at *AB*,

Fig. 56. In commutating-pole motors, brush shifting is not feasible, hence, even if it were necessary, this expedient could not be utilized to maintain the motor speed constant. In the graph of Fig. 56, it will be noted that the motor has a normal speed of 400 r.p.m. which can be, by means of shunt-field control, increased to 1,200 r.p.m. At the normal speed, CD, the regulation is within $1\frac{1}{2}$ per cent., the speed remaining practically constant. At the higher speed, AB, the revolutions per minute actually increase about 2 per cent. or 25 r.p.m. from no-load to full-load.

66. The Speed Characteristics of Shunt Motors of Different Designs are shown in Fig. 49, from which it is evident that the properties, in so far as speed is concerned, of the shunt motor may be subject to considerable variation in machines of various designs.

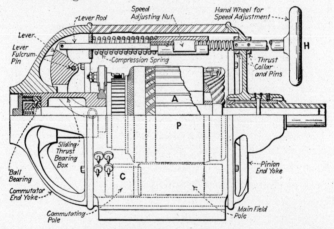

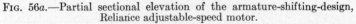

Fig. 56a.—Partial sectional elevation of the armature-shifting-design, Reliance adjustable-speed motor.

66a. The Reliance Adjustable-speed Motor employs a novel method of varying the field which the armature inductors cut whereby the speed of the motor is changed. Typical designs for a motor of this type are shown in Figs. 56a and 56b. The motor is, in essence, as shown in Fig. 56a, a shunt-wound, direct-current, commutating-pole motor of the usual design. However, there are these important differences: (1)

The armature, *A*, together with its shaft, may be shifted longitudinally by a handwheel, *H*, so that the armature may be made to lie wholly or only partially, at the will of the operator, under the influence of the main-field-pole (*P*) flux. (2) The commutating poles, *C* (Fig. 56*a*) are located at the commutator ends of the main poles.

When the handwheel, *H*, is turned to such a position that the armature lies wholly between the main poles then the armature

Fig. 56*b*.—Reliance adjustable-speed motor, type *AS* armature-shifting design.   (Reliance Electric & Engineering Co., Cleveland, Ohio.)

inductors are cutting a maximum of flux and the motor will rotate at its slowest speed.   But, if the handwheel is turned until the armature lies, insofar as it can be made to do so, outside of the influence of the main-field poles, then the armature inductors cut a minimum flux and the armature will rotate at its greatest speed.   Obviously, an infinite number of running speeds between the maximum and minimum are obtainable.   Speed variations of 10 to 1 are, it is claimed, satisfactorily attained in practice.

It is apparent that in a motor of this type the main fields are always saturated because the effective area or cross section of iron which carries flux decreases as the armature is shifted laterally.   The result is that the field distortion is little greater when the armature is rotating at a high speed and carrying full-load current than when it is operating under full-load at low speed with the armature directly under the main poles, where maximum flux cuts its inductors.   A variable-speed motor of this type has a number of attractive features.   Possibly the most important is the simplicity of the entire arrangement and the ease of installation, inasmuch as no speed-adjusting rheostat and the relatively complicated wiring incident thereto is necessary.   Motors of this type are reversible when equipped with reversing type starters.

The motor exhibits the usual adjustable-speed, shunt-motor characteristics.   That is, when adjusted for one given speed, it will rotate at that constant speed under a variable load.   The decrease in speed—the motor being adjusted for operation at some certain speed—from no-load to full-load is said to be very small and to compare favorably with that of the best constant-speed-motor practice.   The United States Government, American Steel & Wire Co., Illinois Steel Co., Pennsylvania Railroad and large users have purchased motors of this type.   It is apparent that they are well adapted for individual drive for machine tools where an adjustable-speed motor is necessary and it is in this service that they have found their widest application.

67. The Speed Characteristics of a Compound-wound, Direct-current Motor (since a motor of this type has both shunt- and series-field windings) partake of the characteristics of both shunt and series motors.   Fig. 57 shows typical performance graphs of one of these machines.   As is evident from the graphs B and C of Fig. 52, a compound-wound motor may, in so far as the speed characteristics are concerned, be made to resemble a series or shunt motor, depending upon the percentage of the field flux due to the series and the shunt windings, respectively.   The motor of graph B (Fig. 52) has a very poor speed regulation, while that of graph *C* has a fairly good regulation—about 12 per cent.

68. Compound-wound Motors may be Either Differential or Cumulative (Fig. 21) as may compound-wound generators. The cumulative compound-wound motor has its series field so connected that it "assists" the shunt winding. Thus, the main field of a motor of this type is strengthened as the load increases. The result is that some of the properties of a series motor—namely, powerful starting torque and rapid acceleration—are obtained. But when the series winding is

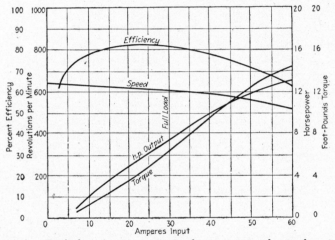

FIG. 57.—Typical performance graphs for a compound-wound motor.

differentially connected (Fig. 21, II), it "opposes" the shunt-field winding. Such an arrangement would tend to compensate for the $I \times R$ drop from no-load to full-load and render the motor a constant-speed machine. That is, as the load increases, the effect of the flux of the shunt field is decreased by the action of the series field. The tendency is then for the speed, instead of decreasing due to the $I \times R$ drop, to remain constant. Differentially wound motors are seldom applied because of operating disadvantages, chief among which are low starting torque and inability to successfully handle overloads.

69. A Comparison of the Speed Characteristics of Shunt, Series- and Compound-wound Motors is given graphically in Fig. 52. This comparison is on the basis of motors of the same general construction and design but having windings of the different types.

70. The Effect of Commutating Poles on the Speed Regulation of Motors.*—At overloads the effect on non-commutating pole motors is a decrease in speed proportional to the load; but on commutating-pole' motors the speed in many cases tends to increase between full-load and 100 per cent. overload. Commutating-pole motors will, therefore, have approximately the same speed at twice full-load as at full-load. If the effect of the commutating poles is too strong, the tendency is to make a commutating-pole motor oscillate in speed. This speed oscillation will cause a similar variation of armature current of gradually increasing intensity, until something gives way; a fuse will blow, a circuit-breaker open or the motor will be injured by "bucking over," that is, flashing across brushes, or burning out the armature.

There is a relation between speed regulation and stability. A commutating-pole motor can be designed to be stable at over-loads. This will increase the drop in speed. Better speed regulation makes stability less certain. Reliable designers of this type of motor strike a happy medium between these two factors and the commercial result is that in most cases these motors can be safely operated on intermittent loads where the maximum load is twice the rated load.

A large reduction in speed, insuring a stable motor, is an advantage in machine-tool applications. It often occurs when long, continuous cuts are taken, that on one part of a casting the depth of cut is greater than on another, due to irregularities in casting. When cutting through the heavy part the speed should be reduced, thus protecting the cutting tools and machine tool as well as the work. For this reason ad-

---

* AMERICAN MACHINIST, Sept. 26, 1912.

71. Classification of Direct-current Adjustable-speed Motors*

Basic principle of speed control	General method	Specific method	Energy supply system
By changing voltage impressed on armature.	Connecting to circuits of different voltages.	Three-wire system, equal voltages. Multiple voltage, three-wire, unequal voltages. Multiple voltage, four-wire system.	Three-wire system, using three wires. Multiple voltage, using three wires. Multiple voltage, using four wires.
	Resistance in armature circuit.		
	Auxiliary motor-generators.	Motor-generator system. Boost-and-retard system. Teaser system.	
By changing field magnetism.	Shunt-field control (by resistance in field circuit).	Standard motors. Compensated motors. Commutating-pole motors.	Single voltage, using two-wires.
	Varying reluctance of magnet-circuit.	Moving poles radially. Moving armature longitudinally.	
	Shunting part of field current.	(Used with series motors.)	
By changing number of conductors in series from brush to brush.	Series-parallel control. Changing number of poles.	(Double-commutator motors.) (Obsolete.)	

* "Adjustable Speed Motors," by A. D. DuBois, ELECTRICAL WORLD, May 18, 1912.

justable-speed motors, with a speed reduction as high as 25 per cent., can be used to advantage.

72. To Compute Either the Kilowatt Input, Horse-power Output, Efficiency, Impressed Voltage or Current of any Direct-current Motor, the other quantities being known, one of the following formulas may be used:

$$(12) \qquad h.p._o = \frac{Kw_i \times E}{74.6} = \frac{E \times I \times E}{74,600} \qquad \text{(horse-power)}$$

$$(13) \qquad E = \frac{h.p._o \times 74.6}{Kw_i} = $$
$$\frac{h.p._o \times 74,600}{E \times I} \qquad \text{(efficiency per cent.)}$$

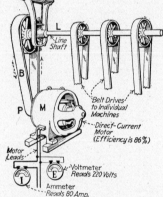

Fig. 58.—Example in computing the horse-power output of a direct-current motor.

$$(14) \qquad Kw_i = \frac{h.p._o \times 74.6}{E} \qquad \text{(kilowatts)}$$

$$(15) \qquad E = \frac{h.p._o \times 74,600}{E \times I} \qquad \text{(volts)}$$

$$(16) \qquad I = \frac{h.p._o \times 74,600}{E \times E} \qquad \text{(amperes)}$$

Wherein, $h.p._o$ = power output of the motor, in horse-power. Kw_i = power input to the motor, in kilowatts. E = efficiency of the motor, in per cent., at the output $h.p._o$. E = the e.m.f. impressed on the motor, in volts. I = the current taken by the motor, in amperes, for the output $h.p._o$.

EXAMPLE.—What horse-power will the direct current-motor, M, of Fig. 58—which has, under the conditions of this example, an efficiency of 86 per cent.—deliver to the line shaft, L, if the e.m.f. impressed across its terminals is 220 volts, and it is taking 80 amp.? Assume that the loss in the belt drive, B, is 3 per cent. SOLUTION.—To ascertain the horse-power delivered by the motor at its pulley, P, substitute in equation (12): $h.p._o = (E \times I \times \mathbf{E}) \div 74,600 = (220 \times 80 \times 86) \div 4,600 = 1,513,600 \div 74,600 = 20.3$ h.p., which is the power delivered at P. Because of the belt loss, the power delivered to the line shaft L, would be 3 per cent. less than this, or, $0.97 \times 20.3 = 19.7$ h.p.

EXAMPLE.—What is the efficiency of the direct-current motor of Fig. 59, under the test conditions there

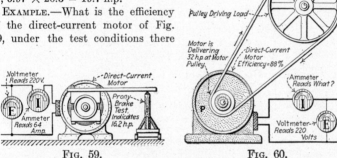

FIG. 59.   FIG. 60.

FIG. 59.—Example in computing the efficiency of a direct-current motor when its horse-power output, its current input and its voltage are known.

FIG. 60.—Example in finding current taken by a motor, its horse-power output, voltage and efficiency being known.

specified? The power output as measured by the Prony brake is 16.2 h.p. The impressed e.m.f. is 220 volts and the current taken by the motor is 64 amp. SOLUTION.—Substitute in equation (13): $\mathbf{E} = (h.p._o \times 74,600) \div (E \times I) = (16.2 \times 74,600) \div (220 \times 64) = 1,208,520 \div 14,080 = 85.8$. Hence, the efficiency of this motor under the conditions illustrated is 85.8 per cent.

EXAMPLE.—What current will be taken by the motor of Fig. 60, it being known that it is delivering 32 h.p. at its pulley, P, that its efficiency at this load is 88 per cent., and that the e.m.f. impressed across its terminals as read by the voltmeter is 220 volts. SOLUTION.—Substitute in equation (16): $I = (h.p._o \times 74,600) \div (\mathbf{E} \times E) = (32 \times 74,600) \div (88 \times 220) = 2,387,200 \div 19,360 = 123.3$ amp. That is, an ammeter, if inserted at I, would read 123.3 amp.

4

MANAGEMENT OF DIRECT-CURRENT GENERATORS

73. To Start a Shunt-wound Generator.*—Note the directions in 76 concerning the oiling arrangements and bringing the machine up to speed. (1) See that the machine is entirely disconnected from the external circuit. This is not always necessary, but is safest. See that the field resistance is all in circuit. (2) Start the armature turning. (3) When the armature has attained speed, cut out field resistance until the voltage of the machine is normal or equal to that on the bus-bars. (4) Close the line switch, watching the ammeter and voltmeter and make further adjustment with the field rheostat if necessary.

74. To Shut Down a Shunt-wound Generator.—(1) Reduce the load insofar as possible by inserting resistance in the shunt-field circuit with the field rheostat. (2) Throw off the load by opening the circuit-breaker, if one is used, otherwise open the feeder switches and finally the main generator switches. (3) Shut down the driving machine. (4) Wipe off all oil and dirt, clean the machine and put it in good order for the next run.

75. Parallel Operation of Shunt Generators.—As suggested in Art. 14 shunt-wound generators do not operate successfully in parallel because they do not divide the load well and the voltage of one is liable to rise above that of another and drive it as a motor. When it is running as a motor its direction of rotation will be the same as when it was generating, hence, the operator must watch the ammeters closely for an indication of this trouble. Shunt generators are now seldom installed and are seldom operated in parallel, although they can sometimes

---

* Westinghouse Elec. & Manfg. Co.

be made to work that way. Where there are several in a plant the best arrangement is to divide the total load between them, giving each its own distinct circuit. Fig. 62 shows the connections for shunt generators that are to be operated in parallel.

76. To Start a Compound-wound Generator.—(1) See that there is enough oil in the bearings, that the oil rings are working, and that all field resistance is cut in. (2) Start the prime mover slowly and permit it to attain normal speed. See that the oil rings are working. (3) When machine is rotating at normal speed, cut out field resistance

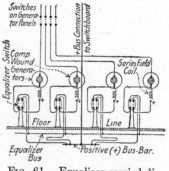

Fig. 61.—Equalizer carried directly between machines.

until voltage of the machine is normal, that is, equal to or a trifle above that on the bus-bars. (4) Throw on the load. If three separate switches are used, as in Figs. 13 and 61, close the equalizer switch first, the series-coil line switch

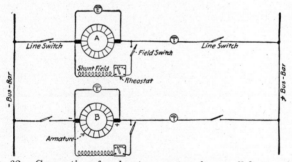

Fig. 62.—Connections for shunt generators for parallel operation.

second, and the other line switch third. If a three-pole switch is used, as in Figs. 22, 63, 64, and 65, all three poles must of course, be closed at the same time. (5) Watch the voltmeter and ammeter and adjust the field rheostat until the machine takes its share of the load. A machine generating the higher voltage will take more than its share of the load and if its voltage is too high it will run the other as a motor.

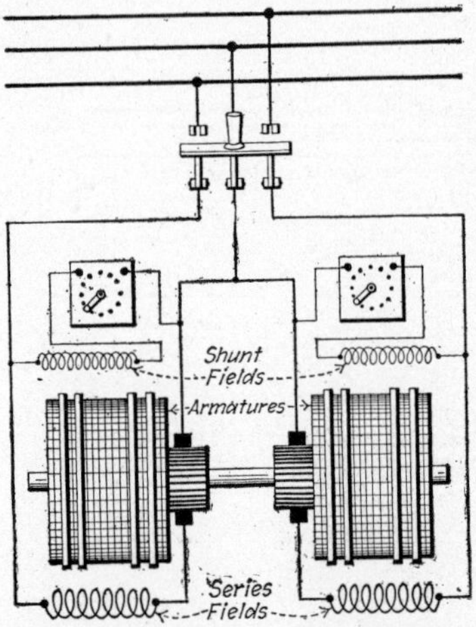

77. To Shut Down a Compound-wound Generator Operating in Parallel with Others.—(1) Reduce the load as much as possible by throwing in resistance with the field rheostat. (2) Throw off the load by opening the circuit-breaker, if one is used, otherwise open the main generator switches. (3) Shut down the driving machine. (4) Wipe off all oil and dirt, clean the machine and put it in good order for the next run. If the machine is operating independently and no motors are connected to the circuit, close the engine throttle valve and permit the engine and generator to come to rest. Turn all resistance in the field rheostat. Open the main switch. Where motors are served they must be disconnected first. If they are not, a loaded motor may stop when the impressed voltage decreases somewhat below normal. Then, since its armature is not turning, it is in effect a short-circuit and may blow fuses or make other trouble.

Fig. 63.—Connections for one unit of two-generators in series serving a three-wire system. (This outfit is not arranged for parallel operation.)

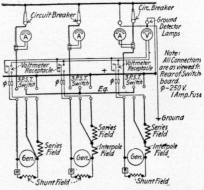

Fig. 64.—Diagram of connections of two direct-current commutating-pole generators in parallel with one generator without commutating poles.

78. In Starting and Shutting Down Three-wire Generators, and two-wire machines serving a three-wire system (diagrams for the parallel operation of which are shown in Figs. 66, 63,

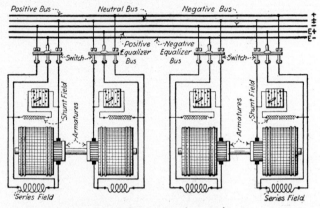

Fig. 65.—Arrangement of two groups of two-wire generators operating in parallel feeding a three-wire system.

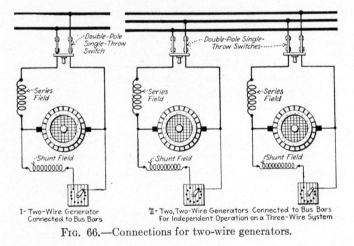

Fig. 66.—Connections for two-wire generators.

44 and 67) the same general procedure is followed as with ordinary two-wire units as above described.

79. Parallel Operation of Compound-wound Generators* is readily effected if the machines are of the same make and

* Westinghouse Elec. & Manfg. Co.

voltage or are designed with similar electrical characteristics. The only change usually required is the addition of an equalizer connection between machines. If the generators have different

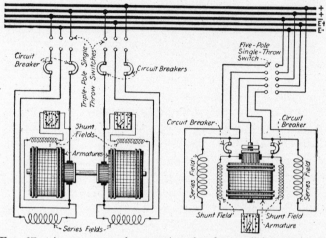

Fig. 67.—Arrangement of connections for the parallel operation on a three-wire system of a three-wire generator and two, two-wire generators in series.

compounding ratios it may be necessary to readjust the series-field shunts to obtain uniform conditions.

80. Testing for Polarity.—When a machine that is to operate in parallel with others is connected to the bus-bars

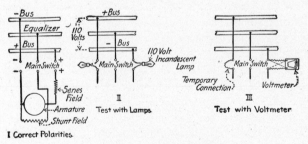

Fig. 68.—Tests for polarity.

for the first time it should be tested for polarity. The + lead of the machine should connect to the + bus-bar

and the − lead to the − bus-bar (Fig. 68, *I*).   The machine
to be tested should be brought up to normal voltage, but
not connected to the bars.   The test can be made with two
lamps (Fig. 68, *II*), each lamp of the voltage of the circuit.
Thus, each is temporarily connected between a machine
terminal and bus terminal of the main switch.   If the lamps
do not burn, the polarity of the new machine is correct,
but if they burn brightly its polarity is incorrect and should
be reversed.   A voltmeter can be used (Fig. 68, *III*).   A
temporary connection is made across one pair of outside terminals and the voltmeter is connected across the other pair.
No deflection or a small deflection indicates correct polarity.
(Test with voltmeter leads one way and then reverse them, as
indicated by the dotted lines.)   A full-scale deflection indicates incorrect polarity.   Use a volt-meter having a voltage
range equal to twice the voltage on the bus-bars.

81. An Equalizer, or Equalizer Connection, connects two
or more generators operating in parallel at a point where the
armature and series-field leads join (see Fig. 13), thus connecting the armatures in multiple and the series coils in multiple, in order that the load will divide between the generators in proportion to their capacities.   The arrangement of
connections to a switchboard* is shown in Fig. 22.   Consider, for example, two compound-wound machines operating
in parallel without an equalizer.   If, for some reason, there
is a slight increase in the speed of one machine, it would
take more than its share of load.   The increased current
flowing through its series field would strengthen the magnetism, raise the voltage, and cause the machine to carry a
still greater amount until it carried the entire load.   Where
equalizers are used, the current flowing through each series coil
is proportional to the resistance of the series-coil circuit and is
independent of the load on any machine; consequently an
increase of voltage on one machine builds up the voltage of
the others at the same time, so that the first machine cannot
take all the load but will continue to share it in proper
proportion with the other generators.

* Westinghouse Elec. & Manfg. Co.

82. Connecting Leads for Compound Generators.—Be certain that all the cables which connect from the various machines to the bus-bars are of equal resistance. This means that if the machines are at different distances from the switchboard, different sizes of wire should be used, or resistance inserted in the low-resistance leads; see Art. 84. With generators of small capacity the equalizer is usually carried to the switchboard, as suggested in Fig. 64, but with larger ones it is carried under the floor directly between the machines (Fig. 61). In some installations the positive and the equalizer switch of each machine are mounted side by side on a pedestal near the generator (Fig. 61). The difference in potential between the two switches is only that due to the small drop in the series coil. The positive bus-bar is carried under the floor near the machines. This permits of leads of minimum length. Leads of equal lengths should be used for generators of equal capacities. If the capacities are unequal (see Art. 84) it may be necessary to loop the leads. See Fig. 61.

83. Ammeters for Compound Generators should, as in Fig. 22, always be inserted in the lead not containing the compound winding. If cut in the compound-winding lead, the current indications will be inaccurate because current from this side of the machine can flow either through the equalizer or the compound-winding lead.

84. To Adjust the Division of Load Between Two Compound-wound Generators.—First adjust the series shunts of both machines so that, as nearly as possible, the voltages of both will be the same at ¼, ½, ¾, and full-load. Then connect the machines in parallel, as suggested in Fig. 13, for trial. If upon loading, one machine takes more than its share of the load (amperes), increase the resistance of the circuit through its series-field-coil path until the load divides between the machines in proportion to their capacities. Only a small increase in resistance is usually necessary. The increase may be provided by inserting a longer conductor between the generator and the bus-bar, or iron or German-silver washers can be inserted under a connection lug. Inasmuch as (when machines are connected in parallel) adjustment of the series-coil shunt affects both machines similarly, the division of load between the two machines cannot be altered by making such adjustment.

85. Operation of a Shunt and a Compound Dynamo in Parallel is not successful because the compound machine will take more than its share of the load unless the shunt machine field rheostat is adjusted at each change in load.

86. Three-wire Direct-current Generators Can be Operated in Multiple* with each other and in multiple with other machines on the three-wire system. See Figs. 40, 41, 42, 43, 44, 45 and 67. When operating a three-wire, 250-volt

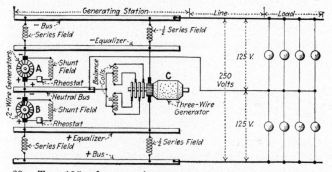

FIG. 69.—Two 125-volt, two-wire generators and one 250-volt three-wire generator connected for parallel operation.

generator in multiple with two two-wire, 125-volt generators (Figs. 40, 67 and 69) the series field of the two two-wire generators must be connected, one in the positive side and one in the negative side of the system, and an equalizer must be run to each machine. Similarly, when operating a three-wire, 250-volt generator in multiple with a 250-volt, two-wire generator (Figs. 41 and 42) the series field of the 250-volt, two-wire generator must be divided and one-half connected to each outside wire. The method of doing this is to disconnect the connectors between the series-field coils and reconnect these coils so that all the north-pole fields

* WESTINGHOUSE PUBLICATION.

will be in series on one side of the three-wire system and all the south-pole fields in series on the other side of the system.

87. The Connections Where Two-wire Generators are Operated to Feed a Three-wire System are, where the units are operated in parallel, shown diagrammatically in Fig. 65. It will be noted that both a positive and a negative equalizer bus are required. Fig. 63 illustrates the connections where only one pair of two-wire generators is utilized to serve a three-wire system and a similar arrangement is shown in Fig. 66, *II*.

88. As There are Two Series Fields, Two Equalizer Buses are Required When Several Three-wire Machines are Installed (see Figs. 40 and 41) and are to be operated in multiple. The two equalizers serve to distribute the load equally between the machines and to prevent cross-current due to differences in voltage on the different generators.

89. An Ammeter Shunt (S_1 and S_2, Fig. 33) is mounted directly on each of the terminal boards of the three-wire machines. The total current output of the machine can thereby be read at the switchboard. As the shunts are at the machine, there is no possibility for current to leak between generator switchboard leads without indicating a reading on the ammeters. Two ammeters must be provided for reading the current in the outside wires. It is important that the current be measured on both sides of the system, for with an ammeter in one side of the system only, it is possible for a large unmeasured current to flow in the other side with disastrous results.

90. Switchboard Connections for Three-wire Generators are shown in principle in preceding illustrations. Fig. 43 is a diagrammatic representation of the switchboard connections for two three-wire generators operated in multiple.* Two ammeters indicate the unbalanced load. The positive lead and equalizer are controlled by a double-pole circuit-breaker; the negative lead and equalizer likewise. Note that both the positive and negative equalizer connections as well as both the positive and negative leads are run to the

*WESTINGHOUSE PUBLICATION.

circuit-breakers in addition to the main switches on the switchboard. It is necessary that this be done in all cases. Otherwise, when two or more machines are running in multiple and the breaker comes out, opening the main circuit to one of them but not breaking its equalizer leads, its ammeter is left connected to the equalizer bus-bars and current is fed into it from the other machines through the equalizer leads, either driving it as a motor or destroying the armature winding. See also Figs. 40 and 42.

91. Commutating-pole Machines Will Run in Multiple with each other and with non-commutating pole machines provided correct connections are made. See illustrations.

The series-field windings on commutating-pole machines are usually less powerful than on non-commutating-pole; and particular attention should, therefore, be paid to insuring the proper drop in accordance with instructions of Art. 84. A connection diagram is shown in Fig. 64.

92. How to Reverse the Direction of Rotation of Direct-current Generators and Motors for a shunt-wound machine is indicated in Fig. 70. Rotation is *clockwise* when, facing the

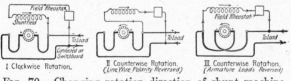

FIG. 70.—Changing rotation direction of shunt machine.

commutator end of a machine, the rotation is in the direction of the hands of a clock. *Counter-clockwise* rotation is the reverse. It is desirable, when changing the direction of rotation, not to reverse the direction of current through the field windings. If it is reversed the magnetism developed by the windings on starting will oppose the residual magnetism and the machine may not "build-up." Connections for reversing compound machines are shown in Fig. 71. A multipolar machine can be reversed as shown by reversing the brushes on the studs and then relocating them on the neutral points.

93. To Reverse the Direction of Rotation of a Commutating-pole Generator (Fig. 25) reverse the shunt and, if there are such, the series fields, as in an ordinary generator. See Figs. 70 and 71.

94. When Starting Up, a Generator May Fail to Excite Itself.*—This may occur even when the generator operated perfectly during the preceding run. Usually this trouble is caused by a loose connection or break in the field circuit, by poor contact at the brushes due to a dirty commutator or perhaps to a fault in the starting box or rheostat, or incorrect position of brushes. Examine all connections; try a temporarily increased pressure on the brushes: look for a broken or burnt-

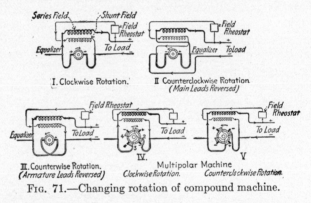

FIG. 71.—Changing rotation of compound machine.

out resistance coil in the rheostat. An open circuit in the field winding may sometimes be traced with the aid of a magneto bell; but this is not an infallible test as some magnetos will not ring through a circuit of such high resistance and reactance even though it be intact. If no open circuit is found in the starting box or in the field winding, the trouble is probably in the armature. But if it be found that nothing is wrong with the connections or the winding it may be necessary to excite the field from another generator or some other outside source as described below.

94a. To Excite a Field from an Outside Source.—Calling the generator it is desired to excite No. 1, and the other ma-

* WESTINGHOUSE INSTRUCTION BOOK.

chine from which current is to be taken No. 2, the following procedure should be followed. Open all switches and
remove all brushes from generator No. 1; connect the positive
brush holder of generator No. 1 with the positive brush holder
of generator No. 2; also connect the negative holders of the
machines together (it is desirable to complete the circuit
through a switch having a fuse
of about 5 amp. capacity in
series). Close the switch.
Where the generator in trouble
is connected to bus-bars fed by
other generators, the same result can be effected by insulating the brushes of the machine
in trouble from their commutator and closing the main
switch. See Fig. 72. If the

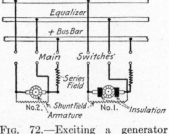

FIG. 72.—Exciting a generator
with an external source of e.m.f.

shunt winding of generator No. 1 is intact its field will show
considerable magnetism. If possible, reduce the voltage of
generator No. 2 before opening the exciting circuit; then
break the connections. If this cannot be done, throw in all
the rheostat resistance of generator No. 1; then open the
switch very slowly, lengthening out the
arc which will be formed until it breaks.

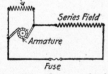

FIG. 73.—One method
of making a compound-
wound generator build
up.

**95. A Simple Means for Getting a
Compound-wound Machine to Pick Up**
is to short-circuit it through a fuse
having approximately the current capacity of the generator. See Fig. 73.
If sufficient current to melt this fuse
is not generated, it is evident that there
is something wrong with the armature,
either a short-circuit or an open circuit. If, however, the fuse
has blown, make one more attempt to get the machine to
excite itself. If it does not pick up, it is evident that something is wrong with the shunt winding or connections.

96. If a New Machine Refuses to Excite and the connections
seem to be all right, reverse the connections, *i.e.*, connect the

wire which normally leads from the positive brush, to the negative brush and the wire which normally leads from the negative brush, to the positive brush.   If this change of connections does not correct the difficulty, change the connections back as they were and locate the fault as previously suggested.

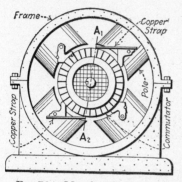

FIG. 74.—Metal-strip brushes in machine which will not excite.

97. Sometimes When a Generator Fails to Excite, tapping the iron of the field structure with a hammer will correct the difficulty. Another method that is often successful is shown in Fig. 74; flat copper strips about ¼ in. wide are held in position by an assistant across the brush-holder studs so that the ends of the strips will contact with the commutator on the line A_1A_2. These strips form a path to the armature which is of much lower resistance than the path through the brushes.   Therefore, when high brush-contact resistance is the difficulty, this expedient is very effective.

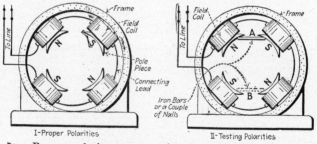

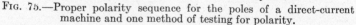

FIG. 75.—Proper polarity sequence for the poles of a direct-current machine and one method of testing for polarity.

98. Polarity of Field Can Be Tested in Two Ways.* (The other "nail" method is described in detail in following Art. 100:—First, by using a compass, bringing it near the various

* Raymond's MOTOR TROUBLES and POWER, July 21, 1914, p. 86.

poles and noting the direction of the deflection of the needle.
Since in all direct-current generators and motors the poles
should alternate in magnetic polarity, Figs. 75 and 76, *I* (in
one pole the magnetism "coming out" and the next "going

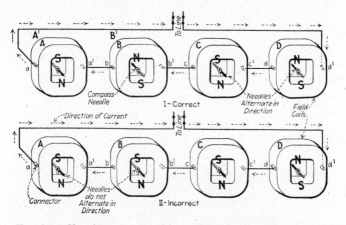

FIG. 76.—Showing correct and incorrect polarities of field coils.

in") it follows that a certain end of a compass needle will
point toward one pole and away from the next when conditions are normal. If, however, two adjacent poles show
similar magnetism, the trouble is located, and the offending
spool should be reversed. This may have to be done by rotating the field coil, on its axis,
through 180° and then recon-
necting it. The mechanical
construction of some coils will
not permit their being turned
end-for-end.

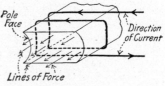

FIG. 77.—Current and magnetization of pole.

**99. Direction of Magnetism
is Determined by the Following Rule.**—"Looking at the
face of an electromagnet (such as the field spool of a motor),
a pole will be north if the current is flowing around it in a
direction opposite to the motion of the hands of a watch," Fig.
77, and south if in the same direction as the motion of the
hands of a watch.

100. Another Method of Determining Whether the Direction of Magnetism of the Poles is Correct is to use two ordinary nails, their lengths depending upon the distance between pole-tips. Instead of using two nails, a piece of iron rod long enough to reach from one pole to another—*A* or *B*, Fig. 75, *II*—may be employed. The point of one nail should touch one pole-tip, the point of the other nail the other pole-tip, and the heads of the nails should touch each other. When the current flows around the field spools, the polarity between any two poles is properly related if the nails placed as suggested stick together by the magnetism or if the iron bar is held strongly between the poles. If there is little or no tendency for the nails or the bar to be

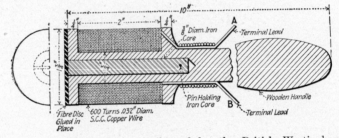

FIG. 78.—A polarity-testing coil used by the British Westinghouse Company.

held to the poles the polarity of the two adjacent poles is the same and therefore wrong.

101. An Inductive Polarity Tester* is shown in Fig. 78. In use the leads *A* and *B* of the coil are connected to a direct-current millivoltmeter. Then, if the coil is moved toward an excited field magnet, the millivoltmeter needle will indicate a momentary deflection in one direction. This direction will change with the polarity of the field coil under test. Usually a greater deflection will be obtained if the testing coil is moved slowly toward the excited field and then quickly withdrawn. If it is withdrawn from a south pole it will move, say to the right. Then if it is withdrawn from a north pole it will move toward the left. Thus, by testing the poles

* ELECTRICAL WORLD, Jan. 9, 1915, p. 102.

around a direct-current machine in rotation it is possible to ascertain whether the connections have been made correctly or incorrectly.   By exercising caution this device can be used with machines which are in operation.   Where a milli-voltmeter is not available a moving-coil ammeter, which has had its shunt disconnected, may be utilized.   Low-reading volt-meters (1 or 3 volts) can be employed provided the test-ing coil is wound with many turns of small-diameter wire.

102. In Placing the Field Coils on a Direct-current Genera-tor or Motor they should be tested, prior to mounting on the machine, to insure that their polarities will alternate as shown in Fig. 76, *I*, around the frame.   Hence, before installation, the coils should be arranged on the floor and connected in series across a source of voltage equal to that which will be im-

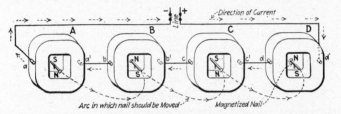

Fig. 79.—Determination of polarities of field coils with a magnetized nail.   (Power, July 21, 1914, p. 86).

pressed on the group of field coils when they are in operation on the machine.   Then, the normal exciting current should be permitted to flow through the coils, and a compass (Fig. 76, *I*) should be held in the core space of each of the coils in succession.   If the coils are correctly arranged, the needle will point alternately north and south in adjacent coils as shown.   But, if the coils are not properly connected the com-pass needle will point in the same direction in adjacent coils, as shown at *A* and *B* in *II*.   Where a coil indicates incorrect polarity it should be turned end for end.   That is, in Fig. 76, *II*, coil *B* should be turned end for end.   If no compass needle is available, a nail, or preferably a short piece of hard-steel wire, may be magnetized and used for a polarity indicator as illustrated in Fig. 79.   Such a piece of metal can be made

5

into a permanent magnet by holding it in the core space of one of the coils. When the coils are properly arranged, the nail or piece of steel wire can be moved from one coil to the other along the curves such as those indicated by the dotted lines in the illustration. In making this test with a nail it is necessary to exercise precaution to insure that the polarity of the nail or wire does not become reversed while the test is being conducted.

103. In Determining the Polarities of Commutating-pole Windings.*—If the armature of a six-pole generator is rotating in a clockwise direction, then the commutating pole which stands in the position corresponding to the 11 o'clock mark of the clock should have the same polarity as the main pole corresponding to the 12 o'clock mark and so on all the way round. On the other hand, each commutating pole of a motor should have the same polarity as the main pole preceding it in the direction of rotation. With a six-pole motor running in a clockwise direction, the commutating pole in the 11 o'clock position should have the same polarity as the main pole in the 10 o'clock position.

103a. Sometimes the Commutating Poles of a Machine Show Correct Polarity When There is a Good Load on the Machine but Behave Irregularly on Light Loads.—This may be due to slight irregularities in the mechanical construction of the machines. If a commutating pole is not in the center of its neighboring poles, but is nearer, say, to the main north pole than to the main south pole, then the commutating-pole tip will show south polarity even if there is no current flowing in its windings. Therefore, with a very light load, the current in a commutating-pole winding, and tending to make the pole, say, a north pole may not be strong enough to overcome the polarity caused by the unequal setting. The same condition will occur if the air gap between the armature and north pole is smaller than that between the armature and south pole.

104. The Management of Brushes on Direct-current Generators is treated under the general heading of brush troubles in Art. 190 and succeeding articles.

* Electrical World, Jan. 9, 1915, p. 102.

105. In Caring for Commutators they should be kept smooth by the occasional use of No. 00 sandpaper.   A small quantity of high-grade, light-body oil may be used as a lubricant.   The lubricant should be applied to high-voltage generators on a piece of cloth attached to the end of a dry stick.   If the commutator becomes "out of true" it should be turned down. By using a special slide rest and tool this can be done while running the engine at a reduced speed without removing the rotating part from the bearings.   Inspect the commutator

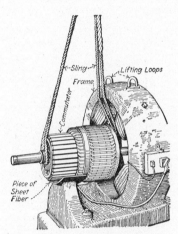

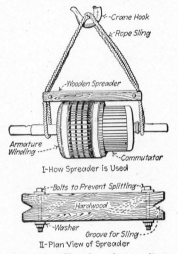

Fig. 80.—The second position in removing an armature.

Fig. 81.—Showing the application of a spreader to prevent abrasion of the armature windings.

surface carefully to see that the copper has not been turned over from segment to segment in the mica and remove by a scraper any particles of copper which may be found embedded in the mica.   Keep oil away from the mica end-rings of the commutator as oily mica will soon burn out and ground the machine.   See Sec. 3 for information relating to commutator troubles and their correction.

106. In Handling an Armature care must be exercised to prevent injury to its windings.   The armature may be removed from a machine with a rope sling, as shown in **Fig. 80.**

After it has been taken out of the frame, a wooden spreader should be arranged in the sling as shown in Fig. 81 to prevent the rope from abrading the winding of the commutator. An armature can be replaced as shown in Fig. 82. Pieces of stiff sheet-fiber should be utilized, as shown in the illustrations, to prevent portions of the frame of the machine from damaging the commutator or winding insulation.

107. Drying Out a Generator or Motor.*—If a generator has been exposed to dampness, before being started in regular service it should be operated with its armature short-circuited beyond the ammeters and with the field current adjusted so as to raise temperature to about 70 deg. C. (See Art. 247 for description of method of measuring the insulation resistance of a machine; the low insulation resistance may indicate moisture and *vice versa*.) The current should then be permitted to flow until the coils become thoroughly dry. The temperature should not be allowed to drop to that of the surrounding atmosphere, as the moisture would then again be condensed on the coils, and the machine brought to the same condition as at the start.

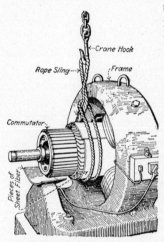

Fig. 82.—The first position in removing or the last position in replacing an armature.

108. There is Always Danger of Overheating the Windings of a Machine When Drying Them with current, as the inner parts, which cannot quickly dissipate the heat generated in them and which cannot be examined, may get dangerously hot, while the more-exposed and more-easily-cooled portions are still at a comparatively low temperature. The temperature of the hottest part accessible should always be observed while the machine is being dried out in this way,

* WESTINGHOUSE INSTRUCTION BOOK.

and it should not be allowed to exceed the boiling point of water. It may require several hours or even days to thoroughly dry out a machine, especially if it is of large capacity. Large field coils dry very slowly. Insulation is more easily injured by overheating when damp than when dry.

SECTION 3

MANAGEMENT OF AND STARTING AND CONTROLL-ING DEVICES FOR DIRECT-CURRENT MOTORS

109. The Management of Direct-current Motors is in many particulars—since (Art. 52) the construction of these motors and generators is the same—similar to that of direct-current generators. It is suggested, therefore, that any reader seeking information on this subject review Sec. 2 on the "Management of Direct-current Generators."

110. Control of Direct-current Electric Motors. Rheostats.*
—A direct-current motor of any capacity, when its armature is at rest, offers a very low resistance to the flow of current and an excessive and perhaps destructive current would flow through it if it were connected directly across the supply mains while at rest.

EXAMPLE.—Consider a motor adapted to a normal full-load current of 100 amp. and having an armature resistance of 0.25 ohm; if this motor were connected across a 250-volt circuit a current of 1,000 amp. would flow through its armature—in other words, it would be over-loaded 900 per cent, with consequent danger to its windings and also to the driven machine. In the case of the same motor, with a rheostat having a resistance of 2.25 ohms inserted in the motor circuit, at the time of starting the total resistance to the flow of current would be the resistance of the motor (0.25 ohm) plus the resistance of the rheostat (2.25 ohms), or a total of 2.5 ohms. Under these conditions exactly full-load current, or 100 amp., would flow through the motor, and neither the motor nor the driven machine would be overstrained in starting. This indicates the necessity of a rheostat for limiting the flow of current in starting the motor from rest.

111. An Electric Motor is Simply an Inverted Generator; consequently when its armature begins to revolve a voltage is generated within its windings just as a voltage is generated in the windings of a generator when driven by a

* The Electric Controller & Manfg. Co.

prime mover. This voltage generated within the moving armature of a motor opposes the voltage of the circuit from which the motor is supplied, and hence is known as a "counter-electromotive force." The net voltage tending to force current through the armature of a motor when the motor is running is, therefore, the line voltage minus the counter-electromotive force. In the case of the motor cited in the above example, when the armature attains such a speed that a voltage of 125 is generated within its windings, the effective voltage will be 250 minus 125, or 125 volts, and, therefore, the resistance of the rheostat may be reduced to

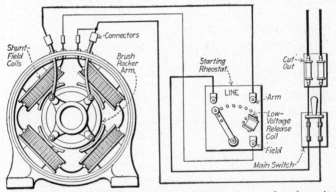
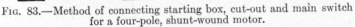

Fig. 83.—Method of connecting starting box, cut-out and main switch for a four-pole, shunt-wound motor.

1 ohm without the full-load current of the motor being exceeded. As the armature further increases its speed, the resistance of the rheostat may be further reduced until, when the motor has almost reached full speed, all of the rheostat resistance may be cut out, and the counter-electromotive force generated by the motor will almost equal the voltage supplied by the line so that an excessive current cannot flow through the armature.

112. In Practice, a Rheostat (Fig. 83) is Provided for Starting a Direct-current Electric Motor.—The conductor providing the resistance is divided into sections and is so arranged that the entire length or maximum resistance of the rheostat is in circuit with the motor at the instant of starting and that the effective length of the conductor, and hence its resistance, may be reduced as the motor comes up to speed. In cutting out the resistance of a starting rheostat it must not be cut out too rapidly. If the resistance is cut out more rapidly than the armature can speed up, a sufficient counter-electromotive force will not be generated to properly oppose the flow of current, and the motor will be overloaded.

113. Rheostatic Controller.—If all the resistance of the starting rheostat (see above paragraph) is not cut out, the motor will operate at reduced voltage, and hence at less

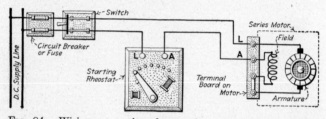

Fig. 84.—Wiring connections for a series motor and its rheostat.

than normal speed. A rheostat (Fig. 84) so arranged that all or a portion of its resistance may be left in a motor circuit to secure reduced speeds is called a "rheostatic controller." Such rheostatic controllers are used for controlling series and compound-wound motors driving cranes and similar machinery requiring variable speed under the control of an operator.

113a. In Starting a Direct-current Motor (see Fig. 85), close the line switch and move the operating arm of the rheostat (Figs. 86, 87 and 84) step by step over the contacts, waiting a few seconds on each contact for the motor speed to accelerate. If this process is performed too quickly the motor may be injured by excessive current; if too slowly, the rheostat may be injured. If the motor fails to start on the first step, move promptly to the second step and if necessary to the third, but no farther. If no start is made when the third step is reached,

open the line switch at once, allow the starter handle to return
to the off position, and look for faulty connections, overload,

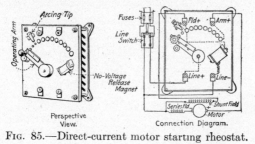

FIG. 85.—Direct-current motor starting rheostat.

etc.   The time of starting a motor with full-load torque should
not, as a general thing, exceed 15 sec. for motors of 5 h.p. and
lesser output, and 30 sec. for those of greater output.

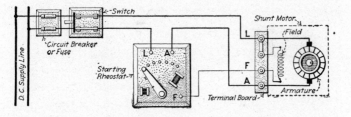

FIG. 86.—Wiring connections for a shunt motor and its starting rheostat.

114. In Stopping a Direct-current Motor, open the line
switch.   The starting-rheostat arm will return automatically

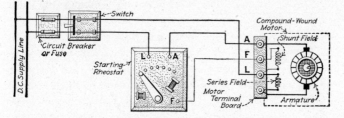

FIG. 87.—Wiring connections for a compound-wound motor and its
rheostat.

to the off position.   Never force the operating arm of any
automatic-starting rheostat back to the off position.

115. Starting Rheostats for Shunt-, Compound- and Series-wound Direct-current Motors vary somewhat in detail, design, and method of connection with the ideas of the different manufacturers. The rheostat shown in Fig. 85 is fairly typical of those for starting motors of outputs up to 120 h.p. Enclosed starting rheostats (Fig. 88) may frequently be employed to advantage.

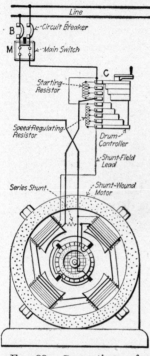

FIG. 88.—Connections of a drum controller with a compound-wound motor.

116. The Low-voltage Release Device on a Starting Rheostat consists of a spring, which tends to return the operating arm to the off position, and an electromagnet, which, under conditions of normal voltage, holds the operating arm in the running position. The coil of this magnet is regularly connected across the circuit with a protecting resistance in series, but can be connected in series with the shunt field of the motor if specially required. If the voltage drops below a predetermined value, the arm is released and returned by the spring to the off position.

117. Arcing Devices on Starting Rheostats.—Arcing tips consisting of pivoted fingers are sometimes mounted near the point where the circuit is opened. In passing to the off position a lug on the end of the arm strikes and deflects the tip, which is in electrical connection with the first stationary contact; the current is diverted to the tip, which snaps back when released and opens the circuit very quickly, thus rupturing the arc. Blow-out coils can, where necessary, be mounted behind the first contact and will disrupt any arc formed in opening the circuit.

118. Overload Release Device on Starting Rheostats.—This device, which is not illustrated, includes an electromagnet, which, in case of overload, attracts its armature and forces an insulating wedge between two contacts, separating them and thereby opening the circuit of the low-voltage release magnet. The operating arm returns immediately to the off position. With some devices, the attraction of the armature closes

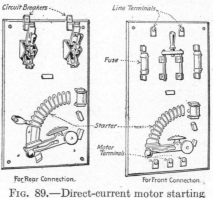

FIG. 89.—Direct-current motor starting panels.

two contacts which places a short-circuit around the low-voltage release magnet, thereby deenergizing it and permitting the operating arm to return to the off position. It should be noted that the *National Electrical Code* rules require the use of fuses or circuit-breakers (see Art. 120 with each rheostat even though it be equipped with an overload release of this nature.

118a. Starting Panels for Direct-current Motors are shown in Figs. 89 and 90. Panels, of which the illustrations are typical, are very desirable in that they concentrate all of the apparatus for the motor's control at one point and greatly simplify the wiring. Where such a panel is used, it is merely necessary to run the two line wires to the line terminals of the panel, run the three leads between the motor and the panel

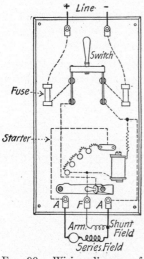

FIG. 90.—Wiring diagram of typical starting panel.

and the installation is ready for operation. The designs of different manufacturers vary in details. The panels can be obtained for either front or rear connection and with circuit-breakers or fuses for over-load protection. Which is preferable is determined by the characteristics of the installation in question.

119. The Advantages and Disadvantages of Fuses vs. Circuit-breakers may be summed thus: (1) Fuses have a time element that unmodified circuit-breakers do not have; that is, fuses will not open an overloaded circuit as quickly as will ordinary circuit-breakers. For this reason fuses may be preferable for motors that are liable to very brief overloads, especially where expert supervision of electrical apparatus is maintained, as in large mills and factories. A supply of extra fuses must be kept available. Where there are many fuse replacements the cost of fuse renewals is considerable. (2) Circuit-breakers can be reset in less time and with less trouble than is required to replace blown fuses, and no extra parts are required. Circuit-breakers may therefore be preferable where time saving is an important consideration. The first cost of the circuit-breaker equipment is more than that for fuses, but for severe service the circuit-breakers are much the cheaper in the long run.

120. The National Electrical Code Rules Require That Each Motor and Its Starter be Protected by fuses or a circuit-breaker and controlled by a switch which must plainly indicate whether on or off. The switch and cut-out (fuses or circuit-breaker) are, preferably, located near the motor and in plain sight of it. All wiring should be neat and workmanlike and the wires should be run in conduit wherever possible. For further information relating to the "Code" requirements (governing the installation of motor-control apparatus) and the reasons and explanations therefor, see the author's WIRING FOR LIGHT AND POWER.

121. In a Series-wound Motor the Speed Varies Inversely as the Load (Fig. 84)—the lighter the load the higher the speed. See also Art. 59 under "Direct-current Motors and Generators." A series-wound motor of any size, when supplied with full voltage under no-load, or a very light load, will "run away" just as will a steam engine without a governor when given an open throttle. For a given load, a series-wound motor with its rheostat in series draws the same current irrespective of the speed and for a given load the speed varies directly as the voltage. The speed at a given load may be varied by varying the resistance in the motor circuit; in the meantime if the load on the motor be constant the current drawn from the line will be constant regardless of the speed.

122. Shunting the Field of a Series Motor.—The above statements relate to the use of a rheostat in series with a series-wound motor. If a resistance or rheostat be placed in parallel with the field of a series-wound motor the speed will be increased instead of decreased at a given load. This is known as shunting the field of the motor. This shunt would never be applied till the motor has been brought up to normal full speed by cutting out the starting resistance. With a "shunted field" a motor drives a load at a speed higher than normal and therefore requires a correspondingly increased current.

123. Shunted Armature Connection of a Series Motor.—If a resistance is placed in parallel with the armature of a series motor, the motor will operate at less than normal speed when all the starting resistance has been cut out. This connection is known as a "shunted armature connection" and is useful where a low speed is desired at light loads and is particularly useful in some cases where the load becomes a negative one, that is, where the load tends to overhaul the motor, as in lowering a heavy weight.

124. Speed Control of Shunt-wound Motors.—A shunt-wound motor (Fig. 86) unlike a series motor, when supplied with full voltage, maintains practically a constant speed regardless of variations in load within the limits of its capacity. See also Art. 63 under "Direct-current Generators and Motors." It automatically acts like a steam engine having a very efficient governor. The speed of a shunt-wound motor may be decreased below normal by a rheostatic controller in

series with its armature and may be increased above normal
by means of a rheostat in series with its field winding. The
latter rheostat is known as a "field rheostat," and, to be effective, must have a high resistance owing to the small current which flows through the shunt-field winding.

125. Speed Control of Compound-wound Motors.—A compound-wound motor (Fig. 87) is a hybrid between a series and
shunt-wound motor and its characteristics are likewise of a
hybrid nature. See also Art. 67 under "Direct-current Generators and Motors." A compound-wound motor will not
"run away" under no-load as will a series motor, but its speed
decreases as the load increases, though not so rapidly as is

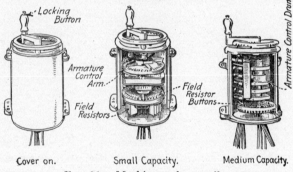

Fig. 91.—Machine-tool controller.

the case with a series-wound motor. The characteristics of
the compound-wound motor render it particularly valuable in
cases where the load is subject to wide variation. It will give
a strong torque in starting and driving heavy loads and will
not race dangerously when the load is suddenly relieved.

126. The Speed of a Compound-wound Motor may be
reduced below normal by means of a rheostat in the circuit
of its armature. The speed may be increased above normal
by shunting and even short-circuiting the series-field winding,
and may be still further increased by means of a field rheostat
in series with the shunt-field winding.

**127. Rotary, Drum or Machine-tool Type Controllers for
Direct-current Motors.**—Although controllers of this type
(Figs. 91, 92 and 93) find their most frequent applications on

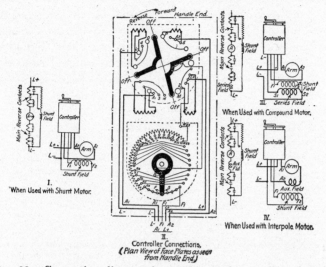

FIG. 92.—Connection diagram for machine-tool controller of small capacity using revolving arms for both armature and field control.

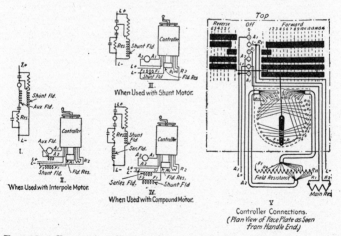

FIG. 93.—Connection diagram for machine-tool controller of medium capacity using drum for armature control and revolving arm for field control.

machine tools, they are very desirable for any service where
the work is severe and where the expense of an enclosed controller is justified.   Machine-tool work usually requires a combination starting and speed-regulating controller, that is, one
whereby the motor is started by cutting out armature resistance.   After the motor is started its speed is regulated by
varying the amount of resistance in series with the shunt fields
These controllers can be purchased for this service and for
control or starting service of practically any type.   The methods
of construction and connection are so numerous that only one
type of drum controller, one which is used for machine-tool
service, will be described here.

128. Advantages of Controllers of the Drum Type are that
the contacts and arm are entirely enclosed and that the movement of a single handle in one direction or the other starts
the motor in a corresponding direction and brings it to the
running speed desired.   The operating arm remains securely
locked at the proper notch until released by the operator by
pressing a button in the handle.

EXAMPLE.—There are two switching devices in the controller shown in
Figs. 92 and 93.   One connects to the armature or starting resistor and
the other connects to the field control resistor.   Both switching devices
are operated by the same handle.   In drum controllers of small capacity
the armature switching device consists of an arm passing over contact
buttons and all of the resistors are mounted within the drum; that is,
the controller is self-contained.   In controllers of large capacity, the
armature resistance is cut in and out by a rotating drum similar to that
used in street-railway service and all of the resistors are mounted external to the controller.   The field resistance is cut in and out by a
rotating arm passing over contact buttons in all but the largest controllers for which a drum is used.   Arc shields between drum segments
and blowout coils are provided where necessary.   The controllers can
be arranged to provide dynamic braking.   Speed ranges of from 1 to 2
to, possibly, 1 to 6 are usually provided.

129. Operation of Drum-type Controllers (see Figs. 92 and
93).—Continuous movement of the operating handle in either
direction first starts the motor in the corresponding direction
of rotation, then cuts out the starting resistance, and finally
cuts in the field resistance until the desired running speed is

reached. The handle should be moved over the starting notches in not over 15 sec. for motors of possibly 10 h.p. capacity and in not over 30 sec. for larger motors. The starting resistance should not be used for speed control. For a quick stop when operating with weakened field, move the handle quickly to the first running notch, hold it there momentarily and then move it to the off position; the application of full field strength when the speed is high causes dynamic braking, thus checking the speed quickly and without shock. For a very quick emergency stop, the handle can be moved to the first reversing notch after checking the speed by dynamic

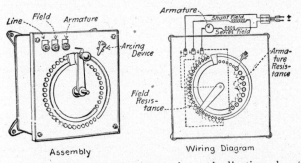

FIG. 94.—Non-automatic starting and speed-adjusting rheostat.

braking, but this operation causes severe mechanical and electrical stresses; and should never be carried beyond the first notch. When the motor is to be at rest for any considerable length of time, open the line switch.

130. A Non-automatic Starting and Speed-adjusting Rheostat for Direct-current Motors is shown in Fig. 94. This device has no low-voltage or overload protection, hence is suitable only for applications where skilled attendance is available. The operating arm makes contact as it is revolved between the circular bars and the resistance contact buttons. There are a number of field-control steps, hence close speed adjustment over a considerable range can be obtained. The contact buttons of the inner circular segment are connected to the starting resistor and the contacts of the outer circle are connected with the running resistor. A reading of the follow-

6

ing paragraph describing the operation of the device will render clear the principles involved.

131. Operation of a Non-automatic Starting and Speed-adjusting Rheostat* (Fig. 94).—To start the motor, close the line switch or circuit-breaker and move the operating arm of the rheostat over the starting buttons to the first running

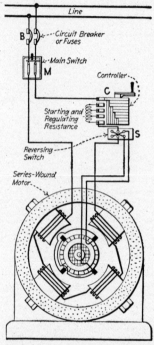

position (the point where the two bar contacts overlap). A motor starting with full-load torque should be brought to this point in approximately 15 sec. Further movement of the operating arm increases the motor speed by field control. The motor can be operated continuously with the arm on any field contact button, but with rheostats of this design must not be allowed to run on any starting button. To stop the motor, open the line switch or circuit-breaker and move the rheostat arm to the off position. The latter movement must not be forgotten, since this rheostat has no automatic features. To protect the motor in case of failure of the power supply and its subsequent return after the motor has stopped, a low-voltage release circuit-breaker should be installed

Fig. 95.—Series motor controlled with a drum controller.

in series with each rheostat. *The rheostat handle must be in the off position* before the circuit-breaker is closed.

132. A Regulating Controller for a Direct-current Series Motor is usually connected substantially as diagrammed in Fig. 95. A non-reversing controller, *C*, is shown. Hence, when it is desired to reverse the direction of rotation of the motor the reversing switch, *S*, must be thrown to the reverse position.

* Westinghouse Elec. & Manfg. Co.

The circuit-breaker or buses are shown at B and the main switch at M.

133. The Connections of a Regulating Controller for a Compound-wound Motor are shown in Fig. 88. The external connections would be the same for either a shunt- or compound-wound motor of either the interpole or non-interpole types. The overload protection and main switch are located as in the previous example.

134. The Principle of the Automatic Starter is illustrated diagrammatically in Fig. 96. Starters of some types employ the solenoid arrangement illustrated, while others (Fig. 99) involve a series of contactors or automatically operated

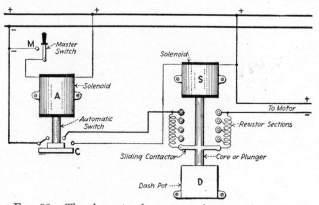

FIG. 96.—The elements of one type of automatic starter.

switches which cut out the starting resistance as the motor speed increases. Where a solenoid-operated type of starter similar to that shown in the illustration is used, a master switch, M, or push button is utilized to close the control circuit through an auxiliary switch. When the auxiliary switch, C, is thereby closed, this completes the circuit through the solenoid, S. Thus the solenoid is energized and the core is pulled up into it, which cuts out of circuit as the core rises the resistor sections of the starting rheostat. A dash pot, D, is provided, the piston in which is attached to the solenoid core. Thereby the core is prevented from rising abruptly and cutting out the resistor sections too rapidly.

135. Multi-switch Starters for Direct-current Motors are used for motors of large output and for motors of medium output that start under severe overloads. Starters of this type are built of capacities of about 50 h.p. and upward. Fig. 97 shows a typical starter of this type. In the starter shown, when each switch is closed it compresses a spring which insures firm contact between the copper block contacts. The first switch of single-pole starters of the design illustrated and the first two switches of double-pole starters, close and open the circuit. These switches are provided with arc-shields and blow-out coils. A mechanical interlocking device makes it impossible to close the switches in any but the proper order.

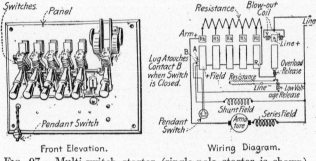

Front Elevation.   Wiring Diagram.

Fig. 97.—Multi-switch starter (single-pole starter is shown).

Each starter is equipped with an overload release and a low-voltage release, which throw open all the switches in event of an overload or a failure of voltage. Both devices are effective while the motor is being started, and the tripping point of each is adjustable over a range. The overload release can be tripped by hand. In order to insure the closing of all the switches a pendant switch in series with the low-voltage release coil must be held closed until the last switch of the starter is closed; if this button is released before the last switch is closed, all the switches promptly open. The last switch automatically closes the release-coil circuit.

A field relay switch is sometimes provided for use in connection with a separate speed-adjusting field rheostat. This switch short-circuits the field rheostat during the acceleration of the motor, so that the motor is always started with full field strength regardless of the position of the rheostat arm. If the field rheostat arm is at the off position, the short-circuit is automatically removed when the motor reaches full speed, but if there is more resistance in series with the motor shunt field than would be safe to insert in one step the field rheostat arm must be first moved to the off position before the rheostat is available for speed adjustment.

136. In Starting a Motor with a Multi-switch Starter (Fig. 97) close the switches, one at a time, in regular consecutive order. With the single-pole type starter the first switch closes the armature circuit with all the resistance in series and connects the shunt field of shunt and compound-wound motors directly across the line; each succeeding switch short-circuits a section of resistance. In the double-pole type the first two switches must be closed in order to admit current to the motor. With full-load torque, the motor should be started in 1 min.; with 50 per cent. overload, in 30 sec. The motor is stopped by tripping the overload release.

137. Magnet-switch Controllers (Figs. 98 and 99) consist essentially of a group of electromagnetically actuated switches. Magnet switches can be arranged into an almost innumerable number of combinations for different services.

Only one arrangement which will illustrate the principles involved will be treated here. For further information see manufacturers' catalogues. The switches are operated by shunt magnet coils. Their action can be manually or automatically governed. Fig. 98 gives cross-sectional views of two kinds of magnet switches. The rate of acceleration is controlled by a series relay the operation of which will be understood by reference to Fig. 99. This diagram shows a compound-wound motor connected to a three-point magnet-switch controller with a one-point master switch. The magnet switches are shown at M_1, M_2 and M_3, the main contacts at *I*, *II*, and *III*, and the interlocking contacts at *a-d*, *b-b*, *f-f*, etc. Main circuits are shown in heavy lines and interlocking circuits in light lines.

The series relay, *h*, is a small electromagnet, the plunger of which carries a contact disc which normally spans two stationary contacts *s-s*, in series with the magnet coil interlocking circuit. The magnet coil is connected in series with the main circuit and the amount of current required to lift the plunger can be adjusted by weights on the plunger. Note that the line switch in the diagram does not close either the motor or the magnet switch circuits. Operation

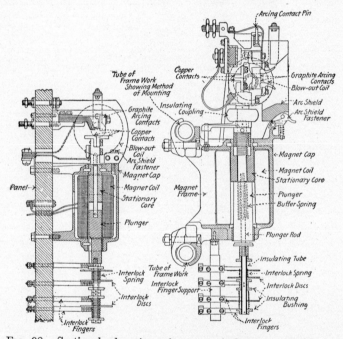

Fig. 98.—Sectional elevation of two typical magnet switches.

does not begin until the master switch is closed. Closing the master switch connects coil M_1 across the circuit; the plunger rises closing contact *I* and bridging *a-a* with disc 1. The motor starts and the high starting current causes the series relay to open gap *s-s*, in the control circuit. As soon as the motor current falls to a point predetermined by the relay adjustment, gap *s-s* is again closed and coil M_2 is connected across the line through *s-s*, *a-a* and *c-c*. Contacts

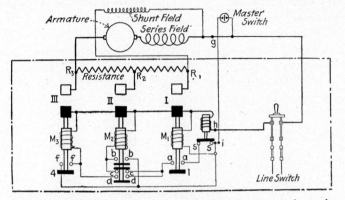

FIG. 99.—Magnet switch controller arranged for the automatic acceleration control of a compound-wound motor.

II are then closed; interlocking contacts *b-b* and *d-d* are
bridged and gap *c-c* is opened.
Contacts *II* short-circuit resistance
R_2-R_1, causing an increase in the
motor current, so that the series
relay again opens *s-s*. But the
opening of *c-c* and the closing of
b-b has meanwhile connected M_2
across the circuit independent of
the relay, so that though the relay
can delay the closing of a magnet
switch, it has no control over one
already closed. When the starting current decreases, gap *s-s* is
again closed; coil M_3 is energized,
closing contacts *III* and connecting the motor directly across the
line. The gap *f-f* is bridged with
contact 4, so that the coil M_3 is
removed from any further control
by the relay.

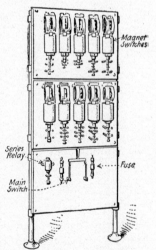

FIG. 100.—Assembly of a
Magnet switch controller for
elevator service showing how
the switches may be mounted.

If the voltage fails the magnet switches drop open. On

return of the voltage (the master switch remaining closed), they close automatically in the correct sequence to start and accelerate the motor. For some kinds of service an overload relay is used. This relay is similar to the series acceleration relay in operation but it is so connected that all but the first magnet switch drops open when an overload occurs. The motor now operates slowly with all the resistance in series with the armature until the overload is removed, after which the open switches close as in starting. The point at which the relay will operate is adjustable by weights on the plunger.

Of the many applications of magnet switches possibly the most important are the control of direct-current machine-tool motors and elevator motors. Fig. 100 shows a front view of a magnetic-switch elevator controller.

138. Field Relay Switches are required where separate rheostats are used for starting and controlling the speeds of motors. This is required by a *National Electrical Code* rule to prevent the possibility of

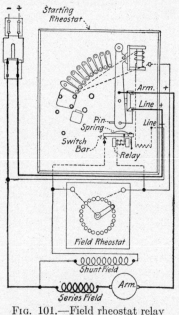

FIG. 101.—Field rheostat relay switch.

starting a motor with weakened field. The switch, shown in Fig. 101, mounted under the starter handle accomplishes this function by short-circuiting the field rheostat during acceleration so that the motor must always start with full field regardless of the position of the field rheostat arm. The switch shown, or a similar one, can be applied to ordinary starting and speed-regulating rheostats and generally should be mounted on the rheostat at the factory of the firm that furnishes it.

139. The Field Relay Switch Shown Consists of a small electromagnet, a pivoted switch bar, and a stationary contact. The switch bar is normally held away from the contact by a helical spring. The magnet-coil, switch bar, and contact are in series with a circuit that parallels the field rheostat. When the operating arm of the starting rheostat is moved to the first step, a pin on its hub presses the relay switch bar against its stationary contact, thus short-circuiting the field rheostat. As the arm is turned the pin on the starter hub soon releases the relay switch bar; but the relay electromagnet, energized when the contacts close, holds this bar temporarily in place. The winding of the relay electromagnet is so proportioned that if there is little or no resistance in series with the motor shunt field, the relay magnet will release the switch bar before the motor is brought to full speed, leaving the field rheostat available for speed adjustment. But if the field rheostat arm is turned so that there is more resistance in series with the shunt field than would be safe to insert in one step, the electromagnet will keep the relay switch closed until the arm of the field rheostat is brought back toward the off position.

140. Starting and Speed-adjusting (Field-control) Rheostats for Direct-current Shunt- and Compound-wound Motors.—There are as many and more designs as there are manufacturers, but the equipment shown in Figs. 102 and 103 is typical and can be used for starting and regulating speed in non-reversing services where speed adjustment by field control is desirable. Fig. 104 shows the application of one of these rheostats to a compound-wound commutating-pole motor. The apparatus is so arranged that the motor is always started with full field strength. In case of failure of the voltage, the field control resistance is automatically short-circuited and the motor is disconnected from the line.

140a. Construction of a Starting and Speed-adjusting Rheostat (Fig. 103).—The rheostat consists of a face plate carrying the contacts, operating arms, and safety devices, mounted in connection with two resistors. One resistor is for starting and one is for adjusting the field strength. The face plate carries three rows of stationary contacts. The upper row is connected with the field adjusting resistor, the second row with the starting resistor; and the lower row contains a long curved segment for short-circuiting the field resistance in starting. A contact for short-circuiting the armature resistance when the arm is in the running position is sometimes provided. The face plate supports two arms, an operating arm and a short-circuiting arm, pivoted to the same hub and arranged so that they cannot pass each other. The operating arm carries the

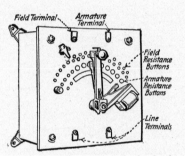

Fig. 102.—Starting and speed-adjusting rheostat.

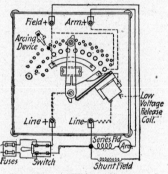

Fig. 103.—Wiring diagram for starting and speed-adjusting rheostat.

handle and two contact fingers, one for the starting contacts and the other for the field contacts. The short-circuiting arm has a contact finger which slides over the contact bar, short-circuiting the field resistance in starting, and the armature resistance while running. In some designs this arm also carries laminated copper brushes which short-circuit the starting resistance when the arm reaches the running position. A spring tends to return the short-circuiting arm to the off position.

Under conditions of normal operation the short-circuiting arm is held in the running position against the force of the spring by an electromagnet connected across the line in series with a protecting resistance. If the voltage falls below a predetermined point, the arm is released and returns to the off position, carrying the operating arm with it. Rheostats for this service are frequently arranged so that the circuit is opened between a lug on the operating arm and a small pivoted finger with a centering spring mounted near the first starting contact and connected to it electrically. The current is always broken abruptly no matter how slowly the

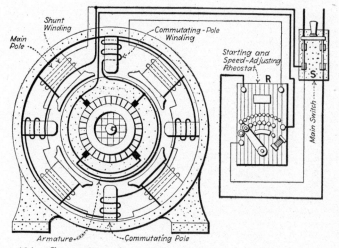

FIG. 104.—Connections of a starting and speed-adjusting rheostat for a shunt-wound, commutating-pole motor.

arm may be moved. Blow-out coils are sometimes mounted on the rear of the face plate to disrupt any arc that may form.

An overload release device can be mounted on all but the largest rheostats of this type. It consists of an electromagnet which, in event of an overload, opens the low-voltage magnet circuit, thus releasing the short-circuiting arm. The tripping point is adjustable. The *National Electrical Code* rules require the use of a circuit-breaker or fuses with a rheostat equipped with an overload release of this character.*

* Westinghouse Elec. & Manfg. Co.

140b. Operation of a Starting and Speed-adjusting Rheostat (Figs. 102 and 103).—The motor is started by moving the operating arm to the running position, stopping a few seconds on each starting contact to permit the speed to accelerate. The retaining magnet holds the short-circuiting arm in the running position where it short-circuits the starting resistor. The operating arm is then moved back over the field-resistance contacts until the desired speed is reached. For motors starting with full-load torque, the time of acceleration should be from 15 sec. to 30 sec.,

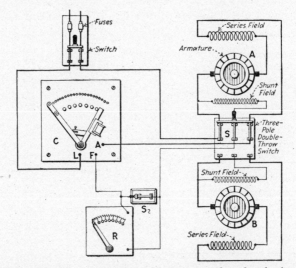

Fig. 105.—Method of connecting two motors so that they both may be controlled by one set of starting and speed-regulating equipment.

depending upon the capacity of the motor. To stop the motor, open the line switch. Both arms then return to the off position automatically.

141. The Arrangement of One Starting and Speed-adjusting Rheostat for the Control of Two Motors, *A* and *B*, is illustrated in Fig. 105. This arrangement was used* to provide emergency service on the other motor if one motor failed. By throwing the three-pole double-throw switch, *S*, the control

* R. L. Hervey in Power, Sept. 19, 1916.

equipment is connected to either motor. The resistance of the field regulator of C not being sufficient to increase the motor speed as desired, an additional rheostat, R, was inserted in the field circuit. The single-pole switch, S_2, was so connected that R could be shunted out of circuit if necessary.

142. Armature Control Speed Regulators (Fig. 106) are used for speed reduction with shunt, compound or series motors in non-reversing service where the torque required decreases with the speed but remains constant at any given speed as with fans, blowers and centrifugal pumps. They can also be used for applications where the torque is independent of the speed, as with job printing presses. However, this method

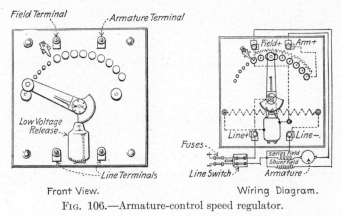

Front View.   Wiring Diagram.

Fig. 106.—Armature-control speed regulator.

of speed control is not suitable for such applications where there is operation for long periods at reduced speed, since such operation is not economical. It is not possible, where the torque varies, to obtain constant speed with these controllers.

143. Construction of an Armature Control Regulator.—In the regulator shown the low-voltage release consists of an electromagnet enclosed in an iron shell, a sector on the pivot end of the operating arm, and a strong spring which tends to return the arm to the off position. The magnet is mounted directly below the pivot of the arm and its coil is connected in shunt across the line in series with a protecting resistance. When the magnet is energized its plunger rises and forces a steel ball into one of a series of depressions in the sector on the arm with sufficient force to hold the arm against the action of the spring; each depression corresponds to a contact. The arm can be easily moved by the operator, however, as the ball rolls when the arm is turned. When the voltage fails, the magnet plunger falls and the spring throws the operating arm to the off position. An overload release, similar to that described in another paragraph, which operates by opening the low-voltage coil circuit, is sometimes furnished on regulators of this type. Standard commercial rheostats of this type are designed to give about 50 per cent. speed reduction on the first notch. See the following paragraph on operation for further information.

144. Operation of Armature Control Speed Regulators (Fig. 106).—Forward motion of the operating arm starts the motor and brings it gradually to maximum speed. Moving the arm over the first few contact buttons increases the shunt field strength if the motor is shunt or compound. The movement over the succeeding buttons cuts out armature resistance and permits the motor to speed up.

145. Objections to Armature Control.*—(*a*) *Bulk of Rheostat.* —This may not be very objectionable if only a few motors are so controlled, but for a number the extra space becomes a factor, and in many cases it is difficult to find sufficient room near the motor.

(*b*) *Inefficiency of the System.*—The same amount of power is supplied at all speeds but at low speeds only a small part of it is converted into useful work, the balance being wasted in the rheostat as heat.

(*c*) *Poor Speed Regulation with Varying Speeds.*—Since the impressed voltage at the armature terminals is equal to the line voltage minus the resistance drop in the rheostat any change in the current drawn by the motor produces a change in the terminal voltage, the counter e.m.f., and therefore the speed.

This condition is illustrated by the graphs of Fig. 107, which are plotted from data obtained from a 4-h.p. motor.

---

* Crocker and Arendts, ELECTRIC MOTORS.

With all of the armature resistance in circuit the speed at full-load—4 h.p.—is 750 r.p.m. whereas at no-load the speed is 1,220 r.p.m. That is, there is a drop in speed of 470 r.p.m. between no-load and full-load, hence the speed regulation is 470 ÷ 1,220 = 38.5 per cent.

146. Crane Controllers for Direct-current, Series and Compound-wound Motors are usually arranged somewhat as indicated in Fig. 108. The switching device consists of a disc of soapstone or other fireproof insulating material carrying stationary contact pieces and a pivoted switch arm carrying four con-

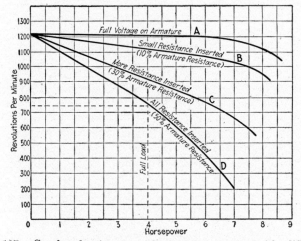

Fig. 107.—Graphs showing speed-load characteristics with different percentages of armature resistance in circuit.

tactors. Blow-out coils are usually provided to effectively rupture the arcs that form when the contactors pass from one contact piece to the next. The resistors may be contained in the controller base, as in small controllers, or may be arranged for separate mounting as in large ones. In Fig. 108 the fine lines within the circle are shading lines which merely indicate that the circle is a soapstone disc. Only the heavy lines within the circle represents electrical connections. Fig. 109 shows two typical controllers.

Movement of the controller handle in either direction past

the off position starts the motor in the corresponding direction of rotation. At each step a section of resistance is short-cir-

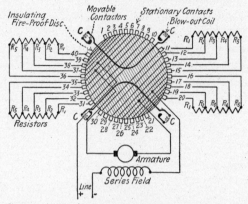

Fig. 108.—Connections of a 16-point crane controller connected to a series motor.

cuited. At the full-speed positions all the resistance is short-circuited. Stops prevent over-running past the full-speed positions. Direct-current crane controllers increase or decrease

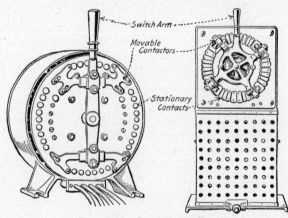

Fig. 109.—Crane controllers.

the amount of resistance in series with the motor and thereby control its speed.

147. Dynamic Braking of Direct-current Motors is effected by allowing a motor to be temporarily driven as a generator by its load. The mechanical energy of the moving machinery or descending load is thus converted into electrical energy and then into heat which is dissipated in resistance. The result is that the speed of the motor is promptly retarded. The amount of braking action can be adjusted by varying the current flowing in the motor armature. A load exercising an active torque on the motor armature, such as an elevator car, cannot be brought to a full stop by this method, since with the decreasing armature speed the braking action also decreases. For final stopping, some form of mechanical brake, which acts automatically, is therefore necessary.

148. Dynamic Braking is Used in connection with motors for elevators, hoists, cranes, coal and ore handling machinery, railway cars, etc. It is employed for reducing the motor speed just before a stop, as in elevator service; or for controlling the speed of moving objects, as in lowering crane loads, retarding the speed of the cars descending grades, and the like.

149. The Principal Advantages of Dynamic Braking are the practical absence of all wear and tear on the apparatus, convenience of application, and ease, accuracy, and certainty of control. In dynamic braking with a properly selected motor, active deterioration is limited to the controller contacts, which can be arranged for quick, easy, and inexpensive renewal. No special or additional apparatus is required for braking except the resistance which can be placed wherever convenient within a reasonable distance from the motor. The braking effect can be adjusted with great accuracy over a wide range by varying the armature current or the field strength by means of suitable resistance. In some instances, notably with railroads, dynamic braking actually returns energy to the circuit; but in industrial service the energy generated is usually dissipated by resistance. In electric cars, during the winter months, this dynamic braking current is in many cases used in the heaters for warming the cars.

150. Heating with Dynamic Braking.—The most important limitation to the use of dynamic braking is the heating of the

7

motor by the generated currents. For simple stopping duty this action is insignificant, as it lasts only a few seconds; but with speed control in lowering a load by dynamic braking, the generated current may flow for an extended length of time and the heating may be considerable, especially as it is added to the heating of the machine when operated as a motor. This additional heating effect due to the braking current must be considered in selecting the motor.

151. Dynamic-braking Connections.—Fig. 110 shows by simple diagrams some of the possible connections. Diagram *I* shows the armature of a shunt motor short-circuited through

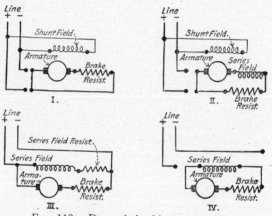

FIG. 110.—Dynamic braking connections.

a brake resistance, the field remaining across the line. Diagram *II* shows the armature of a compound motor short-circuited through the series field and a brake resistance, the shunt field remaining across the line. Diagram *III* shows the armature of a series motor short-circuited through the series field, a protecting resistance for the field, and a brake resistance—the field and its resistance being in series across the line. Diagram *IV* shows the armature and series field of a series motor short-circuited through a brake resistance, all of which are entirely disconnected from the line.

By cutting out the series field in diagram *II* the braking

effect can be diminished, the connections then being as in *I*. The connections shown in diagram *III* are generally preferable for series motors during the first part of the braking operation, in order to insure building up as a generator. As soon as the generator action has begun, the connections can be changed to those shown in diagram *IV*. In each of the cases shown by the four diagrams the braking effect can be increased by short-circuiting sections of the brake resistance and thus increasing the armature current.

152. The Control of Large Direct-current Motors with an Equalizer Flywheel Motor-generator Set (Figs. 111 and 112) is illustrated diagramatically in Fig. 113. Methods of

Fig. 111.—A flywheel, motor-generator hoisting set installed for the North Butte Mining Company. The motors are the largest in the world installed in mining service for hoisting. The direct-current motor is an 1850 h.p., 71 r.p.m. machine. The alternating current motor has a capacity of 1400 h.p. The direct-current generator has an output of 1500 kw. The outfit hoists as much as 10 tons of ore per trip. See Fig. 112 for motor and hoists. (Westinghouse Electric Co.)

control similar to that suggested have been employed for mine-hoist motors and for rolling-mill motors having capacities as great as 15,000 h.p. Energy for driving the roll or hoist motor is supplied from a three-phase, alternating-current line, but this alternating current does not directly drive the roll motor, *R*, but instead merely the motor, *M* (Fig. 113), which drives the flywheel motor-generator set. The energy to the roll motor is supplied directly by the direct-current generator, *G*, of this set. The roll motor, *R*, is controlled by varying the strength and direction of the field current of the direct-current generator, *G*, which field

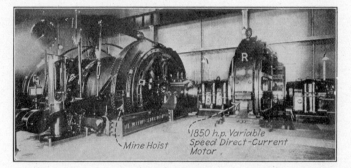

FIG. 112.—Variable speed, direct-current motor and hoist of the North Butte equipment. See Fig. 111 for the flywheel, motor-generator set.

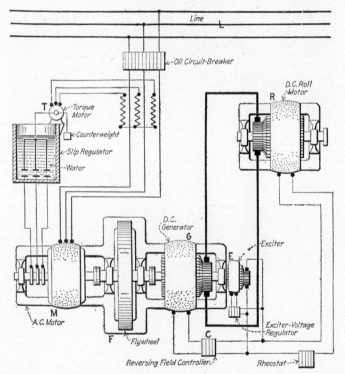

FIG. 113.—Diagram of flywheel-motor-generator control for a large motor operating under service conditions.

current is supplied by exciter E. With this method, to control the speed of and reverse the roll motor, it is merely necessary to vary or reverse the field current of the generator by manipulating controller C. Dynamic braking is used to stop the roll motor.

153. The Function of the Flywheel of the Motor-generator Set is to equalize the draft of energy from the alternating-current line, L. If the mill motor tends to draw a large current from the line, the motor-generator set would tend to slow down. Then the flywheel will impart its stored energy to the system during these moments of heavy load on the roll motor. When the peak load is over, the alternating-current motor will again attain normal speed and store energy in the flywheel. The load on the alternating-current motor is greater than that on the roll motor when the roll motor is lightly loaded. But, when the roll motor, R, is pulling its peak loads, the alternating-current motor, M, carries the smaller load.

154. The Function of the Torque Motor, T (Fig. 113), is to throw the peak load on the flywheel. It does this by introducing resistance into the rotor circuit of the large alternating-current motor, M, thereby reducing its speed. The slip regulator is merely a liquid rheostat having three pairs of electrodes, one pair connected in series with each phase of the rotor circuit of M. The movable electrode of each pair is connected to an arm arranged on the shaft of the small torque motor. When the current in the line, L, tends to decrease due to a heavy draft of energy by R, the torque motor decreases the distance between the electrodes and M increases its speed accordingly.

155. A Float or Tank Switch is illustrated in Fig. 114. Devices of this character are used to stop and start pump motors, such, for example, as those used for draining the sumps in basements of buildings. As the water in the pit rises, the rod, R, is forced upward by the action of the float, F, on the surface of the liquid in the pit. On the rod are two stops, S and S'. When the pit is almost full, the stop, S', will push against the switch arm, A, and when this arm has been forced to move a certain distance, the weighted tumbler, W, flops over and causes the switch to close. This energizes the solenoid of the automatic starter ordinarily used with such motors (Fig. 265) and the motor commences to drive its pump, which raises the water out of the pit. As the water in the pit is lowered, the float falls and finally stop S strikes the switch arm, the control circuit is opened and the motor is stopped.

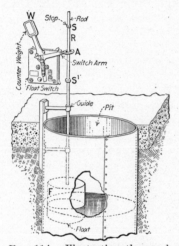

Fig. 114.—Illustrating the mechanism of a float switch.

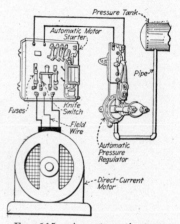

Fig. 115.—An automatic starter arranged in combination with a pressure regulator for controlling a direct-current motor.

156. The Method of Connecting an Automatic Starter for a Pressure-regulator-control, Direct-current Motor is illustrated in Fig. 115. Where a motor is to be controlled by a float switch the general scheme of connections is similar to those illustrated in Fig. 265, which shows the connections for alternating-current motors.

157. Field-discharge Switches and Resistors should be provided in connection with all electrical machines having field circuits, of considerable inductance, which are energized by direct current. Unless some sort of resistor path is provided for the dissipation of the electro-magnetic energy stored in the magnetic field, it will cause destructive arcing at the field

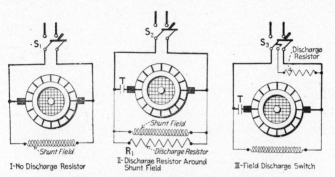

FIG. 116.—Arrangement of discharge resistors.

switch whenever this switch is opened.   The voltage to which

this arcing is due is an e.m.f.
of self-induction, and it may be
(unless a dissipative resistor
is provided) great enough to
puncture the insulation on the
field windings.   Fig. 116 illustrates some of the possible connections as applied to direct-
current motors, but the general
principles there indicated can,
with obvious modifications, be
applied to the shunt-field circuits of all direct-current machines and to the field circuits
of alternating-current machines.   In Fig. 116, *I*, there
is no field discharge resistor or
switch, hence when the main
switch, S_1, is opened, the field
can discharge directly through
the armature.   Where auto-
matic-control equipment is
used with motors a switch, *T*,

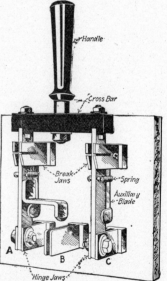

FIG. 117.—A field discharge
switch.   (*A* and *C* connect to field-
winding terminals and *B* connects
to one end of the field discharge
resistance.)

is often inserted between the shunt field and the armature and a field discharge resistor, R, is then arranged across
the shunt field as suggested in the diagram. Where this device is utilized, there is a constant I^2R loss in the discharge
resistor, R_1, so long as the voltage is impressed across the
shunt field. A shunt-field resistor may have a relatively high
resistance, hence this I^2R loss is often negligibly small and
the simplicity of the scheme of II may justify its employment.
At III, a field discharge switch, S_3 (Fig. 117), is employed
which cuts the discharge resistor in circuit with the shunt field
whenever the main switch is opened.

TROUBLES OF DIRECT-CURRENT GENERATORS AND MOTORS

158. Troubles of Direct-current Generators and Motors.*— Since, as explained in Art. 52, the construction of direct-current generators is essentially the same as that of direct-current motors, most of the troubles inherent to one are also encountered with the other—the remedies for generator troubles are about the same as those for motor troubles. Therefore, while some of the matter in this section applies specifically to direct-current motors it may under certain conditions also, with equal force, relate to direct-current generators.

---

* Considerable of the material under this heading is based on articles which have appeared in the magazine POWER (*McGraw-Hill Publishing Company*, New York) and on that in the book, MOTOR TROUBLES, by E. B. Raymond.

159. Direct-current Generator and Motor Troubles.   (From Machinery, by special permission)

Sparking at the brushes	**Brushes**	Not set diametrically opposite.	*A.* Should have been set properly at first, by counting bars, or by measurement on the commutator. *B.* Can be done if necessary while running; move rocker until brush on one side sparks least, then adjust other brushes so they do not spark.	1
		Not set at neutral points.	Move rocker back and forth slowly until sparking stops.	2
		Not properly trimmed.	*A.* Brushes should be properly trimmed before starting. If there are two or more brushes one may be removed and retrimmed. *B.* Clean with alcohol or ether, then grind and reset carefully. *See* lines 1, 4, 38.	3
		Not in line.	Adjust each brush until bearing is on line and square on commutator bar, bearing evenly the whole width. *See* line 13 *A.*	4
		Not in good contact.	*A.* Clean commutator of oil and grit. See that brushes touch. *B.* Adjust tension screws and springs to secure light, firm and even contact. *See* line 38 *B.*	5
	Commutator	Rough; worn in grooves or ridges; out of round.	*A.* Grind with fine sandpaper on curved block, and polish with crocus cloth. Never use emery in any form. *B.* If too bad to grind down turn off true in a lathe or preferably in its own bearings, with a light tool and rest, a light cut; running slowly. *Note.*—Armature should have $\frac{1}{16}$ to $\frac{1}{8}$-in. end motion when running, to wear commutator evenly and smoothly. *See* line 31.	6
		High bars.	Set "high bar" down carefully with mallet or block of wood, then clamp tightly end nuts, or file, grind or turn true. A high bar may cause singing. *See* line 38.	8
		Low bars.	Grind or turn commutator true to the surface of the low bars.	9
		Weak magnetic field.	*A.* Broken circuit } in field coils { Repair if external. *B.* Short-circuit } { Rewind if internal. *C.* Machine not properly wound, or without proper amount of iron—no remedy but to rebuild it.	10

160. Direct-current Generator and Motor Troubles. (From Machinery, by special permission)—*Continued*

Excessive current in armature	Generator	Excessive load.	A.	Reduce number of lamps and load.	11
		Ground and leak from short-circuit on line.	B.	Test out, locate, and repair.	
		Dead short-circuit on line.	C.	*Note.*—Dead short-circuit will or should blow safety fuse. Shut down, locate fault and repair before starting again, and put in a new fuse.	
	Motor	Excessive voltage.	D.	Use proper current only, and with proper rheostat and controller and switch.	
		Excessive amperes on constant-current circuit.	E.	See that controller, etc., are suitable with ample resistance.	
		Friction.	F.	Reduce load on motor to its rated capacity or less. *See 3 B* and 35, 36.	
		Too great load on pulley.	G.	See that there is no undue friction or mechanical resistance anywhere.	

Sparking at the brushes	Armature faults	Short-circuited coils.	A. Remove copper dust, solder or other metallic contact between commutator bars. B. See that clamping rings are perfectly free, and insulated from commutator bars; no copper dust, carbonized oil, etc., to cause an electrical leak. C. Test for cross connection or short-circuit, and if such is found rewind armature to correct. D. See that brush holders are perfectly insulated. No copper dust, carbon dust, oil or dust, to cause an electrical leak. *See 1, 2, 60.*	12
		Broken coils.	A. Bridge the break temporarily by staggering the brushes, until machine can be shut down (to save bad sparking) and then repair. B. Shut down machine if possible, and repair loose or broken connection to commutator bar. C. If coil is inside, rewinding is the only sure remedy. May be temporarily repaired by connecting to next coil, across mica. D. Solder commutator lugs together, or put in a "jumper," and cut out, and leave open the broken coil. Be careful not to short-circuit a good coil in doing this. *See 12.*	13
		Cross connections.	Cross connections may have same effect as short-circuit, treat as such, *see 12.* Each coil should test complete without cross and no ground.	14

161. Direct-current Generator and Motor Troubles. (From MACHINERY, by special permission)—*Continued*

Heating of parts	**Armature**	Overloaded.	Overload. Too many amperes, lights, or too much power being taken from machine. *See* 11, 12, 13, 14. 15
		Short-circuit.	Short-circuited. Generally dirt, etc., at commutator bars. *See* 11, 12, 13, 14. 16
		Broken circuit.	Broken circuit. Often caused by a loose or broken band. *See* 11, 12, 13, 14. 17
		Cross connection.	Cross connection. Often caused by a loose coil abrading on another coil or core. *See* 11, 12, 13, 14. 18
		Moisture in coils.	Dry out by gentle heat. May be done by sending a small current through, or causing machine to generate a small current itself, by running slowly. 19
		Eddy currents in core.	Iron of armature hotter than coils after a run. Faulty construction. Core should be made of finely laminated insulated sheets. No remedy but to rebuild. 20
	Field coils	Friction.	Hot boxes or journals may affect armature. *See* 23, 33 below. 21
		Excessive current. — Shunt.	*A.* Decrease voltage at terminals by reducing speed. Increase field resistance by winding on more wire, finer wire, or putting resistance in series with fields. 22
		Excessive current. — Series.	*B.* Decrease current through fields by shunt, removing some of field winding or rewind with coarser wire.
			Note.—Excessive current may be from a short-circuit or from moisture in coils, causing a leakage. *See* 10, 24.
		Eddy currents.	Pole pieces hotter than coils after short run, due to faulty construction, or fluctuating current; if latter, regulate, and steady current. 23
		Moisture in coils.	Coils show less than normal resistance, may cause short-circuit or body contact to iron of dynamo. Dry out as in 19. *See also* 22 *note*. 24
	Bearings	Not sufficient or poor oil.	*A.* See that plenty of good mineral oil, filtered clean, and free from grit, feeds; but be careful that it does not get on commutator or brush holder. *See* 12. 25
			B. Cylinder oil or vaseline may be used if necessary to complete run, mixed with sulphur or white lead, or hydrate of potash. Then clean up and put in good order.

162. Direct-current Generator and Motor Troubles—*Continued*

Heating of parts	**Bearings**	Dirt or grit in bearings.	A. Wash out grit with oil while running, then clean up and put in order. Be careful about flooding commutator and brush holder. B. Remove caps and clean and polish journals and bearings perfectly, then replace. See that all parts are free and lubricate well. C. When shut down, if hot, then remove bearings and let them cool naturally, then clean, scrape and polish, assemble; see that all parts are free and lubricate well.	26
		Rough journals or bearings.	Smooth and polish in a lathe, removing all burrs, scratches, tool marks, etc., and rebabbitt old boxes and fit new ones.	27
		Journals too tight in bearings; bent shaft.	Slacken cap bolts, put in liners and retighten till run is over, then scrape, ream, etc., as may be needed, bend or turn true in lathe or grinder. Possibly a new box or shaft will be needed.	28 29
		Bearings out of line.	Loosen bearing bolts, line up and block, until armature is in center of pole pieces, ream out dowel and bolt holes and secure in new position.	30
		End pressure of pulley hub or shaft collars.	A. See that foundation is level and armature has free end motion. B. If there is no end motion, file or turn ends of boxes or shoulders on shaft to provide end motion. C. Then line up shaft and belt, so that there is no end thrust on shaft, but that the armature plays freely endways when running.	31
		Belt too tight.	A. Reduce load so that belt may be loosened and yet not slip. Avoid vertical belts if possible. B. Choose larger pulleys, wider and longer belts with slack side on top. Vibrating and flapping belts cause winking lamps.	32
		Armature out of center of pole pieces.	A. Bearings may be worn out and need replacing, throwing armature out of center. *See 36.* B. Center armature in polar space, and adjust bearings to suit. *See 30.* C. File out polar space to give equal space all round. D. Spring pole away from armature; this may be difficult or impossible in large machines.	33

163. Direct-current Generator and Motor Troubles—*Continued*

Noises	Armature or pulley out of balance.	Faulty construction, armature and pulley should have been balanced when made. May be helped by balancing on knife edges now.	34
	Armature strikes or rubs pole pieces.	A. Bend or press down any projecting wires, and secure with tie bands. B. File out pole pieces where armature strikes. *See* 30, 33.	35
	Collars or shoulders on shaft strike or rub box.	Bearings may be loose or worn out. Perhaps new bearings are needed. *See* 30, 31.	36
	Loose bolt connection or screws.	See that all bolts and screws are tight, and examine daily to keep them so.	37
	Brushes sing or hiss.	A. Apply stearic acid (adamantine) candle, vaseline, or cylinder oil to commutator and wipe off; only a trace should be applied. B. Move brushes in and out of holder to get a firm, smooth, gentle pressure, free from hum or buzz. *See* 3, 6, 7, 8, 9, 31.	38
	Flapping of belt.	Use an endless belt if possible, if a laced belt must be used, have square ends neatly laced.	39
	Slipping of belt from overload.	Tighten belt or reduce load. *See* 32.	40
	Humming of armature lugs or teeth.	A. Slope end of pole piece so that armature does not pass edges all at once. B. Decrease magnetism of field, or increase magnetic capacity of tooth.	41
Speed / **Runs too fast**	Engine fails to regulate with varying load.	Adjust governor of engine to regulate properly, from no-load to full-load, or get a better engine.	42
	Series motor, too much current, and runs away.	A. Series motor on constant current—(1) Put in a shunt and regulate to proper current; (2) use regulator or governor to control magnetism of field for varying load. B. Series motor on constant potential—(1) Insert resistance and reduce current; (2) use a proper regulator or controlling switch; (3) change to automatic speed-regulating motor.	43

164. Direct-current Generator and Motor Troubles—*Continued*

Speed	Runs too fast	Shunt motor	Field rheostat not properly set. Not proper current. Motor not properly proportioned.	A. Adjust field rheostat to control motor.	44
				B. Use current of proper voltage and no other, with a proper rheostat.	
				C. Get a better motor, one properly designed for the work.	
	Runs too slow	*See note below table.*		45, same as 42; 46, *see* 11 *A*; 47, short-circuit in armature, *see* 12; 48, rubbing armature, *see* 35; 49, friction, *see* 3 *B*; 50, weak magnetic field, *see* 10.	
Motor	Stop or fail to start		Great overload. *See* 11 *F* and *G*.	Open switch, find and repair trouble. Keep switch open and rheostat "off" to see if everything is right.	51
			Excessive friction. *See* 25, 33, 35.	Shunt motor on constant potential circuit, fuse may blow or armature burn out.	52
		Circuit open	Fuse melted or switch open.	A. Find and repair trouble after opening switch, then put in fuse. *See* 11 *C*.	53
			Broken wire or connection.	B. Open switch, find and repair trouble. *See* 13.	
			Brushes not in contact.	C. Open switch and adjust. *See* 5.	
			Current fails or is shut off at station.	D. Open switch and return starting box lever to off position, wait for current.	
			Short-circuit of field.	Test for and repair if possible. Examine insulation of binding posts and brush holders.	54
			Short-circuit of armature. Short-circuit of switch.	Poor insulation, dirt, oil, and copper, or carbon dust often result in a short-circuit.	56
			Runs backward. Wrong connections.	Connect up correctly per diagram; if no diagram is at hand, reverse connections to brushes or others until direction of rotation is satisfactory.	57

*Note from Line 50.—*45, Engine fails to regulate. 46, Overload. 47, Short-circuit in armature. 48, Striking or rubbing of armature. 49, Friction. 50, Weak magnetic field

165. Direct-current Generator and Motor Troubles—*Continued*

Dynamo or generator	**Reversed residual magnetism**	Reversed current through field coils. Reversed connections. Earth's magnetism. Proximity of another dynamo. Brushes not in right position. *See* 1, 2, 3.	*A.* Use current from another machine or a battery through field in proper direction to correct fault. Test polarity with a compass. *B.* If connections or winding are not known, try one way and test; if not correct reverse connections, try again and test. *C.* Connect up per diagram for desired rotation, see that connections to shunt and series coils are properly made. *See* 57. *D.* Shift brushes until they operate better. *See* 1, 2, 3.	58
		Too weak residual magnetism.	Same as 58 *A*.	59
		Short-circuit in machine.	*See* 12, 54, 56.	60
		Short-circuit in external circuit.	A lamp socket, etc., may be short-circuited or grounded, and prevent building up shunt or compound machines. Find and remedy before closing switch. *See* 54, 56.	61
		Field coils opposed to each other.	Reverse connections of one of field coils and test. Find polarity with compass; if necessary try 58 *A*, *C, D*. If necessary reverse connections and recharge in opposite directions.	62
	Open circuit	Broken wire. Faulty connections. Brushes not in contact. Safety fuses melted or broken. Switch open. External circuit open.	*A.* Search out and repair. *See* 13. *B.* Search out and repair. *See* 37. *C.* Search out and repair. *See* 5. *D.* Search out and repair. *See* 53 *A*. *E.* Search out and repair. *See* 53 *D*. *F.* Search out and repair with dynamo switch open until repairs are completed.	63
		Too great load on dynamo.	Reduce load to pilot lamp on shunt and incandescent machines; after voltage is obtained close switches in succession slowly, and regulate voltage. *See* 11 *A* and 65.	64
		Too great resistance in field rheostat.	Bring up to voltage gradually with rheostat, and watch pilot lamp; regulate carefully.	65

166. Process of Commutation.—The path of the current is as shown in Fig. 118, wherein A is the carbon brush; C, C', C'' are the commutator segments; B, B', B'' are the windings of the armature. At the position shown, coil B is short-circuited by the brush, the current passing into the face of the brush and out again as shown by the dotted line. This local current may be many times greater than the normal intensity and is the one which causes pitting. With perfect commutation, with no sparking or glowing, there should be created in the short-circuited coil under the brush, by virtue of the flux from that pole-tip away from which the armature is revolving, an electromotive force. This should be just great enough to reverse the current within the short-circuited coil and render it equal to the current in the winding proper. Since on one side of the brush the current is in one direction and on the other side in the other direction, the act of commutation beneath the brush reverses this current and permits it to increase to the correct intensity in the opposite direction.

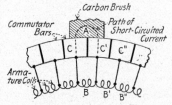

FIG. 118.—Armature coil short-circuited when commutating.

167. With Copper Brushes This Reversal of Current Must be Very Accurately Effected.—With carbon brushes there is a much smaller tendency to spark, hence they will permit of a certain inexactness of commutation adjustment. Experiments indicate that the carbon can resist as much as a 3-volt pressure creating current in the wrong direction and still not spark or glow. This is the property which has necessitated the use of carbon brushes instead of copper on most apparatus. When, however, this voltage, induced in the wrong direction, rises above 3 volts during the passage of the armature coil underneath the brush, trouble from sparking and glowing occurs.

This is the reason that, in a motor, the brushes are pulled backward as far as possible at no-load, so that the coil short-circuited by the brush may enter the fringe or flux

8

from the pole-tip, thus creating the proper reversal of current during the time the coil is passing under the brush. Since adjacent poles are opposite in polarity, only one can provide the proper flux direction for this reversal. In a motor it is always the pole behind the brush and thus the brush requires a backward lead. In a generator it is the pole ahead of the brush in the direction of rotation. Hence, generators require a forward lead.

168. If the Motor Gives Trouble from Glowing and Pitting, the cause is probably this induced current, and the remedy is, first, to insure that the lead of the brushes brings them in the most satisfactory position. If no lead or brush position can be found which will eliminate the trouble, the width of the brush must be changed. The wider the brush the longer does the coil suffer short-circuit, as described. Conversely the narrower the brush, the quicker must the current be reversed. There is, therefore, a width of brush which best satisfies both conditions. Usually, however, where glowing occurs, the cause is too wide a brush, and often serious trouble from this cause can be entirely eliminated by varying the width of the brush perhaps only ⅛ in.; see Art. 196 on "Glowing." Sparking may be due to an open armature circuit; see Art. 200 for a description of the symptoms and the remedy.

169. Sparking Due to Rough Commutator.—The commutator surface may not be perfectly smooth after receiving its last "turn off." The work may have been poorly done by the manufacturer, with the result that the commutator surface, instead of being smooth, is somewhat rough. The result (especially with high-speed commutators) is that the brush does not make good contact with the commutator surface. It may chatter and thus with many motors (especially those of high voltage) the operation will be attended with sparking. As a result, the commutator surface, instead of becoming bright and smooth with time, becomes rough and dull or raw in appearance. Under these conditions the brushes do not make good contact, and, hence, the heat generated, even under proper commutator conditions, owing to the resistance of brush contact, is multiplied several times, with consequent increase of temperature of the commutator. In addition, the friction of brush contact (which should give a coefficient of 0.2) is, with a rough commutator, much higher than it should be, which tends to increase the temperature.

170. Heating of Commutator* may develop from any of the following causes; (*a*) Overload; (*b*) sparking at the brushes; (*c*) too high brush pressure; (*d*) lack of lubrication on commutator.

171. Hot Commutator.—All this (see above) trouble is cumulative. The result is that finally the temperature will rise to a degree where the solder in the commutator will melt, perhaps short-circuiting or open-circuiting the winding. A commutator will stand very slight sparking, but where it is noticeable and where it is continued for long periods of time,

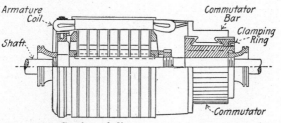

Fig. 119.—Section of direct-current motor armature.

trouble is liable to result. Where the load is usually very light and where full-load or overload are infrequent, a smoothing of the commutator automatically occurs during the light-load period. This is the reason that certain railway motors, which sometimes show sparking under their normal hour rating load, give satisfaction as to commutation. The coasting of the car smooths up the imperceptible damage done by the sparking during the heavy load.

172. Loose Commutator Segments.—A further and more serious cause of sparking and commutator trouble is due to the fact that the commutator may not be "settled" when shipped by the manufacturer. A commutator is made of many parts (Fig. 119), insulated one from another, and all bound together by mechanical clamping arrangements. The segments them-

* Westinghouse Instruction Book.

selves are held by a clamp-ring on each end, which must be insulated from them and which should hold each segment individually from any movement relative to another.   Since the clamp must touch and hold down all segments, a failure to do so in any case results in a loose bar, which moves relatively to the next bar and causes roughness and thus sparking, with all its attendant accumulative troubles.   The roughness of commutators due to poor turning or to poor design is shown uniformly over all the surface of the commutator on which brushes rest.   A roughness due to a high or loose bar is shown by local trouble near the bad bar and its corresponding bars around the commutator.   The jump of the brush occurs at the high bar and is the cause of the sparking.   See also Arts. 174 and 178.

173. Blackening of the Commutator —Sparking due to a loose or high bar causes a local blackening instead of a uniform blackening, which occurs in case of poor design or poor commutator surface resulting from poor turning.   Also, if the speed of the commutator is low enough, there will be a spark at the time the bad segment passes the brush.   At ordinary speeds, or where there are several loose bars, the sparking in appearance will not be different from that due to poor design or poor turning.   In such a case an examination of the commutator surface must be made to identify the cause.   The slightest movement of a bar, especially with the higher-voltage and high-commutator-speed machines, may cause the trouble.   A splendidly designed motor may show very poor operation, due to a commutator fault.

174. Correcting Commutator Roughness.—The proper way to correct the rough surface of a commutator will be determined by the condition of the commutator.   Where the commutator is very rough or eccentric the armature should be taken out of the machine and the commutator turned to a true cylindrical surface in a lathe.   Where the commutator is only reasonably rough it may be trued by filing, using an arrangement similar to that in Fig. 120, which is described in detail in a following paragraph.   Where the roughness is due to poor turning or to ordinary operation, it may then be

smoothed with a piece of ordinary grindstone (Fig. 121). Sandpaper held on a block of wood (Fig. 122) which has been cut

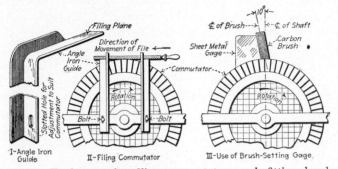

FIG. 120.—Equipment for filing commutators and fitting brushes.
(POWER, Aug. 29, 1916, p. 316.)

to fit the cylindrical surface of the commutator may also be
used for this purpose but it is
not, apparently, as effective as
the grindstone.

**175. To Smooth a Commuta-
tor with a Piece of Grindstone**
(Fig. 121) it should be cut to
convenient size and held by the
hand against the commutator.
If possible, it should be rounded

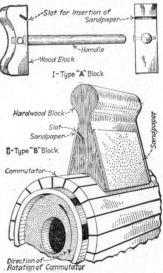

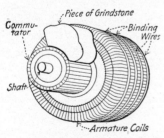

FIG. 121.—Smoothing commutator
with grindstone.

FIG. 122.—Sandpapering blocks
of two different types.

out to the shape of the commutator, though the rounding is
not absolutely necessary except when the surface is exceed-

ingly irregular. A commutator can thus be ground on low-voltage machines without removing the brushes from the commutator and during the ordinary operation of the motor under load. When sparking is due to poor turning, grinding causes the sparking to entirely disappear. This is also a good method of cleaning the surface of brushes which have become coated with copper from the use of sandpaper in fitting them to the commutator surface.

176. Some Kinds of Sandpaper if used to give a brush surface or to smooth a commutator with the brushes down, imbed in the face of the brush hard material which lodges there, cutting the commutator and thus collecting about itself copper from the commutator. An examination of the face of the brush after running a time will show these collections either in spots or all over the face of the brush. The sandstone, used as suggested, removes all this.

177. Where Roughness or Sparking are Due to a Loose Bar, Grinding Will Do No Good.—Then a different process for correction must be used. It consists first in tightening the clamp-rings which hold down the segments so that they touch and hold, each one preventing any relative movements of the bars. After this has been done, produce a smooth commutator surface by turning if the bar is much displaced, or by filing or grinding if it is but slightly displaced.

178. In Truing a Commutator with a File (Fig. 120) a gage or rest of some sort should be employed to insure that the commutator will be improved rather than injured by the filing process. The file rest should be bolted securely to the bearing or to some part of the frame of the machine. The two planes of the rest which project over the commutator should lie exactly parallel to it. Then the armature is rotated at normal speed and a flat smooth file is carefully pushed over the planes. It will cut away the metal of the planes and also that of the commutator. Chalk should be used on the file to prevent it from tearing the copper and the file should be cleaned frequently. At intervals, place a steel straight edge along the commutator surface parallel to the shaft to check the work as it proceeds. After filing, the commutator surface should be finished with very fine sandpaper or preferably with a piece of grindstone (Fig. 121) as described above. A file rest of a type having adjustable filing-surface plates and arranged for bolting to the pedestal bearing of a machine is illustrated in Fig. 123.

179. To Correct Loose-commutator Troubles.—First, force the clamps of the commutator down firm, so that when the commutator is at normal temperature the clamping rings cannot be screwed down further without excessive effort. This is necessary so that all the bars may have a direct pressure from the clamp, rendering any movement, up or down, impossible. Second, after having drawn the clamps down, smooth off the surface of the commutator, using one of the processes described above.

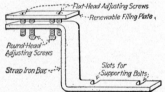
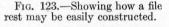

FIG. 123.—Showing how a file rest may be easily constructed.

179a. To Get the Clamps Down Firm run the machine under load; if roughness appears, shut down at a convenient time, and, while hot, tighten the clamping rings. If it is found that the tightening bolts can be screwed up somewhat, the machine should again be put in service for at least four hours at the end of which time shut it down again and again tighten the bolts. If, now, no more slack can be taken up on tightening bolts, the commutator should be surfaced, either by turning with a tool or by grinding.

180. The Slotting of Commutators.[*]—There seems to be a prevalent idea that slotting should cure all commutator troubles, irrespective of their causes. This is not true, but slotting is a cure for certain specific troubles. Where the peripheral speed of the commutator is so slow that the dirt which may collect in the slots between commutator bars will not be thrown out by centrifugal force, slotting may

[*] Alan Bennett, AMERICAN MACHINIST, Sept. 26, 1912.

aggravate rather than correct commutation difficulties. See also Art. 186.

181. The Principal Reason for Slotting Commutators is to relieve the commutators of high mica, that is, mica that projects above the surface. High mica is generally due to one of two causes: either the mica is too hard and does not wear down at an equal rate with the copper, or the commutator does not hold the mica securely between the segments, allowing it to work out by the combined action of centrifugal force and the heating and cooling of the commutator. It is evident that a commutator with a surface made irregular by projecting mica rotating at high speed under a brush, must impart to the brush a vibratory movement, and thus impair the close contact that should exist between the brush and commutator. The result is that sparking takes place more or less violently, depending on the condition of the commutator surface and the rate of speed. This condition generally manifests itself after the machine has been running for some time, and in many cases will account for the development of sparking which did not occur at the time of installation. Often a case of this kind is aggravated by increasing the brush tension, causing a still faster rate of wear of copper over mica, with an attendant increased heating of the commutator.

182. What is Accomplished by Slotting.—A harder brush may at times be used, with the idea of grinding off the mica and thus bringing it down to the commutator surface. Instead of curing the trouble, the commutator will, in the majority of cases, assume the raw appearance of being freshly sandpapered, instead of the glossy surface it should have, and both brush and commutator will wear rapidly. This condition can be restored to normal and the commutator kept to a true surface by slotting, after which, with proper care and the use of proper brushes, commutator troubles will generally cease, provided the electrical design of the machine is not at fault. Even then there are cases that may be benefited to a certain extent by slotting, by reason of the good brush contact obtained. The majority of cases that show improvement are the ones in which the trouble is not inherent in the design of the machine, but is due to mechanical causes.

183. With a Slotted Commutator It is Possible to Use a Brush of Fine Grain and Soft Texture, inasmuch as there is not the same tendency to wear away the brush as with an unslotted commutator. The commutator should then take on the much-desired polish that is generally not attainable with the harder brush. The life of both brush and commutator will be increased, and friction and the consequent heating will be reduced. These advantages will effect a saving that will more than offset the cost of slotting.

184. Various Methods of Slotting.—There is a variety of slotting devices on the market. Some are designed to operate with the armature swung between the centers of a lathe; others use a special tool in a shaper, with the armature secured to its bed. Still others are used by hand with the armature resting on blocks. In all cases the full width of the mica should be removed, and the resulting slot carefully cleaned from burrs and rough edges. It is not necessary that the slotting be carried deeply in the commutator. One-sixteenth of an inch is generally considered sufficient. See also Art. 186.

185. A Slotted Commutator Should Have Proper and Frequent Care, as there is a chance of small particles of copper being dragged across from bar to bar, and for dirt, oil and carbon dust to accumulate in the slots and short-circuit the commutator.

186. High Mica in Commutators.—Some direct-current generators and motors, under certain conditions, roughen up their commutators after a short term of service, although there seems to be no excessive sparking under or at the edges of the brushes. This may occur even though the commutator has been well "settled." The commutator performs as if the mica, used between bars to insulate the various segments one from another, had protruded upward, causing roughness and excessive sparking.

187. Actual Raising of the Mica is a Very Rare Occurrence, and, if it occurs, does so at certain spots and is easily and positively identified. An actual uniform protruding of mica, all over a commutator, as described, is practically an unknown phenomenon. What actually does occur is an eating away of the copper surface of the commutator, leaving the high mica between the bars. A good machine will not spark enough to cause this condition. A poor machine will.

188. The Phenomenon of High Mica is Easily Identified, as the commutator surface appears "raw" all over instead of smooth and bright with a good brown gloss. If allowed to continue, a general roughness appears, accompanied by sparking, until finally the sparking and heating will increase so much that the machine may flash over from brush to brush, blowing the fuses or opening the circuit-breakers. The trouble is aggravated if the motor operates continuously under heavy load. If there are periods of light load, the commutator has an opportunity to be smoothed down by the brushes. This condition is appreciated by railway motor designers. A railway motor coasts a considerable portion of the time. Thus the commutator is smoothed, neutralizing the roughening occurring under load.

189. To Remedy a Roughened, High-mica Commutator. —(1) Use the machine on work where the load is somewhat intermittent; (2) replace it altogether; or (3) slot the commutator. Then, as there are no longer two different materials to wear down or to be worn away by sparking, an unequal surface will not result. The mica need be cut down only $\frac{1}{16}$ in. and a narrow, sharp chisel will do the work satisfactorily. No trouble will result from short-circuiting in this case (if the rotational speed of the machine is sufficiently great) since centrifugal force keeps the slots clean. Some manufacturers ship their machines with the commutators slotted.

190. Brushes, Their Adjustment and Care.*—The position of the brushes on a direct-current machine should be on or

* WESTINGHOUSE INSTRUCTION BOOK.

near the no-load neutral point of the commutator. This neutral point on most standard, non-commutating-pole machines is in line with the center of the pole and the brushes should be set a little in advance of this neutral point. The brushes of non-commutating-pole generators should be given a slight "forward lead" in the direction of rotation of the armature. Motor brushes should be set somewhat back of the neutral point, the "backward lead" in this case being approximately equal to the forward lead on generators. The exact position in either case is that which gives the best commutation at normal voltage for all loads. In no case should the brushes be set far enough from the neutral point to cause dangerous sparking at no-load.

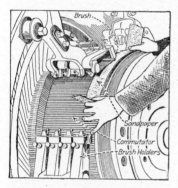

Fig. 124.—Sandpaper should be held close to the commutator.

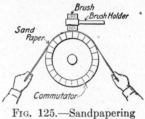

Fig. 125.—Sandpapering brushes.

191. The Ends of All Brushes Should be Fitted to the Commutator so that they make good contact over their entire bearing faces. This can be most easily accomplished after the brush holders have been adjusted and the brushes inserted. Lift a set of brushes sufficiently to permit a sheet of sandpaper to be inserted. Draw the sandpaper under the brushes (Figs. 124 and 125) being careful to keep the ends of the paper as close to the commutator surface as possible to avoid rounding the edges of the brushes. Start with coarse sandpaper and finish with fine sandpaper. The sandpaper should be pulled under the brushes only in the direction of rotation of the commutator because, since brushes always fit loosely in their holders, accurate fitting is otherwise impos-

sible. When pulling the strip of sandpaper back to the starting position the brush should be raised in its holder so that it
does not then touch the sandpaper. Each set of brushes
should be similarly treated in turn. If the brushes are copper-
plated, their edges should be slightly beveled, so that the
copper does not contact with the commutator.

192. A Carbon Brush Should Exert a Pressure of about
$1\frac{1}{2}$ lb. per sq. in. on the commutator. The pressure in
any case may be determined by
using a spring balance as suggested in Fig. 126. Then, the
tension of the spring should be
adjusted so that: *Total pressure
in pounds* ÷ *brush contact area
in square inches* = $1\frac{1}{2}$. The
brush pressure is the reading, in
pounds, of the spring balance
when the tension exerted is just
sufficient to raise the brush
from the surface of the commutator.

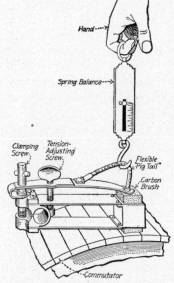

**193. Brush Contact Resist-
ance.**— If adjustment of brush
position gives no relief, the fit
of the brush upon the commutator may be poor. Any resistance in series with a motor
armature causes a drop in speed
as the load comes on, the drop

FIG. 126.—Method of determining pounds brush pressure
with a spring balance.

increasing almost directly in proportion to the armature-
circuit resistance (see Art. 58).

The resistance of surface contact of a carbon brush is a
formidable factor, particularly with low-voltage and high-cur-
rent machines. This contact resistance is, at ordinary brush
densities, about 0.028 ohm per sq. in. The specific resistance
of carbon itself is 0.002 ohm. Hence, for ordinary carbon, the
contact resistance only is of consequence. The resistance of
the carbon is negligible.

EXAMPLE.—An ordinary carbon brush operates at a current density of 35 amp. per sq. in. Then assuming a machine having one brush of 1 sq. in. cross-section for each polarity the brush contact voltage drop for the machine is $2 \times 35 \times 0.028 = 1.96$ volts. The specific resistance is 0.002 ohm, giving a voltage drop through the carbon itself, assuming a length of brush of $1\frac{1}{2}$ in., of 0.21 volt, which is negligible as compared with the drop of 2 volts due to surface contact.

194. The Drop in Voltage Due to Contact Resistance is Greatly Increased if the Fit of the Brushes or the Commutator is Poor, which may be due either to the cutting of grooves in its face by the use of coarse sandpaper, or to a part of the carbon not touching the commutator. Hence, when the drop of speed is excessive, this condition should be carefully inspected. Finally, the spacing of the brushes must be checked. Unequal spacing may not only produce a large drop in speed, but will reduce the efficiency and life of both brushes and commutator.

195. Sparking of the Brushes may be due to one of the following causes* (see also Dynamo-troubles Table): (a) The machine may be overloaded; (b) the brushes may not be set exactly at the point of commutation—a position can always be found where there is no perceptible sparking, and at this point the brushes should be set and secured; (c) the brushes may be wedged in the holders; (d) the brushes may not be fitted to the circumference of the commutator; (e) the brushes may not bear on the commutator with sufficient pressure; (f) the brushes may be burnt on the ends; (g) the commutator may be rough; if so, it should be smoothed off; (h) a commutator bar may be loose or may project above the others; (i) the commutator may be dirty, oily or worn out; (j) the carbon in the brushes may be unsuitable; (k) the brushes may not be equally spaced around the periphery of the commutator; (l) some brushes may have extra pressure and may be taking more than their share of the current; (m) high mica, (n) vibration of the brushes. The above are the more common causes, but sparking may be due to an open circuit or loose connection in the armature (see Art. 200).

* WESTINGHOUSE INSTRUCTION BOOK.

196. Glowing and Pitting of Carbon Brushes may be due to either of two causes, poor design or a wrong position of the brushes on the commutator.   The error of design may be only in the choice of width of carbon brush used.   The pitting is due to glowing.   If the glowing is at the edge of the carbon it is plainly visible and easily located.   It may, however, occur underneath the carbon so that it can be seen only with difficulty.   Such glowing pits the carbon face by heat disintegration.   With some machines three-fourths of the brush face may be eaten away and the pits may be, perhaps, $\frac{1}{4}$ in. to $\frac{1}{2}$ in. deep when discovered.   A usual (incorrect) decision is that the current per square inch of contact is too great, the calculation being made by dividing the *line amperes* by *the square inch cross-section of either the positive or the negative brushes*. If this calculation gives a value under 45 or 50, it is certain that the cause of the trouble has not been judged correctly.

197. The Real Cause of Glowing is, to be sure, excessive current through the brush, but this is not the line current if the calculation, as stated, shows a brush-face density below 50 amp. per sq. in.   It is a local current caused by the short-circuiting of two or more segments of the commutator by the brush resting upon them.   The usual overlap of a carbon brush is about two segments, and while these two segments are under the brush, the armature coils connected to them are short-circuited.   If the design of the machine is such that the coil so short-circuited encloses stray flux from the pole-tip, this flux will create in the short-circuited coil a current, perhaps many times larger than the brush is capable of carrying, with the result that the glowing and pitting occurs.

198. Blow Holes in Machine Frame Castings Sometimes Cause Sparking.—Such blow holes, Fig. 127, may be large enough to increase the reluctance of the magnetic circuit sufficiently that the field intensity in the air gap is not sufficient to eliminate sparking.   It has been proposed* to use X-ray apparatus to locate blow holes in electrical machine castings when the indications are that high reluctance in the magnetic circuit is the cause of brush difficulties.

* ELECTRICAL WORLD, May 1, 1915, p. 1122.

199. Chattering of Brushes is sometimes experienced on direct-current machines. Chattering under certain conditions may become so prominent as to not only be of annoyance, but as to actually break the carbons. An examination of the commutator will reveal no roughness, the surface being, perhaps, perfectly smooth and bright. This trouble occurs principally with the type of brush holder which has a box guide for the carbon. The spring which forces the brush into contact rests on top of the carbon which has fairly free play in the box guide. Chattering usually occurs with high-speed commutators, running at 4,000 to 5,000 ft. per min., peripheral speed.

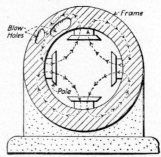

Fig. 127.—Showing "blow holes" in a direct-current machine frame.

Such brush holders are necessary for commutators which, like those on engine-driven machines, may run out of true on account of the shaft play in the bearings caused by the reciprocating motion of the engine. The clamped type of holder is usually free from bad chattering but rocks on a commuta

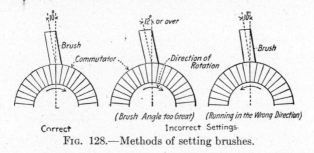

Fig. 128.—Methods of setting brushes.

tor that runs out, causing poor contact and perhaps sparking. Lubricating the commutator causes the chattering to immediately disappear, but there is no commutator compound which gives a lubricating effect lasting over possibly a half hour. Thus it is not practical to lubricate often enough to prevent the chattering.   There will be no chattering if the angle of the brush with the radial line, passing through the center of the carbon and the center of the commutator, is less than 10 deg. and if the carbon trails on the commutator instead of leads.   Fig. 128, *I*, shows the setting which will stop all serious chattering and Fig. 128, *II* and *III* show settings which may give trouble.

200. Sparking may be Due to an Open Armature Circuit. —The "open" may be in the winding of the armature proper or it may, and more frequently, be due to a loose or broken connection where the armature lead is soldered to a commutator bar.   (Open circuits in armatures may be located by testing methods as described in Art. 213.)   Where an armature lead is thus broken, the most effective remedy is resoldering.   If the location of the open circuit is within the winding and hence not readily available, the commutator bars on each side of the "open" can, for a temporary repair, be shunted by bridging a piece of copper, by soldering or otherwise, across the two segments on either side of the break.

201. The Symptoms of Trouble Due to an Open Armature Circuit are vicious sparking when the machine is in operation. The sparking due to this defect is unlike that due to any other because the resulting spark is "long" and "heavy" and frequently appears to extend around the entire circumference of the commutator.   A bright spark will occur each time the break passes the brush position.   It is particularly destructive in its action and shortly "eats away" the mica between the two segments on each side of the open.   Thus, on a machine which has been in operation, the offending coil may be located by the damaged segments to which it connects.   The temporary bridge referred to above should be arranged between these two segments and around the "eaten-away" mica.

202. Ring Fire* is the name that has been given to that type of sparking where rings of fire embrace the circumference of the commutator, wholly or partially encircling it.   Ring fire

---

* See article, "Ring Fire and Flashing" by Gordon Fox, POWER, March 28, 1916, p. 440.

may be subivided into two classifications: (1) ordinary ring fire which is of a reddish color and which may exist to a limited extent with all machines; (2) ring fire caused by armature defects, which is a bluish-green color and more intense than the ordinary type. Ring fire is ordinarily due to minute arcs between adjacent commutator bars. The condition may be aggravated by conducting materials lodged in or on the surface of the mica insulation between bars. Current passing through these conducting paths between the bars renders the particles incandescent. The fine carbon ground from the brushes by the normal operation of the machine or particles of copper from a newly turned commutator are the most frequent causes of this difficulty. Secondary causes are oil, paraffin and commutator compounds which are sometimes used, in which particles of conducting material may lodge. Furthermore, oil may carbonize on the mica segments, forming a conducting path. Where mica insulation between segments has been eaten away in certain isolated locations it is probable that the difficulty is due to the carbonizing of oil or some other materials above suggested.

Undercut commutators, particularly those rotating at low peripheral speed, are particularly subject to ring fire because oils, greases and conducting materials can readily lodge between segments due to the undercutting, hence the commutators of slow-speed machines should be cleaned frequently with a stiff brush to prevent the lodgment of foreign materials in them. High-peripheral-speed commutators will not, ordinarily, require such treatment, because with them the centrifugal force developed is usually sufficient to prevent the retention of the dirt in the slots between segments. In machines of certain designs the voltage between the adjacent segments under the pole-tips may be great enough to produce ring fire. The compensated winding (Art. 37) provides an effective correction for this difficulty. Where the mica segments are thin, ring fire is more liable to occur. Furthermore, it may be encountered more frequently with slow-speed than with high-speed machines because with a high-peripheral-speed commutator the segments do not remain in the zones where the ring

9

fire is developed for a sufficiently long period to permit the formation of the minute arcs.

203. Flashing is that sort of commutator sparking where an arc attains considerable length and flashes between brush holder studs. It may occur in a normal machine at the instant when an excessively high e.m.f. is impressed across the machine or it may be due to the cumulative effect of a number of the causes which promote sparking. Flashing is more liable to occur in motors than in generators.

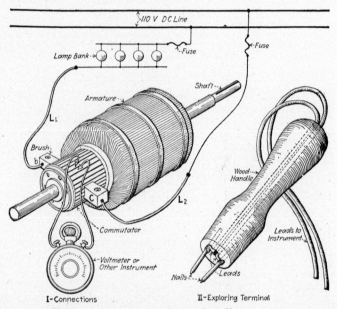

Fig. 129.—Circuit and equipment for testing direct-current armatures for trouble with direct-current.

204. Direct-current Armatures can be Tested for the Common Troubles with the arrangement of Figs. 129 and 131. Terminals b and c are clamped to the commutator at opposite sides and connected with a source of steady current through an adjustable resistance and, preferably but not necessarily, an ammeter. The terminals of a low-reading voltmeter (a galvanometer can often be used) are connected to two bare metal points or "exploring terminals," which are separated by an insulating block, j. Exploring terminals may also be

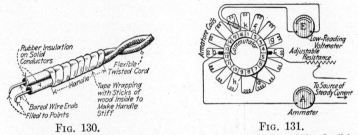

FIG. 130.

FIG. 131.

FIG. 130.—A type of easily-made exploring terminals. (The flexible cord leads are soldered to the solid copper wires within the tape-wrapping handle.)

FIG. 131.—Method of testing an armature.

arranged as shown in Figs. 129, *II* and 130. In use, the current is adjusted to produce a convenient deflection of the

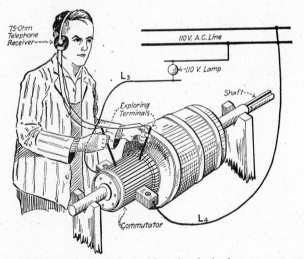

FIG. 132.—Illustrating a method of locating faults in an armature with alternating current.

voltmeter when each of the points rests on an adjacent bar. The points are moved around the commutator and bridged across the insulation between every two bars. If the voltmeter deflection is the same for every pair of bars it indicates that there is no short-circuit in the armature.

205. In Testing Armatures Where Only Alternating Current or Low-voltage Cells are Available a telephone receiver (Figs. 132, 133 and 134) may be used instead of an electrical-measuring

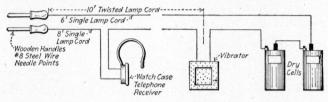

Fig. 133.—Fault-locating outfit consisting of telephone receiver, vibrator and dry cells.

instrument for a detector. The variations or appearance or disappearance of the sound in the receiver, as the test is being conducted, enables the operator to localize the trouble. The alternating current (Fig. 132) will cause a hum in the telephone receiver and the pulsating current produced by the vibrator (Figs. 133 and 134) effects the same result. The vibrator may

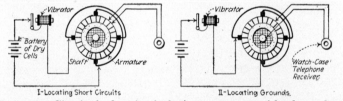

Fig. 134.—Circuits for locating faults in an armature with a low-voltage source and a vibrator.

be an ordinary vibrating bell or buzzer connected in series in the circuit as shown in the illustrations.

206. High-voltage Alternating Current for Testing Armatures is sometimes used (Fig. 135) for high-resistance grounds which may not be detectable where a low e.m.f. is used for testing. Such high-resistance grounds may not in normal operation make their presence known until there is also a ground on the supply system feeding the motor. In using this apparatus the procedure is merely to connect one terminal, A, of the high-voltage source to the commutator, and the other terminal, B, to the shaft. When the high voltage, E_H, is impressed on the armature, this will, usually, break down the insulation at the weak point and render the location of the ground apparent by the smoke which will emanate from the point of breakdown. Fuses, or circuit-breakers, C_1, C_2, should be inserted in the supply circuit to prevent the disastrous effects of a short-circuit.

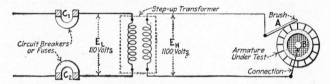

FIG. 135.—Method of obtaining and applying "high potential" for armature fault location.

207. An Alternating-current Inducing Coil is Sometimes Used for Localizing Armature Troubles.*—Such a coil is illustrated in Fig. 136 while the methods of its application are illustrated in Fig. 137. The inducer is merely an alternating-current magnet having a U-shaped core composed of sheet-steel laminations. The laminations should be interleaved and hinged at the point H so that the core may be opened or closed to most effectively accommodate armatures of different diameters. In use the core should be opened to such a width that its two poles, P_1 and P_2, will have a separation corresponding to the throw of one armature coil. As shown in Fig. 137 the poles should not touch the armature iron when a test is being made, but an air gap of approximately $\frac{1}{4}$ in. should be allowed.

208. The Principle of Operation of the Inducer is This.— The alternating flux developed by the current in the inducer winding sets up an e.m.f. in the armature coils and if a coil is short-circuited it will cause a current to circulate in that

* PRACTICAL ENGINEER, Oct. 1, 1914, p. 965.

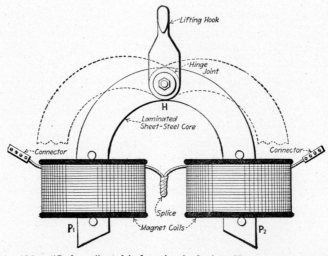

Fig. 136.—"Inducer" used in locating faults in a direct-current armature winding.   It induces an alternating e.m.f. in the armature winding.

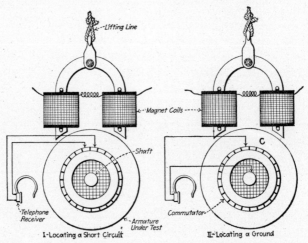

Fig. 137.—Arrangements for locating short circuits and grounds with the alternating-current inducer.

coil. Thus, in making a test the excited inducer is held over the armature, which is rotated. Now, if the armature is slowly rotated, while a small piece of metal is held lightly on the commutator so that it will bridge the segments between each of the bars, there will be, as the armature is rotated, an arc produced each time one of the segments is bridged, provided the segments connect to a normal coil. But, if a coil is open, short-circuited or reversed, there will be no sparking. To determine whether the difficulty is due to an open or a short-circuit, the small iron test strip is bridged across the armature slots. When the coil is short-circuited the induced current which will flow in it will create a flux around the sides of the coil which can be detected with an iron test strip which is moved over the armature coil slots. Furthermore, a short-circuited coil will be quickly heated by the local current flowing in it.

209. The Telephone Receiver Detector Used with the Inducer, Fig. 137, affords a more accurate but somewhat slower method than that described in preceding Art. 207. To locate a short-circuit, Fig. 137, *I*, an exploring terminal connected to the receiver is held on the commutator while the armature is rotated. When the exploring points are bridging a normal coil there will be a hum in the receiver due to the induced alternating current flowing through it. When the points bridge a short-circuited coil there will be little or no hum in the receiver, depending upon the number of short-circuited turns. When the exploring-needle points bridge an open coil, an alternating current of considerable intensity will flow through the receiver and a loud click will be heard. Where a coil is reversed, several of the coils adjacent to it will test "silent." To definitely locate the incorrectly connected coil, it will be necessary to raise some of the coils and trace them out by inspection. To locate a ground, the connections are made as shown in Fig. 137, *II*, and the armature is slowly rotated. When, as the armature is rotated, contactor *C* is on the segment connecting to the grounded coil, no sound will be heard in the receiver but at other locations there will be a sound, the sound diminishing in intensity as the segment connecting to the grounded coil is approached. For locating partial grounds, this method may

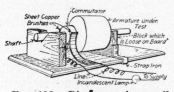

FIG. 138.—Rig for testing small armatures. (ELECTRICAL REVIEW.)

be ineffective, in which case that involving a high alternating voltage (Art. 206) whereby an insulation breakdown may be produced, should be employed.

210. A Rack for Testing Small Armatures using the methods of Figs. 131, 132 and 134 is detailed in Fig. 138. Ordinarily a man and a helper are necessary in testing out an

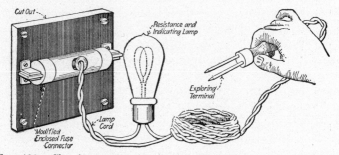

FIG. 139.—Showing application of the "modified fuse connector" for connecting test lamp in series in the testing circuit.

armature but with the appliance shown one operator can locate the faults.

211. A Convenient Arrangement of a Test Lamp and Exploring Terminal is shown in Fig. 139. The flexible cord, and the indicating lamp, which also serves as a resistor for limiting the current, and the exploring terminal can be cut in series with the supply circuit by means of a fuse connector as detailed in Fig. 140.

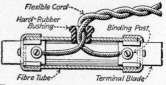

FIG. 140.—Sectional elevation of fuse connector.

With this arrangement the testing set can be quickly cut in service at any point where there is a cut-out. Where it is used, it may be necessary to close the line with a temporary switch or otherwise on the load side of the cut-out. An Edison plug or a ferrule contact fuse can be used instead of the knife-blade contact fuse of Fig. 140 by adopting obvious modifications.

212. A Poor Connection between a Bar and Coil Leads will cause a considerable deflection of the voltmeter (Fig. 131) when one of the points rests on the bar in trouble and the other rests on either of the adjacent bars.

213. An Open-circuited Coil, as *h*, Fig. 131, will prevent the flow of current through its half of the armature. There will be no deflection on that half of the armature until the "open" is bridged, when the voltage of the testing circuit will be indicated.

214. Tests for Open Armature Circuits.—Another method (Fig. 141) is to apply to the commutator, at two opposite points, a low voltage, say from a battery or from a dynamo

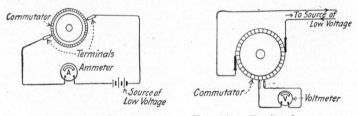

Fig. 141.—Testing for armature open-circuit with an ammeter.

Fig. 142.—Testing for armature open-circuit with a voltmeter.

with a suitable resistance (incandescent lamps for example) in series. Place an ammeter in circuit and clean the surface of the commutator so that it is bright and smooth. The terminal ends leading the current into and out of the commutator should be small, so that each rests only on a single segment (Fig. 141). Note the ammeter reading and rotate the armature slowly. At the point where the open circuit exists the ammeter needle will go to zero if the leads to the commutator bar have become entirely open-circuited. This is because the segment is attached to the winding through the commutator leads.

If the armature does not show the above symptoms, try connecting a low-reading voltmeter or a galvanometer to two adjacent segments while the current is passing through the armature as described from some external low-voltage source (Fig. 142). Note the deflection. Pass from segment to segment in this manner, recording the drop between the successive pair of bars. This drop, if the current is maintained constant from the external source, should be the same between each pair of adjacent segments. If any pair shows a higher drop than the others near it, a higher resistance connection exists there, perhaps causing sparking and biting of the commutator insulation, to a less degree, to be sure, than with an actual open circuit, but enough, perhaps, to cause the trouble requiring the investigation.

215. The Test for Armature Short-circuits, described in the preceding paragraph (Art. 204) is called a "bar to bar" test. It is most valuable in locating faults in armatures. It is the method to use if a short-circuit from one segment to another is suspected. When the section in which the short-circuit, or partial short-circuit, exists comes under the contacts, a low or perhaps no deflection is shown on the galvanometer or voltmeter, thus locating the defective place. Such short-circuits, if they occur when running, owing to defective insulation, burn out the coil short-circuited. When the coil passes through the active field in front of the pole-piece, an immense current is induced in it, causing a destruction of the insulation. When this occurs the coil should be open-circuited if the burning has not already short-circuited it. If practical, it should be bridged over, as suggested in a preceding paragraph.

216. If Two Bars or a Coil is Short-circuited as at f and g (Fig. 131) respectively, there will be little or no voltmeter deflection when the two bars connecting to the "short-circuit" are bridged by the point.

217. A Grounded Armature Coil can be detected in practically the same manner as indicated in Fig. 143 for a field coil. Fig. 144 shows the connections. Impress full voltage on the terminals A and B, clamped to the commutator. Ground one side of the voltmeter on the shaft or spider as at G and touch a contactor C connected to the other side of the voltmeter to all the bars in succession. The minimum deflection will obtain when the bars connecting to the grounded coil are touched. A battery of dry cells, E (Fig. 144), having in series a resistor, R, may be used as a source of energy. A bank of lamps connected in parallel will serve as a resistor. Instead of using a voltmeter as in Fig. 142 a galvanoscope, F (Fig. 144), may be used. Such a galvanoscope may be improvised by winding a coil of wire around a pocket compass but where this device is employed the galvanoscope must be used far enough away from the machine under test so that the compass needle will not be affected by the magnetization of the machine under test.

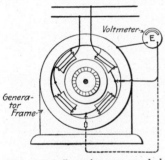

Fig. 143.—Locating a grounded field coil.

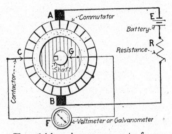

Fig. 144.—Arrangement of connections for locating a ground in an armature.

218. Crossed Coil Leads as at a (Fig. 131) are indicated by a twice normal deflection when the points bridge the bars to which the crossed coils should rightly connect. The crossing of the coil leads connects two coils in series, hence causes twice normal drop. Bridging the bars to which coil h connects will produce a normal deflection, but it will be reversed in direction.

219. Reversed Armature Coil.—Instead of the armature winding progressing uniformly around from bar to bar of the commutator, there may at some point be a coil connected in backward. Such a reversed coil often causes bad sparking. One way to locate such a trouble is to pass a current through the armature, at opposite points on the commutator. Then with a compass explore around the armature the direction of magnetism from slot to slot. If a coil is reversed when the compass comes before it, the needle will reverse, giving a very definite indication of the improperly connected coil.

220. Heating of Armature.*—Heating of the armature may develop from any of the following causes: (*a*) Too great a load; (*b*) a partial short-circuit of two coils heating the two particular coils affected; (*c*) short-circuits or grounds on armature or commutator.

221. Hot Armature Coils.—Sometimes when a new machine is started, local heating occurs in the armature, following the exact shape of the armature coil. This may be because, in receiving its final turning off, the commutator bars were bridged with copper from one segment to another by the action of the turning tool. An examination of the commutator surface will reveal this bridging. When it is removed, satisfactory operation will ensue if the trouble has not gone too far and seriously injured the insulation of the coil.

222. "Flying Grounds," "Flying Short-circuits" and "Flying Open Circuits" sometimes occur in armature windings. These are intermittent troubles which may assert themselves when the machine is hot, after running underload, and its component parts expanded. Then, when it cools, the trouble may automatically correct itself. Sometimes the reverse condition occurs, that is, the fault will be present when the machine is cold, but will be temporarily corrected when it is hot. Furthermore, centrifugal force due to the rotation of the armature may be a factor in the situation, in which case the defect may be present when the armature is rotated at normal speed, but not present when the armature is stationary. Obviously, such troubles are very difficult to locate. About the only way to localize them is to run the machine until the defect has "burnt itself out" or otherwise rendered its presence sufficiently evident that it can be located by the usual testing methods described above.

223. A Grounded Field Coil can be Located (Fig. 143) by connecting a source of voltage to the machine terminals

* WESTINGHOUSE INSTRUCTION BOOK.

having first raised the brushes from the commutator, if it is a direct-current machine. Connect one terminal of the voltmeter to the frame and the other to a lead with a bared end. Tap with the bared end exposed parts of the field circuit. The

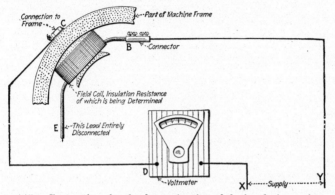

Fig. 145.—Connections for the determination of the insulation resistance of one field coil.

voltmeter deflection will be least near the grounded coil. The insulation resistance of a field coil may be determined with the arrangement of Fig. 145.

224. A Method of Locating an Open-circuited Field Coil is illustrated in Fig. 146. Connect one terminal of the voltmeter to one side of the field-coil circuit and with the bared end of a wire or a contactor, successively touch the junctions of the field-coil leads around the frame. When the open coil is bridged the voltmeter will show a full deflection. Another way: Connect the field-coil circuit terminals to a source of voltage. Con-

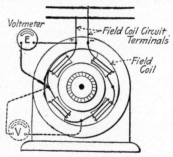

Fig. 146.—Locating an open field coil.

nect the voltmeter successively across each coil as indicated by the dotted lines in Fig. 146.   There will be no deflection on the voltmeter until the open coil is bridged, when the full voltage of the circuit will be indicated.

225. Open Field Circuit.—If, on closing the field switch, no magnetization is detected by trial with any piece of iron, a key for example, there is an open circuit within one of the spools or in the wires leading to these spools. The open circuit can be located by cutting out one spool at a time and allowing current to flow through the rest until the defective spool is discovered. On a two-pole motor try first one spool and then the other. For a very short time, say, 10 min., double voltage can be carried on a spool. On a motor having four or more poles, three spools can always be left in circuit during the search for the open-circuit.

226. Heating of Field Coils* may develop from any of the following causes: (*a*) Too low speed; (*b*) too high voltage; (*c*) too great forward or backward lead of brushes; (*d*) partial short-circuit of one coil; (*e*) overload.

227. Reversed Field-spool Connection.—There may be cases where the manufacturer has shipped a motor with one or more field spools reversed. If such is the case no torque, or, perhaps, very weak torque, will result. Under such conditions a trial with a key or other piece of iron will show proper field magnetism, yet the weakness or total absence of torque will be present, and a trial for polarity (Art. 98) should be made.

228. If a Direct-current Motor will not Start When the Starting Box is Operated and when current is flowing in the armature, an investigation should be made to see if there is a field flux. This can be done by holding a piece of iron, such as a key, against the pole-piece. If the flux exists the key will be drawn strongly against the pole-piece; if there is no flux there will be practically no attraction.

229. Sometimes a Motor When Started will Run in the Wrong Direction.—The only change necessary is to reverse the field connection. Thus Fig. 147 shows at the right the connection for one direction of rotation and at the left, that for the other. Note that in Fig. 147 *I*, the brushes *A* and *A*[1] are

* WESTINGHOUSE INSTRUCTION BOOK.

shifted backward against the direction of rotation. For the opposite rotation, a backward, lead as shown in Fig. 147, *II*, must be chosen.

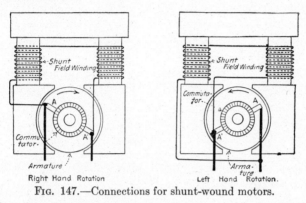

Fig. 147.—Connections for shunt-wound motors.

230. Bearing Troubles of Motors and Generators.—

Modern generators and motors, both alternating- and direct-current, have self-oiling or

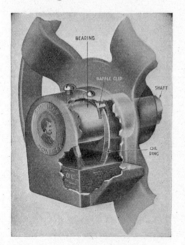

Fig. 148.—Showing the construction of self-oiling bearings used in small-capacity Lincoln Electric Company motors.

(for some machines of the smaller capacities) ball bearings, (Figs. 148 and 149). The self-oiling bearings should be filled to such a height that the rings will carry sufficient oil upon the shaft. If the bearings are too full, oil will be thrown out along the shaft. Watch the bearings carefully from the time the machine is first started until the bearings are warmed up, then note the oil level. The expansion of the oil due to heat and foaming raises the level considerably during that time. The oil should be renewed about once in six months, or oftener if it becomes dirty or causes the bearings to heat.

231. Bearings Must be Kept Clean and Free from Dirt.— They should be examined frequently to see that the oil supply is properly maintained and that the oil rings do not stick. Use only the best quality of oil. New oil should be run through a strainer if it appears to contain any foreign substances. If the oil is used a second time it should first be filtered and, if warm, allowed to cool. If a bearing becomes hot, first feed heavy lubricant copiously, loosen the nuts on the bearing cap, and then, if the machine is belt-connected, slacken the belt. If no relief is afforded by these means, shut down, keeping the machine running slowly until the shaft is cool, in order

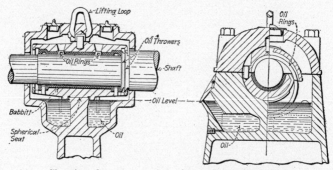

Fig. 149.—Showing the construction of a modern, ring-oiling bearing for a medium, and large-capacity electrical machine.

that the bearing may not "freeze." Renew the oil supply before starting again. A new machine should always be run at a slow speed for an hour or so in order to see that it operates properly. The bearings should be inspected at regular intervals to insure that they always remain in good condition. The higher the speed, the more care should be taken in this regard.

232. A Warm Bearing or "Hot Box" is probably due to one of the following causes: (1) Excessive belt tension. (2) Failure of the oil rings to revolve with the shaft. (3) Rough bearing surface. (4) Improper lining up of bearings or fitting of the journal boxes.

233. Ball Bearings are now being used for electrical machinery, particularly for units of medium and small capacity.

Typical examples of these applications are shown in Figs. 150, 151, and 152. Ball bearings involve less friction loss than do

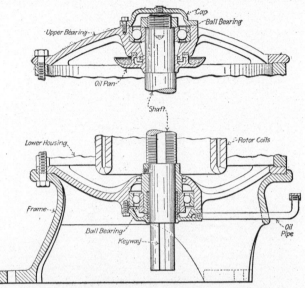

FIG. 150.—Gurney ball bearings in a vertical induction motor. With this arrangement no thrust bearings are necessary.

FIG. 151.—Application of ball bearings to a polyphase squirrel-cage induction motor. (Gurney Bearing Co.)

those of the babbitted type, the friction loss with them being approximately one-quarter of that which obtains with bab-

10

bitted bearings of good construction. This means that where an electrical machine is fitted with ball bearings its bearing friction loss will be negligible. Another desirable feature of ball bearings is that because of their very small friction the wear in them is very slight so that low bearing troubles and variations in air gap due to wear, which is encountered with babbitted bearing machines after they have been in service for a considerable period, is greatly minimized. Experience has indicated that ball bearings, if properly designed and prop-

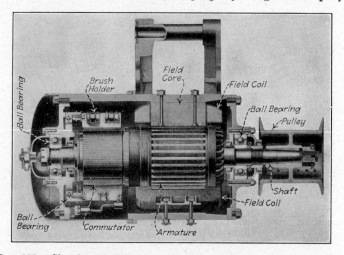

Fig. 152.—Showing application of Gurney ball-bearings in a direct-current, train-lighting generator.

erly applied, will show no measurable wear after many years of continued service. Where bearings of this type are used on vertical motors (Fig. 150), if suitably designed, individual thrust bearings are unnecessary, which tends toward a reduction in weight and initial cost. Good ball bearings need no other attention than a change of the lubricating oil a couple of times a year.

234. To Insure That an Armature is Properly Balanced— if it is not balanced it will probably cause noise when rotating at normal speed—it is necessary to remove the armature from the machine. It is then placed on a balancing stand or on level knife-edge bars (Fig. 153) to ascertain which is the heavy side. If the armature is properly balanced, it will each time, after having been rotated by hand, stop in no particular position, but if it is out of balance it will always stop in the same

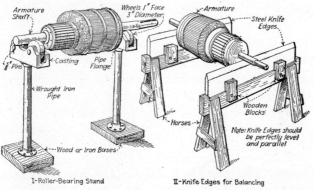

Fig. 153.—Roller-bearing armature stand and knife-edge leveling rig.

position on the balancing rig (Fig. 153), with the heavy side down. The counterbalancing weight which should be added to the light side to properly balance the member may consist of a screw which is turned into a tapped hole in some iron part of the commutator structure. By filing just the proper amount of metal from the screw head, very accurate balance will be obtained. Or instead, a small ball of solder may be sweated to the light side or some of the metal filed from the heavy side. Ascertain by trial just how much metal should be added or removed before attempting to make a permanent correction.

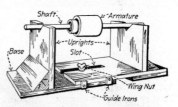

Fig. 154.—A rack for medium-size armatures. (Elec. Rev.)

235. A Rack for Supporting Medium-size Armatures may be constructed as shown in Fig. 154. Such an outfit will not alone be found very convenient but will likely prove a profitable investment in that if used it will tend to prevent damage to the armature winding and end connections.

TESTING OF DIRECT-CURRENT GENERATORS AND MOTORS

236. Motor Testing.—In all of the discussion of this subject, of testing for both direct-current and alternating-current motors, it is assumed that the motor is loaded in the usual way by belting or direct-connecting it to some form of load, and that the object is then to determine whether the motor is over- or underloaded, and approximately what per cent. of full-load it is carrying. All commercial motors have nameplates, giving the rating of the motor and the full-load current in amperes. The per cent. of full-load carried by the machine can, therefore, be determined approximately by measuring the current input and the voltage. If an efficiency test of the apparatus is required, it becomes necessary to use some form of absorption dynamometer, such as a Prony (Art. 239) or other form of brake. The output of the motor can then be determined from the brake readings. The accuracy of all tests is, obviously, dependent upon the accuracy of the instruments employed. Before accepting the results obtained by any test, particularly under light or no-load, one should be certain that the instruments employed are accurate under the conditions encountered.

237. The Horse-power, Torque and Speed Formulas For All Electric Motors follow from the general formula for horse-power, the derivation of which is suggested in Art. 238. Thus,

$$(17) \quad h.p. = \frac{2 \times 3.14 \times T \times r.p.m.}{33,000} = \frac{6.28 \times T \times r.p.m.}{33,000}$$

Then, dividing both numerator and denominator of (17) as simplified, by 6.28:

$$(18) \qquad h.p. = \frac{T \times r.p.m.}{5,252} \qquad \text{(horse-power)}$$

and

(19) $$T = \frac{5{,}252 \times h.p.}{r.p.m.}$$ (pound-foot)

hence

(20) $$r.p.m. = \frac{5{,}252 \times h.p.}{T}$$ (rev. per min.)

Wherein, $h.p.$ = horse-power output of the motor, when it is running at the $r.p.m.$ speed and developing torque T. T = torque in pounds-feet, or, say-ing the same thing in another way, the torque in pounds at 1-ft. radius. $r.p.m.$ = speed of motor, in revolutions per minute.

238. How To Determine the Horse-power Output of an Electric Motor with a Prony Brake is explained in the fol-lowing example (Fig. 155). The principle involved has as its basis the concept of *torque* which is discussed in the au-thor's PRACTICAL ELECTRICITY.

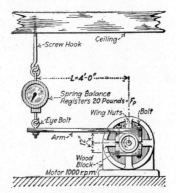

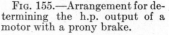

FIG. 155.—Arrangement for de-termining the h.p. output of a motor with a prony brake.

EXAMPLE.—The torque (Fig. 155) is 20 lb. at 4-ft. radius, or 80 lb.-ft., or 80 lb. at 1-ft. radius. Since the motor pulley is turning at the rate of 1,000 r.p.m., a point on its circumference travels: $2 \times \pi \times radius \times r.p.m.$ = $2 \times 3.14 \times 1 \times 1{,}000 = 6{,}280$ *ft. per min.* At its circumfer-ence the pulley is then "overcoming" a resistance of 80 lb. Therefore, it is doing work at the rate of: $80 \times 6{,}280 = 502{,}400$ *ft.-lb. per min.* Since, when work is done at the rate of 33,000 ft.-lb. per min., a horse-power is developed, the motor is then delivering: $502{,}400 \div 33{,}000 = 15.2$ *h.p.* It should be noted that, though the torque at the circumfer-ence of the motor pulley was considered in this example, it is not neces-sary to take the torque at this point. The torque may be taken at any point, if the radius to that point is used, instead of the radius of the pulley. Substituting the values from the above example in formula (18) of Art. 237: $h.p. = (80 \times 1{,}000) \div 5{,}252 = 15.2$ *h.p.* This is the same result secured by the former and longer method.

239. There are Several Different Forms of Prony Brakes, the most important of which are illustrated in Figs. 155, 156 and **157**.   With the brakes of Figs. 155 and 156: *torque, in pounds-feet* $= F_p \times L$.   Where $F_p =$ force, measured in pounds, at the end of the brake arm; and $L =$ the effective length

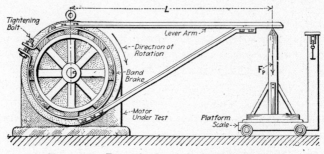

Fig. 156.—Prony brake of the band-brake type.

of the brake arm, in feet, that is, the distance from the center of the shaft to the point at which the force is measured.   For measuring small torques, the self-regulating brake (Fig. 157, *I*)

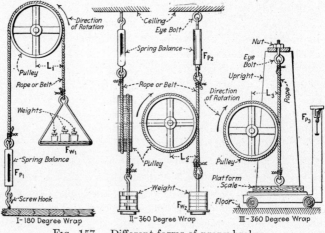

Fig. 157.—Different forms of prony brakes.

may be arranged by setting copper rivets in a leather belt. The rivets per unit of surface should increase from zero at one end of the working surface to a maximum at the other.

Where very small torques are to be measured, a round belt
in a grooved pulley can be used for the band.* The belt
should have a small steel wire wound around it spirally. The
turns of the wire around the belt should increase from zero
at one end to a maximum number at the other.

With the arrangement of Fig. 157, $I : T = (F_{w1} - F_{p1}) \times L_1$.
The distance, L_1, should be measured from the center of the
shaft to the center of the band or belt. At $II : T = (F_{w2} - F_{p2})$
$\times L_2$. With the brake of $III : T = F_{p3} \times L_3$. In all of these
determinations, if F and L are measured in pounds and feet,
respectively, T will be the torque in pounds-feet.

**240. A Direct-current Motor or Generator Magnetization-
curve Test** may be conducted as shown in Fig. 158. See Fig.
18 for a magnetization curve. The object of this test is to

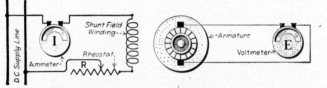

Fig. 158.—Arrangement for obtaining data for plotting a magnetization
graph for a direct-current motor or generator.

determine the variation of armature voltage, without load on the
machine, with different intensities of current flowing through
the field circuit. The armature should be driven at normal
speed. The effective resistance of the rheostat, R, in the field
circuit is varied and the voltage across the armature measured.
The curve obtained by plotting a series of these two values
is usually called magnetization curve or graph of the generator.
It is usual to start with a high resistance in the field circuit
so that very small field current flows, gradually increasing this
current by cutting out the field resistance. When the highest
no-load voltage required is attained, the field current is then
diminished, and the data for what is called the descending (as
opposed to the ascending) magnetization curve are obtained.
The difference in the two curves is due to the lag of the

* H. N. Scheibe, Electric Journal; vol. iv, p. 118.

magnetization behind the magnetizing current, and is due to the hysteresis of the iron in the armature core.

241. A Load and Speed Test of a Direct-current Shunt Motor may be made with the equipment diagrammed in Fig. 159. The procedure in this test is to maintain the voltage applied to the motor constant, and to vary the load by means of a Prony brake (Art. 238) and determine the corresponding variation in speed of the machine and in the current drawn from the supply circuit. If the motor is a constant-speed machine the field resistance is maintained constant. For starting the machine, an ordinary starting rheostat should be inserted.

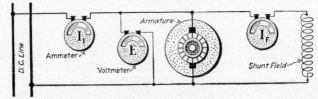

Fig. 159.—Connections for a load and speed test on a direct-current shunt motor.

242. In Making a Temperature Test of a Direct-current Shunt Motor or Generator by the "Loading-back" Method the equipment may be disposed as illustrated in Fig. 160. In making temperature tests on a small generator (this method is not illustrated) it is usual to drive the generator with a motor and to load the generator with a lamp bank or resistance, the voltage across the generator being maintained constant, and the current through the external circuit adjusted to full-load value. The temperatures are then recorded. When they reach a constant value above the temperature of the atmosphere, the test is discontinued. Similarly in making a test on a small motor, the motor is loaded with a generator and the load increased until the input current reaches the normal full-load value of the motor, the test being conducted as for a small generator.

When, however, the apparatus, either motor or generator, is of considerable capacity it becomes necessary, in order to

economize energy and thus decrease the cost of testing, to use
what is called the loading back method.   The apparatus for
this is shown in Fig. 160.   The motor is started in the usual
way, with the generator belted to it, the external circuit of the
generator being open.   The field current of the generator is
then so adjusted that the generator voltage is equal to that of
the line.   The generator is then connected to the circuit and
its field resistance varied until it carries normal full-load current, or slightly less than full-load current.   Under these conditions, if the motor and generator are of the same type and
size, the motor will carry slightly in excess of full-load, the

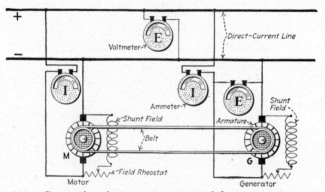

Fig. 160.—Connections for temperature test of shunt generator or motor
by the "load-back" method.

difference being approximately twice the losses of the machines.   Under these conditions the total power drawn from
the line is equal to twice the loss of either machine.   Temperature readings are taken as in other temperature tests.

**243. The Determination of the External Characteristic of a
Direct-current, Compound-wound Generator Under Adjustable Load** may be effected with apparatus arranged as shown
in Fig. 161.   The object of this test is to determine the relation
between armature voltage and armature current when the
shunt-field current is maintained constant.   The shunt field
is adjusted to give normal voltage across the armature when
the external circuit is open.   The load is then imposed by

means of an adjustable resistance or lamp bank, *R*, and readings of external voltage and current recorded.   If the machine is normally compounded (Fig. 15) the external voltage will remain practically constant throughout the load range.   If the machine is under-compounded, the external voltage will drop with load, while if over-compounded, (Fig. 14) there will be a rise in voltage with increase in load.

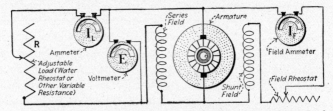

Fig. 161.—Testing arrangement for determining the external characteristic of a compound-wound direct-current generator.

244. A Test to Determine the External Characteristic of a Shunt-wound Direct-current Generator is diagrammed in Fig. 162.   The external characteristic of a shunt generator is a graph (Fig. 10, *I*) showing the relation between the current and voltage of the external circuit.   The shunt-field current is so adjusted by manipulating rheostat, *R*, that the machine im-

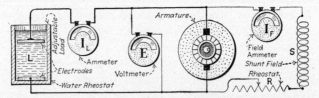

Fig. 162.—Arrangement for obtaining data for external characteristic of a shunt-wound generator.

presses, on its external circuit, normal voltage when the external circuit is open.   The field current is then maintained constant and the external-circuit current varied by varying the resistance in the circuit with the rheostat, *L*.   By plotting, on squared paper, voltage along the vertical, against the corresponding amperes along the horizontal, the external characteristic graph is obtained.

245. Measurement of the Insulation Resistance of Generators and Motors will give an indication of the average condition of the insulation as regards moisture and dirt, but will not always detect weak spots.* The higher the insulation resistance, the better the general condition of the insulating material. The approximate figure of 1 megohm per 1,000 volts of rated e.m.f. when the machine is at its normal full-load temperature may be taken as indicating a fairly satisfactory condition of the armature insulation. The insulation resistance of the field will be much higher in proportion to the e.m.f. of the exciting current and will seldom give appreciable trouble. Since large armatures have much greater areas of insulation, their insulation resistance will be proportionally lower than that of small machines. Even though the material

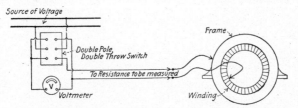

FIG. 163.—Measuring generator insulation resistance.

is in exactly the same condition, the insulation resistance of any machine will be much lower when hot than when cool, especially when the machine is rapidly heated.

246. The Only Feasible Way of Increasing the Insulation Resistance When the Machine is Complete is by "Drying Out."—Armature winding and field coils are dried out by heat; baking in an oven is to be preferred, but is often impracticable. They are usually heated by the passage of current. In the case of the armature this may be accomplished by short-circuiting the leads and running the generator with a low field charge, just sufficient to produce the proper current. See Art. 107.

247. Insulation Resistance may be Conveniently Measured with a High-resistance Voltmeter, preferably one especially

* Westinghouse Elec. & Manfg. Co.

designed for the purpose. Voltmeters having a resistance of 1 megohm are now made for this service so that, if one of these instruments is used, the calculation is somewhat simplified. A double-pole switch arranged as indicated in Fig. 163 is convenient for changing the voltmeter connections. If a grounded circuit is used for making this measurement, care must be taken to connect the grounded side of the line to the frame of the machine to be measured, and the voltmeter between the windings and the other side of the circuit. Fig. 145 illustrates the method of determining the insulation resistance of a field coil. See the author's AMERICAN ELECTRICIAN'S HANDBOOK for a description and examples of the method and figuring used in making determinations of insulation resistance with a voltmeter.

PRINCIPLES, CONSTRUCTION AND CHARACTERISTICS
OF ALTERNATING-CURRENT GENERATORS

248. Modern Commercial Alternating-current Generators or Alternators usually are arranged as suggested diagrammatically in Fig. 164. Electromagnets, excited by a small direct-current generator or exciter, are mounted on a wheel-like structure which revolves within a circular stationary frame in the inner surface of which are armature coils. The revolving part is the revolving field; the stationary part is the armature. The direct current is fed to the field coils through collector rings. Armature coils are, in practice, arranged in slots in the inner circumference of the armature structure. Alternating e.m.fs. are induced in the armature by the lines of force from the revolving field magnets cutting the armature coils. The alternating voltage can be varied, within limits, by adjusting the field rheostats.

249. There are Several Types of Alternators or alternating-current generators. They are: (1) Revolving-armature alternators (Fig. 165) wherein the armature revolves and the field magnets are stationary; revolving-armature machines are now ordinarily manufactured only for capacities of less than about 30 kva.; (2) revolving-field alternators, wherein the field magnets revolve and the armature is stationary (Fig. 166); (3) inductor alternators, wherein both field magnets and armature are stationary and iron cores revolve between the armature core and the field-magnet poles. Modern alternators of moderate and large capacity are practically all of the revolving-field type because the stationary armature offers better opportunity for insulation and a high voltage is not necessary on the collector rings. Fig. 166 shows a modern installation of a small revolving-field alternating-current generator. In

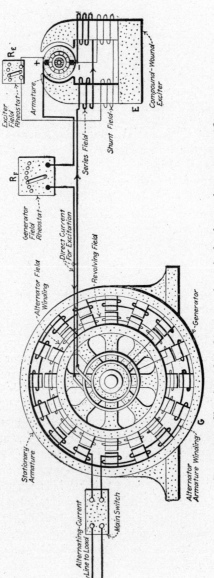

Fig. 164.—Showing the elements of a single-phase alternator outfit.

Fig. 165.—A small revolving-armature generator. (This Westinghouse belted alternator is rated at 20-kva., three-phase or 14-kva. single phase, 60-cycles, 1800 r.p.m., 120, 240, 480 or 600 volts, three- or single-phase.

Fig. 166.—A Ridgway 75-kva., 277-r.p.m., three-phase, 60-cycle, 240-volt, direct-connected, engine-type generator, driven by a 12 × 14 106-h.p. high speed Ridgway engine. The exciter is belt-driven and has an output of 5 kw.

Fig. 167 are illustrated two revolving field turbo-generator units.

Fig. 167.—Two 500 kva., Ridgway, mixed-pressure, turbo-alternator units.　2200 volts, three-phase, 60-cycles.

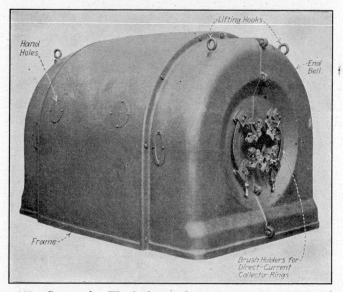

Fig. 168.—Stator of a Westinghouse alternating-current generator for steam-turbine drive.

250. The Construction of Turbo-alternators—that is alternating-current generators arranged for steam-turbine drive

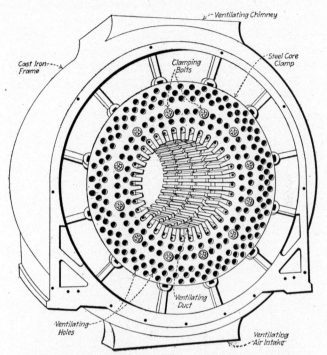

FIG. 169.—Stator (alternating-current armature) of a turbo generator without armature windings and with end bells removed.

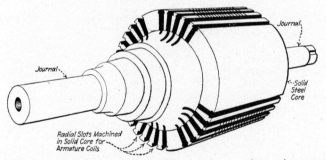

FIG. 170.—Rotor (direct-current field) core for an alternating-current turbo generator. This shows one of the "radial-slot" type.

11

(Figs. 168 to 171)—is somewhat different from that utilized for machines which are to be driven at moderate speeds. However, these are always revolving-field machines. Steam turbines, if they are to develop their maximum economies, must operate at high speeds and it follows that generators which are to be driven directly by them must be capable of operating

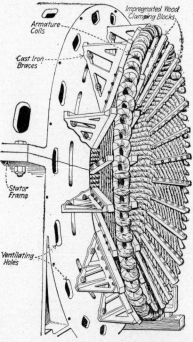

Fig. 171.—End-view of a turbo-alternator armature with the winding and braces in position.

at the same speeds; 1,200, 1,800 and 3,600 r.p.m. are speeds frequently encountered in practice. These machines ordinarily require forced ventilation, hence are usually enclosed as shown in Fig. 168. Since the rotors (fields) revolve so rapidly, they must be of very secure construction. Hence, for small and medium-capacity machines, the field structure is frequently machined from a steel forging as shown in Fig.

170.   The field core for the large machines is assembled from dishes cut from steel slabs or plates.

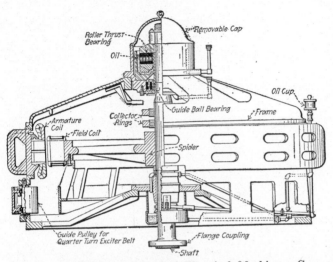

Fig. 172.—Sectional elevation of an Electrical Machinery Company vertical waterwheel generator.   (See Fig. 173 for a photographic reproduction.)

Fig. 173.—Showing an Electrical Machinery Company's vertical waterwheel generator with a belted exciter.   (See Fig. 172 for a sectional elevation of a generator of this type.)

251. A Sectional View of a Vertical Water-wheel Generator, as manufactured by The Electrical Machinery Company, is shown in Fig. 172. The stator rests on a circular cast-iron base which carries a split, babbitted, self-oiling, steady bearing below the rotor. The vertical shaft is arranged to couple direct to the waterwheel shaft. A thrust bearing of the roller type which carries all of the revolving parts is at the top. This machine is shown installed in Fig. 173.

252. The Electromotive Force in an Alternator is Generated as Suggested in Fig. 174.—As each field coil, D for instance, sweeps past the armature coils the lines of force from the field coil cut the armature coils. As coil D passes from A to C an alternating e.m.f. represented by the graph ABC will be generated in the armature. It should be understood that in

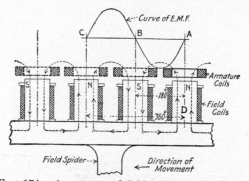

Fig. 174.—Armature and field structure developed.

commercial alternators the armature coils are set in slots and differently arranged than in Fig. 174, which only illustrates a principle. For a simple but rather complete explanation of how and why alternating e.m.fs. are generated by alternators, see the author's PRACTICAL ELECTRICITY.

253. The Relation Between the Speed, Frequency and Number of Poles of any Alternating-current Generator is expressed by the following formulas:

$$(21) \qquad f = \frac{p \times r.p.m}{120} \qquad \text{(frequency)}$$

$$(22) \qquad p = \frac{120 \times f}{r.p.m,} \qquad \text{(number of poles)}$$

$$(23) \qquad r.p.m. = \frac{120 \times f}{p} \qquad \text{(speed)}$$

Wherein, f = frequency, in cycles per second. *r.p.m.* = revolutions per minute of rotor. p = the number of field poles. A table will be found in the author's AMERICAN ELECTRICIANS' HANDBOOK, showing the synchronous speeds for alternating-current generators for all of the commonly used number of poles from 2 to 100, and for frequencies of 25 to 133 cycles. See the author's PRACTICAL ELECTRICITY for a much more complete discussion of the subject of frequency.

EXAMPLE.—What is the frequency developed by a two-pole alternating-current generator which is rotated at 3,600 r.p.m.? SOLUTION.—Substitute in the above equation (21): $f = (p \times r.p.m.) \div 120 = (2 \times 3,600) \div 120 = 7,200 \div 120 = 60$ *cycles per sec.*

EXAMPLE.—How many poles must a 25-cycle alternator which operates at 100 revolutions per minute have? SOLUTION.—Substitute in the equation (22): $p = (120 \times f) \div r.p.m. = (120 \times 25) \div 100 = 3,000 \div 100 = 30$ *poles.*

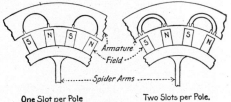

One Slot per Pole   Two Slots per Pole.

FIG. 175.—Single-phase armature windings.

254. Single-phase Alternators.—The circumferential distance from the center line of one pole to the center line of the next pole of the same polarity constitutes 360 magnetic degrees. See Fig. 174, which shows how a single-phase e.m.f. is generated. See the author's PRACTICAL ELECTRICITY for explanations of the terms "single-phase," "two-phase" and "three-phase." Fig. 164 is a diagrammatic illustration of a single-phase alternator and Fig. 175 shows, diagrammatically, two different kinds of single-phase windings. Single-phase alternators are seldom made now. If single-phase service is demanded the manufacturers furnish a three-phase machine instead and give it a single-phase rating equal to about 70 per cent. of the three-phase rating. The single-phase load is then carried on any two of the three leads of the three-phase generator. See "Three-phase Alternator" (Art. 258).

255. A Table of Average Performance Values for Standard Two- and Three-phase Generators of capacities up to 2,000 kva., will be found in the author's AMERICAN ELECTRICIANS' HANDBOOK. In this table are given the current values, the efficiencies at various loads and the exciter capacities ordinarily required for 240, 480, 600, 1,200, 2,200 and 2,400-volt machines.

256. Performance Guarantees on Alternating-current Generators are, in the United States, now practically always made on the continuous rating (A. I. E. E. Std. Rule 281)* bases. That is, the generators are rated at the kilovolt-ampere outputs at which they will operate continuously without excessive temperature rise. The maximum temperature rise specified is usually 50 deg. on the basis of a 40-deg. reference, ambient† or "room" temperature. These temperature rises are based on operating the machines on normal excitation, voltage and frequency at a specified power-factor—usually 80 per cent. That is, the "normal" method of rating whereunder an overload—possibly 25 per cent. for two hours—was guaranteed, is no longer used by the leading manufacturers of electrical machinery. The above temperatures are all based on the thermometer method of observation.

257. Two-phase Alternator.—In a generator of the type indicated in Fig. 176 the centers of the two component coils *I* and *II* are 90 electrical deg. apart and the single-phase electromotive forces generated in coils *I* and *II* by the passage of the field system past them, differ in phase by 90 deg. This property has given rise to the term quarter-phase for this type of machine, but it is more frequently called a two-phase machine. The electromotive force in coil *I* is zero when that in coil *II* is a maximum, and *vice versa*. The

---

* "A machine rated for continuous service shall be able to operate continuously at its rated output without exceeding any of the limitations referred to in 260."

† The ambient temperature (A. I. E. E. Std. Rule No. 303) is the temperature of the air or water, which in coming into contact with the heated parts of a machine, carries off its heat. See also Art. 47b.

curves of electromotive force in coils *I* and *II* may be plotted as indicated in Fig. 177. Fig. 178 shows two methods of connecting the armature windings of two-phase alternators. The armature coils can be arranged in one or

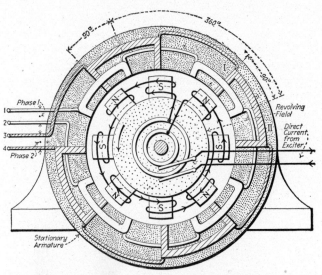

FIG. 176.—Diagram for two-phase alternator.

more slots per pole as diagrammatically suggested in Fig 179. In commercial machines the windings are almost always arranged in more than one slot per pole. See the author's PRACTICAL ELECTRIC-ITY for further information in regard to two-phase currents.

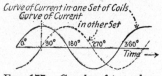

FIG. 177.—Graphs of two-phase current.

258. Three-phase Alternator Coils are arranged as illustrated diagrammatically by coils *I*, *II* and *III* of Fig. 180, and the curves of instantaneous electromotive force are displaced from one another by 60 deg. as indicated in Fig. 181. This arrangement of coils is really a six-phase grouping, and in connecting the winding for three-phase, the coils of one of the phases must be connected in the reverse sense from the other two.   This will give the true three-phase arrangement in which the e.m.f. curves are as in Fig. 182.   These curves

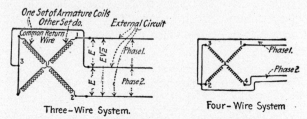

Three-Wire System.   Four-Wire System

Fig. 178.—Methods of connecting two-phase generator armature windings.

also represent the e.m.fs. for the winding in Fig. 183 with the three phases connected in the same sense.   Here three

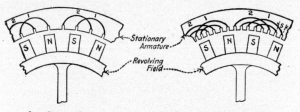

One Slot per Pole.   Two Slots per Pole.

Fig. 179.—Two-phase generator armature windings.

coils are distributed over a double-pole pitch, and the phase displacement between the e.m.fs. is 120 deg.

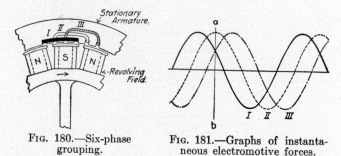

Fig. 180.—Six-phase grouping.

Fig. 181.—Graphs of instantaneous electromotive forces.

259. The Two Methods of Connecting Three-phase Armature Windings are shown in Fig. 184.   These methods

are discussed in more detail in the author's PRACTICAL
ELECTRICITY. Armature windings can be arranged in one
or more slots per pole (Fig. 185). The Y method of connection is almost invariably
used for modern three-phase
generators.

**260. Exciters for Alternat-
ing-current Generators** are
usually compound-wound, flat-
compounded, and rated at 125
or 250 volts. It is especially
desirable that they be "stable,"
if direct-connected to the shaft

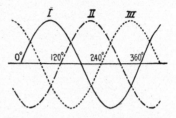

FIG. 182.—Curves of three-phase
currents.

of an alternator. By a stable generator is meant one that does
not have an excessive rise or fall in terminal voltage with a
corresponding change in speed. Standard direct-current ma-

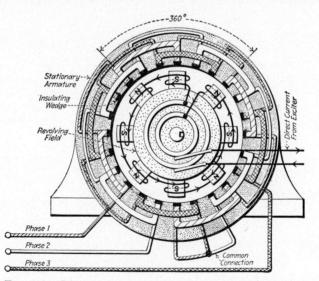

FIG. 183.—Diagram for three-phase, Y-connected alternator.

chines of the desired rating are used where the exciters are
separately driven. Separately-driven exciters are usually preferable for most applications on account of the fact that the

system is thereby rendered much more flexible; any drop in the speed of the alternator does not cause a corresponding drop in the exciter voltage, and the regulation of the plant as a whole is improved. Furthermore, if the exciter is not direct-connected, an accident to it will not necessitate shutting down the generator, assuming that there is a duplicate exciter set.

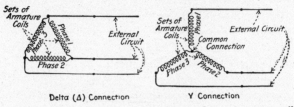

Fig. 184.—Methods of connecting three-phase armature coils.

261. It Is Necessary That the Exciter Capacity be Ample to Provide Reserve Capacity.

—To make the exciter plant as reliable as possible, storage batteries are being installed in connection with the exciting generators in some plants in such a way that current may be furnished to the field circuits of the alternators, even though all rotating apparatus be at

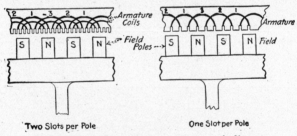

Fig. 185.—Three-phase armature windings.

a standstill. As an example of the amount of reserve capacity that is sometimes installed: in the first power plant of the Niagara Falls Power Company four exciters are installed, each one having sufficient capacity to excite the entire plant, and each driven by its own turbine, fed by a separate penstock.

262. Exciter Drives.

—It is apparent that where separately-driven exciters are used the prime movers should be such that the exciters may be started independently of the energy furnished by the alternators. Steam-, water-, or gas-driven units are necessary unless a storage battery or power from an external source is available for excitation of the plant when first starting up. With the bus-bars excited, motor-driven units may be operated and they are preferable in many cases.

263. Exciter Capacity.—General figures for the capacity of an exciter for any machine run from 2.5 per cent. of the capacity of the alternator, for moderate speeds and small sizes, to 0.5 per cent. of the alternator capacity, or a trifle less, for large, high-speed, turbine units. Two per cent. is a value commonly used in the absence of definite data. This is too low in a very few cases, but more often in error on the safe side.

264. A Belt-driven Exciter for a Vertical Waterwheel Alternator is shown in Fig. 173 and 186. Note that a quarter-twist belt is used for driving the direct-current machine. A sectional view of an alternator of the type shown in this illustration is given in Fig. 172.

265. Field Discharge Switches and Resistors should be provided for automatically

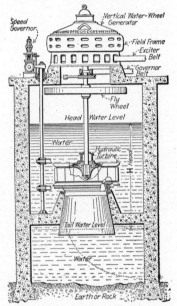

FIG. 186.—An example of a vertical, waterwheel generator installation.

discharging the field circuits of alternating-current generators when the field switch is opened. If such provision is not made, the high e.m.f. of self-induction developed when the switch is opened, is liable to puncture and possibly ground the field winding of the machine. See Figs. 116 and 117 for information relating to field-discharge switches and resistors as applied to direct-current motors and generators.

266. Explanations of the Derivations of the Following Formulas and Rules will in most cases be found in the author's PRACTICAL ELECTRICITY. To explain here why the formulas given are correct would require considerable space and would in effect be a repetition of material which is treated rather fully in the other book just referred to.

267. To Compute the Horse-power Required to Drive an Alternating-current, Single-phase Generator, on the Basis of its Kilovolt-ampere Output, the following equation may be used:

$$(24) \qquad h.p._i = \frac{kva._o \times p.f.}{E \times 0.746} \qquad \text{(horse-power)}$$

$$(25) \qquad kva._o = \frac{h.p._i \times E \times 0.746}{p.f.} \qquad \text{(kilovolt-amperes)}$$

$$(26) \qquad p.f. = \frac{h.p._i \times E \times 0.746}{kva._o} \qquad \text{(power-factor)}$$

$$(27) \qquad E = \frac{kva._o \times p.f.}{h.p._i \times 0.746} \qquad \text{(efficiency)}$$

Wherein, $h.p._i$ = the horse-power input to the generator. $kva._o$ = the kilovolt-ampere output of the generator. $p.f.$ = the power-factor of the load which the generator is serving. E = the efficiency of the generator, for the conditions under consideration, expressed decimally.

EXAMPLE.—What horse-power is required to drive a single-phase generator which is delivering 625 kva. at 80 per cent. power-factor, it being assumed that the efficiency of the machine at this load is 90 per cent.? SOLUTION.—Substitute in equation (24): $h.p._i = (kva._o \times p.f.) \div (E \times 0.746) = (625 \times 0.80) \div (0.90 \times 0.746) = 745 \ h.p.$

268. To Compute for an Alternating-current Single-phase Generator, Either the Horse-power required to Drive It, Its Voltage, Current, Efficiency, Power Factor, When the Value for Only One of These Quantities is Not Known, one of the following formulas may be used:

$$(28) \qquad h.p._i = \frac{E \times I_1 \times p.f.}{E \times 746} \qquad \text{(horse-power)}$$

(29) $$E = \frac{h.p._i \times \mathbf{E} \times 746}{I_1 \times p.f.}$$ (volts)

(30) $$I_1 = \frac{h.p._i \times \mathbf{E} \times 746}{E \times p.f.}$$ (amperes)

(31) $$p.f. = \frac{h.p._i \times \mathbf{E} \times 746}{E \times I_1}$$ (power-factor)

(32) $$\mathbf{E} = \frac{E \times I_1 \times p.f.}{h.p._i \times 746}$$ (efficiency)

Wherein, $h.p._i$ = the power input to the generator, in horse-power. E = the voltage impressed by the generator on the external circuit. I_1 = the current circulated in the external circuit by the generator. $p.f.$ = the power-factor of the load on the external circuit, expressed decimally. $\mathbf{E}$ = efficiency'of the generator, expressed decimally.

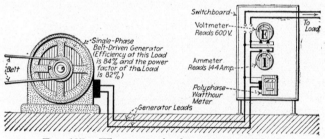

FIG. 187.—What power in the generator taking?

EXAMPLE.—What horse-power would be required to drive the single-phase generator of Fig. 187 with the conditions as there specified, it being assumed that under these conditions the efficiency of the machine is 84 per cent., the e.m.f. impressed on the external circuit is 600, the current is 144 amp. and the power-factor of the load is 82 per cent.? SOLUTION. —Substitute in equation (28): $h.p._i = (E \times I_1 \times p.f.) \div (\mathbf{E} \times 746) = (600 \times 144 \times 0.82) \div (0.84 \times 746) = 113\ h.p.$ That is, under these conditions the engine would have to deliver 113 h.p. at the generator pulley, P.

269. To Compute the Kilowatt Output of Any Alternating-current, Single-phase Generator, this equation may be used:

(33) $$kw._o = \frac{E \times I_1 \times p.f.}{1,000}$$ (kilowatts)

$$(34) \qquad E = \frac{kw._o \times 1,000}{I_1 \times p.f.} \qquad \text{(volts)}$$

$$(35) \qquad I_1 = \frac{kw._o \times 1,000}{E \times p.f.} \qquad \text{(amperes)}$$

$$(36) \qquad p.f. = \frac{kw._o \times 1,000}{E \times 1_1} \qquad \text{(power-factor)}$$

Wherein, all of the symbols have the same meanings as in the above Articles except that $kw._o$ = power output of the generator in kilowatts.

270. To Compute the Kilovolt-ampere Output, the Current or the Voltage of any Alternating-current, Single-phase Generator one of the following formulas may be used:

$$(37) \qquad kva._o = \frac{E \times I_1}{1,000} \qquad \text{(kilovolt-amperes)}$$

$$(38) \qquad E = \frac{kva._o \times 1,000}{I_1} \qquad \text{(volts)}$$

$$(39) \qquad I_1 = \frac{kva._o \times 1,000}{E} \qquad \text{(amperes)}$$

Wherein, the symbols have the same meanings as above.

271. To Compute the Kilovolt-amperes Output, the Current or the Voltage of Any Three-phase, Alternating-current Generator one of the following formulas may be used:

$$(40) \qquad kva._o = E \times I_3 \times 0.00173 \qquad \text{(kilovolt-amperes)}$$

$$(41) \qquad E = \frac{kva._o \times 577}{I_3} \qquad \text{(volts)}$$

$$(42) \qquad I_3 = \frac{kva._o \times 577}{E} \qquad \text{(amperes)}$$

Wherein, $kva._o$ = the output of the generator, in kilovolt-amperes. E = the e.m.f. impressed by the machine between phase wires on the external circuit in volts. I_3 = the current, in amperes, in each of the three-phase wires, it being assumed for all of this notation that the load on the three phases is balanced.

EXAMPLE.—What is the kilovolt-ampere output of the three-phase, alternating-current generator of Fig. 188 when it is delivering, as shown, a current of 54 amp. in each of the three-phase wires and impressing on the external circuit a voltage of 2,200? SOLUTION.—Substitute in equation (40): $kva._o = E \times I_3 \times 0.00173 = 2,200 \times 54 \times 0.00173 = 205.5$ *kva.*

272. To Compute for a Three-phase, Alternating-current Generator, Either the Horse-power Required to Drive It, the Kilowatt-ampere Output, the Power Factor or the Efficiency, When the Value for Only One of these Quantities is Not Known, one of the following formulas may be used:

(43) $$h.p._i = \frac{kva._o \times p.f.}{E \times 0.746}$$ (horse-power)

(44) $$kva._o = \frac{h.p._i \times E \times 0.746}{p.f.}$$ (kilovolt-amperes)

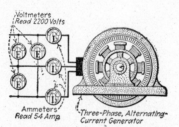

FIG. 188.—Example in computing Kva. Output of a three-phase generator.

(45) $$p.f. = \frac{h.p._i \times E \times 0.746}{kva._o}$$ (power-factor)

(46) $$E = \frac{kva._o \times p.f.}{h.p._i \times 0.746}$$ (efficiency)

Wherein, all of the symbols have the same meanings as in the above articles except that $kva._o$ = the kilovolt-ampere output of the generator.

EXAMPLE.—A three-phase generator has a full-load rating of 600 kva. When delivering full-load kilovolt-amperes to the load at 80 per cent. power-factor, what horse-power would be required to drive this machine, assuming that its efficiency is 90 per cent.? SOLUTION.—Substitute in equation (43): $h.p._i = (kva._o \times p.f.) \div (E \times 0.746) = (600 \times 0.80) \div$

$(0.90 \times 0.746) = 715 \ h.p.$ Therefore, under these conditions it would require 715 $h.p.$ to drive the generator.

273. To Compute for Any Alternating-current Generator, Either the Kilowatt Output, the Voltage, the Current or the Power Factor, When the Value for Only One of These Quantities is Not Known, one of the following equations may be used:

(47) $kw._o = E \times I_3 \times p.f. \times 0.00173$ (kilowatts)

(48) $E = \dfrac{kw._o \times 577}{I_3 \times p.f.}$ (volts)

(49) $I_3 = \dfrac{kw._o \times 577}{E \times p.f.}$ (amperes)

(50) $p.f. = \dfrac{kw._o \times 577}{E \times I_3}$ (power-factor)

Wherein, all of the symbols have the same meanings as specified above except that $kw._o$ = the output of the generator in kilowatts.

274. To Compute for Any Three-phase Generator, the Horse-power Required to Drive It, Its Voltage, Current, Efficiency or Power Factor, When the Value of Only One of These Quantities is Not Known, one of the following formulas may (it being assumed that the electrical load is equally balanced between the three phases) be used:

(51) $h.p._i = \dfrac{E \times I_3 \times p.f.}{\mathbf{E} \times 430.7}$ (horse-power)

(52) $E = \dfrac{h.p._i \times \mathbf{E} \times 430.7}{I_3 \times p.f.}$ (volts)

(53) $I_3 = \dfrac{h.p._i \times \mathbf{E} \times 430.7}{E \times p.f.}$ (amperes)

(54) $p.f. = \dfrac{h.p._i \times \mathbf{E} \times 430.7}{E \times I}$ (power-factor)

(55) $\mathbf{E} = \dfrac{E \times I_3 \times p.f.}{h.p._i \times 430.7}$ (efficiency)

Wherein, $h.p._1$ = the power input to the generator, in horse-power. E = the e.m.f. in volts impressed by the machine between phase wires on the external circuit. I_3 = the current circulated by the machine in each of the three-phase wires. *p.f.* = power-factor of the load served by the generator. **E** = efficiency of the machine, expressed decimally, for the conditions under consideration.

EXAMPLE.—What horse-power input would be required at the pulley, *P*, of the three-phase generator shown in Fig. 189 when the machine is impressing 2,200 volts on the external circuit and circulating a current of 23 amp., it being assumed that the power-factor of the load is 85 per cent. and that the efficiency of the generator is 90 per cent.? SOLUTION.—Substitute in equation (51): $h.p._i = (E \times I_3 \times p.f.) \div (\mathbf{E} \times 430.7) = (2,200 \times 23 \times 0.85) \div (0.90 \times 430.7 = 111\ h.p.$

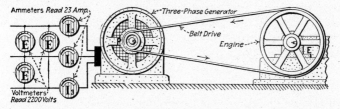

FIG. 189.—Size engine required to drive a three-phase alternating-current generator.

275. To Find the Size Engine Required to Drive an Alternating-current Generator

the same general procedure may be followed as that used in ascertaining the engine capacity for direct-current machines, which is described in Art. 51. However, with an alternating-current generator it must be remembered that the kilovolt-ampere rating of the machine must be multiplied by the power-factor of the load which will be served in order to ascertain the power load in kilowatts. One of the preceding equations can be used in determining the horse-power necessary at the generator pulley or shaft to pull a given electrical load. In the author's AMERICAN ELECTRICIANS' HANDBOOK are given tables showing the actual efficiencies of commercial alternating-current generators. It should be noted (see Art. 253) that with alternating-current generators the speed is determined by the number of poles on the generator and by the frequency which it is desired to produce.

12

MANAGEMENT OF ALTERNATING-CURRENT GENERATORS

276. In the Management of Alternating-current Generators many of the principles already discussed in Sec. 2, "Management of Direct-current Generators," apply. In general, the alternators should receive the same care in regard to oiling (Art. 76), cleanliness and general attention as do direct-current dynamos. The reader is advised to review Sec. 2.

277. Synchronizing.*—Two or more alternating-current generators will not operate in parallel unless (1) *their voltages, as registered by a voltmeter, are the same;* (2) *their frequencies are the same;* and (3) *their voltages in phase.* If the machines are not in phase, even if their indicated voltages and their frequencies are the same the voltage of one will, at given instants, be different from that of the other and there will be an interchange of current between the machines. When two or more generators all satisfy the three above requirements they are "in step" or in synchronism. Synchronizing is the operation of getting machines into synchronism. Incandescent lamps or instruments are, as described in other paragraphs, used for indicating when machines are in synchronism.

278. Synchronizing a Single-phase Circuit with Lamps.— The Elementary Principle involved in determining synchronism is indicated in Fig. 190. If the voltage and frequency of generators *A* and *B* are the same and the machines are in phase, point *a* will be at the same potential at every instant as will point *a'*. Hence the lamps between *a* and *a'* will not light so long as the three conditions are satisfied. So long as the

---

* For a complete discussion of the various methods, and for diagrams of all synchronizing circuits in common use for both lamps and synchroscopes see ELECTRIC JOURNAL, articles by Harold Brown, May, 1912, and July, 1912. The material on this subject herein is largely from these articles.

conditions are not satisfied there will be a fluctuating cross-current from a to a' and a constant fluctuating of the brilliancy of the incandescent lamps.   When the lamps become dark and remain so, the generators are in synchronism and may be thrown together.   Had the connection at a' been made to the b' generator lead, the lamps would be bright when the generators were in synchronism, but for reasons outlined in another paragraph the connection shown which provides the "dark lamp" method of synchronizing is preferred.   The second pair of lamps between b and b' is provided to insure against accident in case the a–a' set were broken.   The same conditions occur in the a–a' set as in the b–b' set.   A voltmeter of

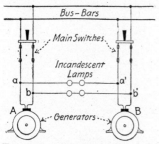

FIG. 190.—Circuits for synchronizing with lamps.

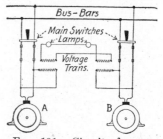

FIG. 191.—Circuits for synchronizing high-voltage circuits with lamps.

proper rating can be substituted for the lamps.   Where the voltage generated is so high that it is not desirable to connect a sufficient number of lamps in series for it, a single pair of lamps fed through voltage transformers can be used for synchronizing, is suggested in Fig. 191.

279. Phasing Out.—Prior to connecting the leads from a polyphase generator (which is to operate in parallel with others) to the generator switch, the circuits must be "phased out."   That is, the leads must be so arranged that each lead from the generator will, when the generator switch is thrown, connect to the corresponding lead of the other generator.   If this is not arranged there may be considerable damage done due to an interchange of current when the two machines are paralleled. After once phasing out it is necessary to synchronize but one phase of the machine with the corresponding phase of the other machine.

280. Connections for Phasing Out Three-phase Circuits are shown in Fig. 192. If voltage transformers are not used the sum of the voltages of the lamps in each line should be approximately the same as the voltage of the circuits. On 440-volt circuits, two 220-volt or four 110-volt lamps should be used in each phasing-out lead. To phase out, run the two machines at about synchronous speed. If the lamps do not

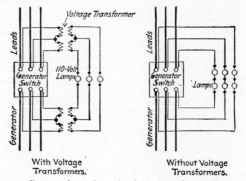

Fig. 192.—Connections for phasing out three-phase circuits.

all become bright and dark together, interchange any two of the main leads on one side of the switch, leaving the lamps connected to the same switch terminals, after which the lamps should all fluctuate together, indicating that the connections are correct. The machines are in phase when all the lamps are dark.

281. The Synchronizing Connections for More Than Two Three-phase Generators are shown in Fig. 193 although only two machines are illustrated in this diagram. A synchronizing plug may be used instead of the single-pole synchronizing switch shown. The illustration indicates the connections used where machines are to be synchronized to a bus. Where only two machines are to be synchronized, the connections are the same as shown in Fig. 193 except that the bus transformer and the corresponding lamp are omitted and one plug or synchronizing switch is required instead of two.

282. Synchronizing Dark or Light.—Synchronizing dark appears to be the preferable method.   All the connections shown in this book are for "synchronizing dark."   When the lamps are "dark" the machines are in phase and it is necessary to close the switch when the variation in light is the slowest obtainable or ceases altogether, that is, at or just before the middle of the longest dark period.   Should a filament break, the synchronizing lamps would remain dark and thus apparently indicate synchronism and possibly cause an accident.   Therefore, it is considered desirable by some to reverse

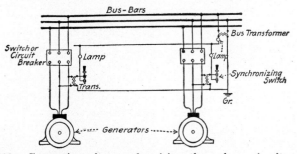

Fig. 193.—Connections for synchronizing three-phase circuits where transformers are required.

the synchronizing circuit connections and thereby synchronize "light."   Synchronizing light eliminates the danger due to the breaking of a filament, but has the disadvantage that the time of greatest brilliancy is difficult of determination.   The "light" period is relatively long compared with the dark period, so that synchronizing light is usually considered the more difficult and were it not that with the "synchronizing light" method the danger due to filament breakage is eliminated, the method would never be used.   The probability of a filament breaking just at the time of approaching synchronism and when the machines are not in phase is remote.   If it occurs at any other time in the operation it will be noticed. As a protection against accidents due to such breakage, two synchronizing lamps should always be placed in multiple.

283. The Number of Lamps to Use in a Group to Indicate Synchronism is determined by the voltage of the generators. With high-voltage circuits it is not feasible to use a sufficient number of lamps, so a transformer is then employed (Fig. 193) that has a voltage sufficient for a 110-volt lamp. See the diagrams. The greatest voltage impressed on the lamps is double that of the voltage transformers or generators. Thus the maximum voltage on the lamps where two 220-volt generators are being synchronized is 440 volts. The dark period may be shortened by impressing a voltage higher than their normal on the lamps. For two 220-volt machines, for example, three 110-volt lamps might be used.

284. Synchroscopes are instruments that indicate the difference in phase between two electromotive forces at every instant. They show whether the machine to be synchronized is running fast or slow and indicate the exact instant when the machines are in synchronism. The companies which manufacture the instruments furnish literature describing the theory involved and which gives complete circuit diagrams.

285. While for Successful Parallel Operation, it is not necessary that alternating-current generators (Fig. 194) be of the same type, output, and speed, it is universally conceded that the question of wave shape or form is important, since if the waves are of different shapes, cross-currents will always be present. Similar wave shapes are more readily obtained with machines of similar type. Satisfactory parallel operation, the previously mentioned conditions being fulfilled, consist in obtaining: (1) Correct division of the load among the machines; and (2) Freedom from hunting.

286. Division of Load.—Machines with similar characteristics tend to divide the common load uniformly. Such a proportional load division may be disturbed if the steam supply to the engines is defective or variable from any cause. The steam supply is regulated by the engine governors, and defects in one or more of these governors will give rise to poor load division. It is essential that the governors of all the engines shall have similar speed-regulation characteristics so that a sudden change in the load shall cause the same amount of regulation on each engine.   Correct load division is, therefore, essentially a problem of engine governor design.   It is sometimes arranged to govern all the engines from a common throttle valve, but this plan is not often employed.   A more usual plan consists in running all the machines except one, with their stop valves full open and their governors fixed, so that the remaining engine may take up any variations in the common load.

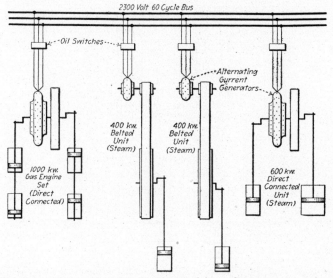

Fig. 194.—Internal-combustion engine-driven alternator, operating in parallel with steam-engine driven machine, Shreveport, La., plant of the Southwestern Gas and Electric Company.   (ELECTRIC WORLD, July 4, 1914, page 37.)

287. Varying the Voltage of an Alternator Running in Parallel With Others by Adjusting Its Field Rheostat Will Not Vary the Load on It as With a Direct-current Generator.— To increase the energy delivered by an alternator it is necessary that the prime mover be caused to do more work.   An engine should be given more steam or a waterwheel more water.

288. Adjustment of Field Current.—When the rheostats of two alternators, running in parallel at normal speed, are not adjusted to give a proper excitation, a cross-current will flow between the armatures. The intensity of this current depends only upon the difference in field excitation of the machines. It may vary over a wide range, from a minimum of zero when both field excitations are normal, to more than full-load current when they differ greatly. The effect of this cross-current is to increase the temperature of the armatures and, conse-

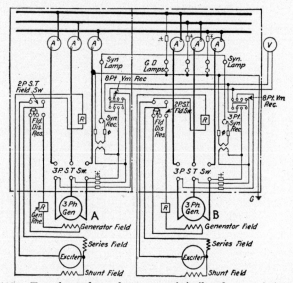

Fig. 195.—Two three-phase alternators of similar characteristics operating in parallel.

quently, to decrease the output of the generators. It is important that the rheostats be so adjusted as to reduce it to a minimum. This cross-current registers on the ammeters of both generators and usually increases both readings. The sum of the ammeter readings will be a minimum when the idle or cross-current is zero.

In general, the proper field current for a machine running in parallel with others is that which it would have if running alone and delivering its load at the same voltage. In order to determine the proper position of the rheostats it is necessary to make trial adjustments after the alternators are paralleled, until that position is found at which the sum of the alternating-current ammeter readings is a minimum.

EXAMPLE.—To illustrate this method consider two similar alternators, A and B, Fig. 195, operating in parallel. When the generator field rheostats of both are properly adjusted no cross-currents will flow through the armatures and the main ammeters (A, A, and A) will show equal readings if each machine is receiving the same amount of power from its prime mover. If the rheostat of A be partly cut in so as to reduce its field current, a cross-current, lagging in B and leading in A, will flow between the armatures, the effect of which will be to strengthen A's magnetization and weaken B's until they are approximately equal. The resultant e.m.f. of the system will thereby be lowered.

On the other hand, if the rheostat of B be partly cut out so as to increase its field current, a cross-current leading in A and lagging in B will flow between the armatures, strengthening A's magnetization and weakening B's magnetization until they are again equal. The resultant e.m.f. of the system will thereby be raised. A cross-current of the same character is, therefore, produced by decreasing one field current or increasing the other, *i.e.*, in both cases it will lead in the first machine and lag in the second machine. The e.m.f. of the system will, however, be decreased in one case and increased in the other.

It is obvious that by simultaneously adjusting the two rheostats, the strength of the cross-current may be varied considerably and the e.m.f. of the system maintained constant.

For the first trial adjustment cut in A's rheostat several notches and cut out B's the same amount, so as not to vary the e.m.f. of the system. If this reduces the sum of the main ammeter readings, continue the adjustment in the same direction until the result is a minimum. After this point is reached a further adjustment of the rheostat in either direction will increase the ammeter readings. If the first adjustment increases the sum of the ammeter readings it is being made in the wrong direction, in which case move the rheostats back to the original positions and then cut out A's rheostat and cut in B's. If both adjustments increase the sum of the ammeter readings the original positions of the rheostats are the proper ones.

In making these adjustments of the rheostats it may be found difficult to locate the exact points at which the cross-current is a minimum, as it may be possible to move the rheostats over a considerable range when near the correct positions without materially changing the ammeter readings. When the adjustment is carried this far, it is close enough for practical operation.   If the generators are provided with power-factor meters, the same result may be obtained by adjusting all these to read the same.

289. Hunting* is a term employed to describe the oscillations of the revolving masses of the machines when they are accelerated and retarded above and below the normal average speed.   If this hunting or swinging be allowed to exceed a certain amount, the regulation of the machines becomes unstable and they may break out of step.   Freedom from cumulative hunting is consequently essential.   The swinging action is set up primarily by variations in the rotative speed resulting from irregularity in the turning force.   A perfectly uniform turning moment or turning force cannot be obtained with reciprocating engines.   The irregularity in the turning moment during a revolution results from the following causes: (1) Defective distribution of steam in cylinders.   (2) Short connecting rod.   (3) Inertia of moving parts.

If one of two machines running in parallel momentarily lags behind the other, its armature receives a current which tends to pull the machine into phase and accelerate it so that at the instant it reaches the correct phase position its speed is a little greater than that of the other machine, which is now in turn accelerated.   The machines are now alternately lagging and leading with relation to one another.   In other words, hunting is set up.

Whichever engine is, for the instant, accelerating, will have its steam supply cut down by the governor.   If the governor is too sensitive, it will over-govern, cutting down the steam and the speed too far.   An instant later, the over-governing will be in the opposite sense, and this process will repeat itself. Similar occurrences will simultaneously be taking place on the other engine, and thus we have a case of hunting governors. By this hunting, the steam supply is rendered periodic and varies between two limits.

290. Surging is the term used to designate the current variations during hunting.   The case above described is an instance of hunting in the governors due to change of load and

* STANDARD HANDBOOK.

to over-sensitiveness of the governors. If, however, the governors are sluggish, a time interval elapses between an accidental acceleration and its correction by the governor. This lag will, in response, tend to set up hunting.

291. Prevention of Hunting.—The variations in turning moment and angular speed may be greatly reduced by the use of a heavy flywheel, as this tends to keep the rate of revolution uniform by virtue of storing energy and giving it out again during the course of each revolution. The flywheel, however, must not have too great a moment (that is, it must not be too big) as it adds to the inertia of the moving parts and may prolong hunting if once started. Hunting may sometimes be overcome by damping the governor so that it shall not respond to small and quick variations in speed such as occur during one revolution, but shall only respond to steady and continued changes in speed. This result is obtained by fitting each governor with a suitable dash pot so that it is rendered more sluggish and will make no alteration in the steam supply except when the force acting on the governor is continued for some length of time.

292. Liability to Hunt May Sometimes Be Prevented by Synchronizing the Engines so that the cranks on all the engines are in step, and the variations in turning moment are coincident in all the engines. This plan is sometimes effective, so far as the prevention of hunting in the generating station is concerned, but it cannot always be utilized owing to the time taken to get the cranks in step, especially as an engine must be run up in a few minutes when the load is coming on quickly. It also is apt to intensify the hunting of the apparatus in distant substations. With steam turbine-driven generators, this hunting difficulty is rare—practically unknown—and the use of high and uniform speeds facilitates the problem of parallel running.

293. The Tendency of Generators to Hunt May Be Minimized by fitting the pole-pieces of the field magnets with copper bands or "dampers" (see Fig. 240) in which eddy currents are induced by the shifting and distortion of the field. These currents react on the field and oppose the shifting and thus damp the oscillations. A suitable construction consists of a grid of copper embedded in the pole face. It is very seldom necessary to provide such "dampers" on pole-pieces of generators for modern steam-engine or waterwheel drive. They are usually necessary for internal-combustion engine-driven generators.

294. To Start a Single Alternator.*—(1) See that there is plenty of oil in the bearings and that the oil rings are free to turn and that all switches are open. (2) Start exciter and adjust for normal voltage. Start generator slowly. See that the oil rings are turning. (3) Permit the machine to reach normal speed. Turn the generator field rheostat so that all of its resistance is in the field circuit. Close the field switch. (4) Adjust the rheostat of the exciter for the normal exciting voltage. Slowly increase the alternator voltage to normal by cutting out the resistance of the field rheostat. (5) Close the main switch.

295. To Start an Alternator to Run in Parallel with Others. —(1) Bring the exciter and generator to speed as described in the above paragraph. Adjust the exciter voltage and close the field switch, the generator field resistance being all in. (2) Adjust the generator field resistance so that the generator voltage will be the same as the bus-bar voltage. (3) Synchronize, as outlined in Art. 277. Close the main switch. (4) Adjust the field rheostat until cross-currents (Art. 288) are a minimum and adjust the governors of the prime movers so that the load will be properly distributed between the operating units in proportion to their capacities.

296. To Cut Out a Generator Which is Running in Parallel with Others.*—(1) Preferably cut down the driving power until it is just sufficient to run the generator with no-load. This will reduce the load on the generator. (2) Adjust the resistance in the field circuit until the armature current is a minimum. (3) Open the main switch. It is usually sufficient, however, to simply disconnect the machine from the bus-bars, thereby throwing all the load on the remaining machine

---

*WESTINGHOUSE INSTRUCTION BOOK.

without having made any previous adjustment of the load or of the field current.   Caution.—*The field circuit of a generator to be disconnected from the bus-bars must not be opened before the main switch* has been opened; for, if the field circuit be opened first, a heavy current will flow between the armatures.

SECTION 8

PRINCIPLES, CONSTRUCTION AND CHARACTERISTICS OF INDUCTION AND REPULSION MOTORS

297. The Principle of Operation of the Induction Motor is illustrated in Fig. 196, which indicates diagrammatically a two-phase revolving-field generator and a two-phase induction motor having a rotor that is simply a bar of iron. The induction motor depends for its operation on a rotating magnetic field. There is no electrical connection between the revolving and stationary parts of an induction motor. Windings of the types shown in the illustration are not used in commercial machines, but the general theory involved is the same as with commercial windings. The revolving field (see illustration) of

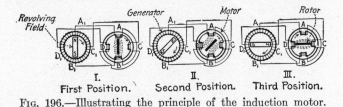

First Position. Second Position. Third Position.

Fig. 196.—Illustrating the principle of the induction motor.

the generator, in turning in the direction shown by the arrow, generates a two-phase current which is transmitted to the motor. For a more extended explanation of the operating principles of induction motors see the author's PRACTICAL ELECTRICITY. What then occurs may be explained thus:

EXPLANATION.—The current, in conductors of one phase, magnetizes poles A and B and that in the other phase the poles C and D. The winding is so arranged that a current entering at A will at a given instant produce a south pole at A and a north pole at B. At the instant shown at I, the motor poles A and B are magnetized while poles C and D are not, because it is a property of a two-phase circuit that when the current

190

in one of the phases is at a maximum value, the current in the other phase is at a zero value. Hence, the bar iron rotor will assume the vertical position shown.

At another later instant, represented at *II*, the currents in both of the phases are equal and in the same direction; the motor poles will be magnetized as shown and the rotor will be drawn into the position indicated. At the instant illustrated at *III*, because of the properties of two-phase currents, there is no current in the phase the conductors of which are wound on poles *A* and *B*, but the current in the phase the conductors of which magnetize poles *C* and *D*, is a maximum. Hence the rotor is now drawn into a horizontal position. Similar action occurs during successive instants and the rotor will be caused to rotate in the same direction within the motor frame so long as the two-phase current is applied to the motor terminals. Considering it in one way, the rotating magnetic field rotates within the motor frame and drags the rotor around with it.

The magnetic attraction or drag exerted on the rotor in a simple motor built as illustrated would be pulsating in effect, hence the torque exerted by such a motor would not be uniform.

298. Commercial Induction Motors operate because of the principles outlined in Art. 299, but their construction is considerably different from that shown in Fig. 196. In commercial induction motors the stator or primary winding is distributed over the entire inner surface of that portion of the stator structure which is of laminated iron and which conducts the magnetic flux. The rotor consists of a laminated iron cylinder which has a winding of insulated wire or of copper rods or bars embedded in slots uniformly spaced around the periphery of the core. Where bars or rods are used they are short-circuited at both ends by heavy copper conductors forming a completely short-circuited rotor.

299. In the Commercial Induction Motor the Magnetic Field of the Rotor Which Reacts on the Magnetic Field of the Stator is Produced by Currents in the Rotor Conductors. —These currents are generated by the rotor conductors being cut by the lines of force of the rotating field which was described in a preceding paragraph. Consider a polyphase induction motor with its rotor at rest. Now connect a source of the proper polyphase current to the motor terminals thereby energizing the stator winding. A rotating magnetic field will be produced by the stator winding. As this magnetic field swings around within the stator structure it will cut the copper bars imbedded in the surface of the rotor. Currents will thereby be induced in the bars and these currents will generate magnetic fields around and within the rotor. Due to the interaction between the rotor and stator magnetic fields, rotation of the rotor will be produced.

It is, therefore, evident that the turning speed (revolutions per minute) of the rotor can never be quite equal to that of the rotating magnetic field as there must always be a sufficient difference in speed or "slip" (Art. 317) that the rotor conductors will be cut by the lines of force of the rotating field. Obviously, if the rotor speed were the same as that of the revolving field, no lines of force could be cut by rotor conductors and there would not be sufficient magnetic interaction between the stator and rotor fields to produce rotation of the rotor and pull a load. The intensity of the current induced in the rotor, and, therefore, the torque, is determined by the amount of "slip" between the rotor and the rotating magnetic field. The greater the torque required, the greater will be the slip.

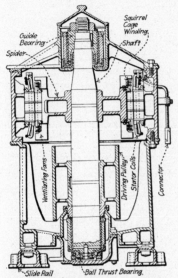

FIG. 197.—Sectional elevation of a Westinghouse, vertical, induction cement-mill, motor (220 volts, three-phase, 60 cycles).

300. Special Alternating-current Motors of various types are manufactured. Examples of these are the types adapted for paper mill, textile mill, cement mill, (Figs. 197 and 198) mining and other purposes. The vertical cement-mill motor illustrated is manufactured in capacities of from 75 to 200 h.p. and operates at 940 r.p.m.

301. General Characteristics of Polyphase Squirrel-cage Induction Motors.—Their speed is practically constant at all loads.   Hence they are used for constant-speed service where starting and reversing are infrequent.   The starting torque is relatively small and a large starting current, 2 to 6 times full-load current, depending on the design of the motor, is drawn from the line if the motor must start full-load torque.   Simple and rugged construction is a feature of these motors, the bearings being the only parts subject to wear.   Since there are no sliding electrical contacts there can be no sparking and the motors are, therefore, particularly suitable for operation in places where there are inflammable gases or dust.

If the resistance of the rotor be increased the motor can be built, in the smaller capacities, for high starting torque, rapid acceleration, and frequent starting.   Motors built thus can be profitably used for operating punches, shears and the like, where simplicity of control is desirable, as with them a large drop in speed produces but a slight increase in torque, permitting the stored energy in

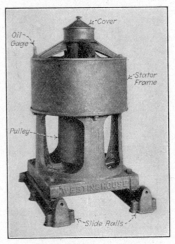

FIG. 198.   Photographic reproduction of Westinghouse vertical cement-mill motor.

the flywheel to be delivered to the machine when a heavy load occurs.   In this respect such an induction motor resembles a compound-wound direct-current motor.   If the torque imposed on any induction motor reaches 2 to 4 times full-load torque the motor will stop or "pull-out."   See Art. 313.   Since the output and torque of an induction motor varies as the square of the applied voltage it is desirable to maintain the voltage at normal value.

302. The Electrical Behavior of the Polyphase Induction Motor on the *input* side is the exact *electro-magnetic equivalent* of a *stationary transformer* with a large amount of magnetic leakage between the primary and the secondary coils.   On its *output side* the *polyphase induction motor* is the exact *electro-mechanical* equivalent of the *continuous-current shunt-wound motor* with a large value of "armature reaction."   The connecting link between the output and the input sides is the magnetic field, which may be considered as two or more superposed magnetic fields stationary with reference to each primary coil but alternating in value at the supply frequency, or it may with equal accuracy and convenience be considered as a single resultant field, of practically constant strength, but revolving in space with reference to the primary circuit.

303. Factors Affecting the Performance of the Induction Motor.*—The greater the maximum output or breaking-down point in a given size of motor, the poorer its efficiency, power-factor, etc., at normal load.   To get excellent all-round results it is desirable to choose a reasonable value for the maximum output of the motor.   The characteristics interesting to a purchaser are:

1. *Efficiency*, that is, the ratio of the energy given out by the motor to the energy put in.

2. *Maximum output*, that is, the greatest horsepower that the motor will carry without unduly slowing down, or perhaps stopping altogether.

3. *Current taken at the instant of starting*, sometimes called impedance current.   When the switch is closed, impressing e.m.f. on an induction motor, there is (unless provisions are adopted to prevent it) a rush of current which may cause disturbances of voltage on the line to which the motor is connected, thus giving occasion for complaints, especially if the circuit is supplying lights.   If no lights are on the circuit, the disturbance may extend to other motors on the circuit, causing trouble with them.

4. *Current Taken when Running without Load.*—With an induction motor, the field is produced by a current drawn from the line through the same wires that supply the energy.   This current, called the magnetizing or wattless current, lags behind the electromotive force, and pulls down the voltage of the

* From Raymond's MOTOR TROUBLES.

circuit, from which it flows, to a much greater extent than does an energy current, so that it is desirable to have as small a magnetizing current as possible. For a well-designed stationary motor for ordinary purposes, this no-load current should be not over 30 per cent. of the total full-load current.

5. *The power-factor*, see the author's PRACTICAL ELECTRICITY, which is the ratio of the component of the current, representing energy, to the total current flowing into the motor (the total current being the resultant sum of the energy current and the magnetizing current). Thus, in a motor taking 1,500 watts per phase (about 2 h.p.), at 100 volts per phase with a magnetizing current of 6 amp. per phase, the total current per phase flowing into the motor is found approximately as follows:

$$(56) \qquad Total\ current = \sqrt{6^2 + \left(\frac{1{,}500}{100}\right)^2} = 16\ amp.$$

EXAMPLE.—Let 1, 2, Fig. 199, equal the electromotive force applied to the phase; let 1, 5 represent, in direction and in length, the energy component of the current, and 1, 4 the magnetizing current; then line 1, 3 represents the total current, or resultant of the currents 1, 4 and 1, 5. This combination of currents is characteristic of alternating circuits. That is, currents combine directly only when in phase. When not in phase, their resultant is obtained

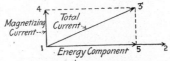

FIG. 199.—Phase relation of currents in an alternating-current motor.

with the parallelogram of forces, as shown with 1, 4 and 1, 5 in Fig. 199. The power-factor, therefore, is the ratio of the line; 1, 5 to 1, 3, or the ratio of the energy component of the current to the total current and this can be roughly estimated as shown.

304. Loss of Efficiency of an Induction Motor at Reduced Speeds.*—When an induction motor is operated at reduced speeds by increasing the slip, as by increasing the secondary resistance or decreasing the primary voltage, the efficiency is lowered by an amount nearly proportional to the speed reduction, as expressed by the formula:

$$(57) \qquad E_2 = E_1\left(\frac{100 - S_2}{100 - S_1}\right) \qquad \text{(efficiency)}$$

* B. G. Lamme, National Electric Light Association Convention, Niagara Falls, June, 1897.

in which E_1 = the efficiency of the motor when running at a given torque and a slip S_1. E_2 = the efficiency when the motor is developing the same torque but with a different slip S_2, efficiencies and slips being expressed in per cent.

EXAMPLE.—Suppose a given 60-cycle, 8-pole motor with a synchronous speed of 900 r.p.m. has a normal full-load speed of 855 r.p.m. (slip 5 per cent.) and an efficiency of 90 per cent., the efficiency at 810 r.p.m. (slip 10 per cent.) with full-load torque will be:

$$E_2 = 90 \left(\frac{100 - 10}{100 - 5} \right) = 90 \times \frac{90}{95} = 85.2 \text{ per cent.}$$

305. Effect of Changes in Voltage and Frequency on Induction-motor Operation. *—Some variations from normal voltage and frequency are generally permissible with any induction motor, but such variations are always accompanied by changes from normal performance. With either the voltage or the frequency differing from normal the following performance changes must be expected:

Conditions	Power-factor	Torque	Slip
Voltage high	Decreased	Increased	Decreased
Voltage low	Increased	Decreased	Increased
Frequency high	Increased	Decreased	Per cent. slip unchanged.
Frequency low	Decreased	Increased	Per cent. slip unchanged.

Usually a variation of either voltage or frequency not exceeding 10 per cent. is permissible, and within this limit the efficiency remains approximately unchanged. The voltage and frequency should not be varied simultaneously in opposite directions, that is, one decreased and the other increased. If an induction motor must operate on frequency other than standard, the performance will be better if the voltage is changed in proportion to the square root of the frequency. Thus a 400-volt, 60-cycle motor operating on $66\frac{2}{3}$ cycles will have very

* Westinghouse Elec. & Manfg. Co. INSTRUCTION BOOK.

nearly its normal operating characteristics if the voltage is raised to:

$400 \times \sqrt{\dfrac{66\frac{2}{3}}{60}} = 442$ *volts.* Decreasing the voltage much below normal is seldom permissible on account of resulting increased temperature rises.

306. Tables of Performance Data for Polyphase Induction Motors of standard capacities ranging from $\frac{1}{2}$ to 200 h.p., are given in the author's AMERICAN ELECTRICIANS' HANDBOOK. In these tables are shown the synchronous speeds, per cent. slips, approximate full-load speeds, full-load currents, starting currents, starting torques, efficiencies and power-factors for the motors of the various ratings and standard voltages.

307. Performance Guarantees on Alternating-current Motors are now usually made on the so-called "normal" basis. However, it is probable that all motors made in this country will shortly be rated on the continuous (Art. 47a) basis. The normal rating usually given these motors specifies that they will operate continuously at their horse-power rated (nameplate) outputs with a temperature rise not to exceed 40 deg. C. and furthermore that they will operate at a 25 per cent. overload for two hours with a temperature rise not to exceed 55 deg. C. All of the above temperature rises are based on a "room" reference or ambient (Art. 47b) temperature of 25 deg. C.

308. Characteristics of Polyphase Induction Motors Having Wound Rotors and Internal Starting Resistance.—Motors of this type of the ordinary design give about $1\frac{1}{2}$ times full-load torque with approximately $1\frac{1}{2}$ times full-load current, making them suitable for use on lighting circuits and for other applications where a minimum starting current is desirable. In general, motors of this type are not built in capacities exceeding 200 h.p. because of the mechanical difficulties encountered in arranging the internal resistance.

309. Compared with the Squirrel-cage Motor, One with a Wound Rotor and internal resistance will develop a greater starting torque per ampere, but it should not be used for applications involving great inertia or excessive static friction.

If used for such applications, full starting current may be required for a considerable period before the apparatus attains full speed. Since the capacity of the internal resistance is small, excessive temperatures may result and cause trouble.

310. Characteristics of Polyphase Slip-ring or Wound-rotor Induction Motors Having External Starting Resistance.— These motors have insulated wire or bar windings on the rotor and are provided with collector rings whereby an external resistance can be connected in the rotor circuit. The speed of the motor can be varied by varying the amount of external resistance in the rotor circuit. These motors may be used in moderate and large capacities for nearly all variable-speed ap-

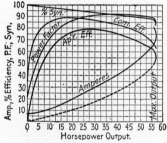

Fig. 200.—Typical performance graphs of a 20-h.p., three-phase induction motor.

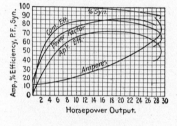

Fig. 201.—Performance graphs of the motor shown in Fig. 202, when running single-phase.

plications. They are also used for constant-speed applications where the starting current must be low. The motors operate with characteristics similar to those of direct-current motors having resistance in the armature circuit. When the external resistance is short-circuited, the motors really become squirrel-cage machines and operate with the characteristics of such machines.

311. Characteristic Graphs of the Induction Motor.—Those of Fig. 200 are fairly typical of the average commercial induction motor. It will be noted that the normal rating of the motor is taken at such a point that both the power-factor and the efficiency are the highest possible. The motor could be so designed that either the power-factor or the efficiency, but not both, could be higher than shown at normal load, but the design of an induction motor is a compromise resulting in the best efficiency and power-factor obtainable with suitable overload and starting characteristics.   Fig. 201 shows the curves of the same motor running single-phase.

312. The Torque Graphs of an Induction Motor with a Wound Rotor, from rest to synchronism, running both three-phase and single-phase with resistance and without resistance, are shown in Fig. 202.   Graph *A* shows the torque from rest to synchronism without resistance in the rotor circuit.   If resistance is inserted, graph *B* is obtained and the starting torque is 440 lb. against 170 lb. without resistance.   It should

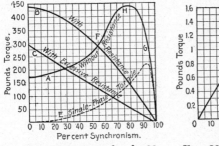

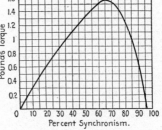

Fig. 202.—Torque graphs of a 30-h.p. induction motor.

Fig. 203.—Torque graph of a 1-h.p., three-phase induction motor, running single-phase.

be noted that the "pounds torque" values given in the graphs of Figs. 202 to 205 represent the pounds torque at a 1-ft. radius and are, therefore, equivalent to "pound-foot torque. See Art. 238.   Graph *C* indicates the torque where too much resistance is used in the rotor.   Graph *E* illustrates the torque single-phase, which is zero at starting.   An induction motor starts as shows on graph *B* until it reaches the point *F*, when the resistance is cut out and the motor adjusts itself to its operating position at *G*.   Thus, if the torque required of the motor for which the graph is shown, is greater than 440 lb., shown at *H*, the motor will break down and come to rest.   With the resistance in the rotor, a starting torque of 440 lb. is available, but this load cannot be brought up to normal speed. The motor can only bring the torque represented by the point *F*, in other words 290 lb., up to normal speed.

In Fig. 203 it will be noted that the torque of a three-phase motor running single-phase at starting is zero, rising to a maximum and reaching zero at synchronism. This means that an induction motor never runs at synchronous speed. The three-phase motor, Fig. 204, starts with a reasonable torque, reaches its maximum output and goes to zero again at synchronism.

Figs. 204 and 205 show the torque curves of squirrel-cage motors without resistance in the rotor circuit. With resistance inserted in the armature, the torque is greater at starting and

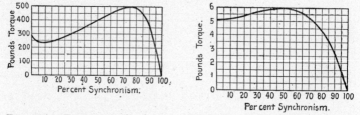

FIG. 204.—Torque graph of a 20-h.p., three-phase induction motor.   FIG. 205.—Torque graph of a 1-h.p., three-phase induction motor.

less later. This is the reason that it is advantageous to introduce resistance at starting and cut it out as synchronism is approached.

313. The Pull-out Torque of an Induction Motor.—All induction motors will "pull out" at some certain torque if they are overloaded. The "pull-out" limit—the maximum torque that can be developed—is that point at which further increase in torque will cause the motor speed to decrease rapidly and then to stop. This point is usually at between 2 and 4 times the full-load rated torque, depending on the design and the capacity of the motor. See the typical induction-motor curve, Fig. 200.

314. Starting Torque and Starting Current of Alternating-current Motors.[*]—In what follows the starting torque is ex-

[*] F. D. Newbury, N. E. L. A. Convention Paper, 1911.

pressed in terms of the full-load torque, and the starting current in terms of the full-load current. The smaller values given for synchronous motors cover the requirements of motor-generator sets and air compressors and pumps when the apparatus can be started without load. The larger values refer to motors for driving pumps and fans, which must be started under practically full-load conditions. The wide variation in the starting current comes from differences in construction of the motor or differences in the proportions of the motor, since, by increasing the size and cost of synchronous motors, the starting performances can be materially improved.

SINGLE-PHASE INDUCTION MOTORS, WITH CLUTCH, SPLIT-PHASE STARTER.—Starting torque, 1 to $1\frac{1}{4}$, starting current, $4\frac{1}{2}$ to 6.

SINGLE-PHASE INDUCTION MOTORS, WITHOUT CLUTCH, SPLIT-PHASE STARTER.—Starting torque, 2; starting current, $3\frac{1}{2}$ to $4\frac{1}{2}$.

POLYPHASE INDUCTION MOTORS, CAGE-WOUND TYPE, AUTO-TRANSFORMER STARTER.—Starting torque, 2; starting current, 7 to 8.

POLYPHASE INDUCTION MOTORS, WOUND-ROTOR TYPE, STEP-BY-STEP RESISTANCE STARTER.—Starting torque, 1; starting current, $1\frac{1}{4}$. Starting torque, 2; starting current, $2\frac{1}{2}$.

SYNCHRONOUS MOTORS, AUTO-TRANSFORMER STARTER.— Starting torque, 0.3 to 0.5; starting current, $1\frac{1}{2}$ to $2\frac{1}{2}$. Starting torque, 0.7 to 1; starting current, 4 to 8.

ROTARY CONVERTERS, AUTO-TRANSFORMER STARTER.—Starting torque, 0.2; starting current, $1\frac{1}{2}$. Starting torque, sufficient to start itself.

315. The Relations Between Speed, Frequency and Number of Poles of an Alternating-current Motor of the Synchronous or Induction Type follows from the equation for alternating-current generators given in Art. 253. For synchronous motors, these equations of Art. 253 are correct, but for induction motors which do not, when loaded, operate at synchronous speeds, the following formulas should be used:

$$(58) \qquad r.p.m. = \frac{120 \times f \times (1.00 - s)}{p} \qquad \text{(speed)}$$

$$(59) \qquad f = \frac{p \times r.p.m.}{120 \times (1.00 - s)} \qquad \text{(frequency)}$$

$$(60) \qquad s = 1.00 - \frac{p \times r.p.m.}{120 \times f} \qquad \text{(slip)}$$

$$(61) \qquad p = \frac{120 \times f \times (1.00 - s)}{r.p.m.} \qquad \text{(number of poles)}$$

Wherein, f = frequency in cycles per second. $r.p.m.$ = revolutions per minute of rotor. p = number of poles. s = the slip, expressed decimally. The method of determining slip is described in Art. 317. In the author's AMERICAN ELECTRICIANS' HANDBOOK will be found a table showing the per cent. slip at full-load for 25- and 60-cycle motors of the commonly used capacities and speeds.

EXAMPLE.—What will be the speed of a 6-pole, 60-cycle, induction motor at full-load, if its full-load slip is known to be 7 per cent.? SOLUTION.—Substitute in the equation (1): $r.p.m.$ = (120 × f × [1.00 − s]) ÷ 6 = (120 × 60 × [1.00 − 0.07]) ÷ 6 = 6,696 ÷ 6 = 1,116 $r.p.m.$

316. Speed Regulation of Induction Motors. Slip.—The speed regulation is the percentage drop in speed between no-load and full-load based on the maximum speed; it is usually called the "slip." The "slip" at full-load is usually about 5 to 7 per cent. At other loads it is approximately proportional to the load, therefore, at twice full-load the drop in speed will be approximately 10 to 15 per cent. Refer to the author's AMERICAN ELECTRICIANS' HANDBOOK for a table showing the slips to be expected from commercial induction motors.

317. The Slip of an Induction Motor is the ratio of the difference between the rotating magnetic-field speed (revolutions per minute or angular velocity) and the rotor speed to the rotating magnetic-field speed. The speed of the rotating magnetic field is equivalent to the synchronous speed (Art. 253) of the machine (see table of synchronous speeds in the AMERICAN ELECTRICIANS' HANDBOOK) which is determined by the frequency of the current and the number of poles of the machine. Then:

$$(62) \qquad Slip = \frac{synchronous\ speed - actual\ speed}{synchronous\ speed}$$

When there is no load on a motor the slip is very small, that is, the rotor speed is practically equal to the synchronous speed.

EXAMPLE.—What is the slip at full-load of a 4-pole, 60-cycle induction motor which has a full-load speed of 1,700 r.p.m. SOLUTION.—From formula 23 the speed of the rotating field or the synchronous speed of a 4-pole, 60-cycle motor is 1,800 r.p.m. Then substituting in the above formula:

$$Slip = \frac{sync.\ speed - act.\ speed}{sync.\ speed} = \frac{1,800 - 1,700}{1,800} = \frac{100}{1,800} = 5.5\ per\ cent.$$

Therefore the slip is 5.5 per cent. The voltage of the motor or whether it is single-phase, two-phase, or three-phase are not factors in the problem.

318. The Induction Motor Inherently a Constant-speed Motor. The Regenerative Feature.*—A characteristic of the induction motor is that it tends to rotate at a definite synchronous speed irrespective of whether the motor is driving or being driven, providing there is no starting resistance in the rotor circuit. For illustration, when a load is being lowered and the motor is connected to a source of energy, it acts as an alternating-current generator, the descending load furnishing the driving power. The motor delivers energy to the line. When load is being raised the motor absorbs energy from the line. This returning of energy to the line by a motor is termed regeneration. Consider an installation where cars loaded with ore are lowered down a slope on a railroad and the empty cars are hoisted back. The motor delivers about as much power to the line when lowering as it consumes when hoisting, with the result that practically no energy is consumed in operating the system. The proof of this is that the watt-hour meter for such an installation runs backward about as much as it runs forward.

EXAMPLE.—Another interesting example is a balanced passenger hoist wherein the passenger cars run over varying grades and sometimes one is loaded, at other times the other is loaded. The cars, when equipped with induction motors connected to a source of energy, run at a practically uniform speed without the use of brakes, whether the load overhauls the motor or not. This characteristic will not obtain if starting resist-

* PRACTICAL ENGINEER.

ance is included in the rotor circuit, for then the motor will slow down when it is delivering power to the cars and will operate at an overspeed if the cars are delivering power to the motor.

319. To Compute Either the Horse-power Output, Current, Voltage, Power-factor or Efficiency of any Three-phase, Alternating-current Motor, the other quantities being known, one of the following formulas may be used:

$$(63) \qquad h.p._o = \frac{E_3 \times I_3 \times p.f. \times \mathbf{E}}{430.7} \qquad \text{(horse-power)}$$

$$(64) \qquad E_3 = \frac{h.p._o \times 430.7}{I_3 \times p.f. \times \mathbf{E}} \qquad \text{(volts)}$$

$$(65) \qquad I_3 = \frac{h.p._o \times 430.7}{E_3 \times p.f. \times \mathbf{E}} \qquad \text{(amperes)}$$

$$(66) \qquad p.f. = \frac{h.p._o \times 430.7}{I_3 \times E_3 \times \mathbf{E}} \qquad \text{(power-factor)}$$

$$(67) \qquad \mathbf{E} = \frac{h.p._o \times 430.7}{p.f. \times I_3 \times E_3} \qquad \text{(efficiency)}$$

Wherein, $h.p._o$ = power output of the motor in horsepower. E_3 = voltage between any two of the three wires of the balanced three-phase system. I_3 = current, in amperes, in each of the three wires of the three-phase system. $p.f.$ = power-factor of the motor, expressed decimally. $\mathbf{E}$ = efficiency of the motor, expressed decimally.

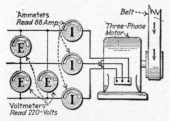

FIG. 206.—Example in determining horsepower output of a three-phase motor.

EXAMPLE.—What will be the horse-power output of a 220-volt, three-phase induction motor, Fig. 206, if its efficiency at full-load is known to be 87 per cent., its full-load power-factor 85 per cent., and its full-load current 88 amp.? SOLUTION.—Substitute in equation (63): $h.p._o = (E_3 \times I_3 \times p.f. \times \mathbf{E}) \div 430.7 = (220 \times 88 \times 0.85 \times 0.87) \div 430.7 = 14{,}316.72 \div 430.7 = 33.2\ h.p.$

EXAMPLE.—The three-phase induction motor shown in Fig. 207 is known to be delivering 50 h.p. at the pulley, P. The impressed e.m.f. is 440 volts. The power-factor at this load is known to be 86 per cent. and the efficiency 90 per cent. What current is being taken by the motor under these conditions? SOLUTION.—Substitute in equation (65):

$I_3 = (h.p._o \times 430.7) \div (E_3 \times p.f. \times \mathbf{E}) = (50 \times 430.7) \div (440 \times 0.86 \times 0.90) = 21,535 \div 340.56 = 63.2$ amp.

EXAMPLE.—The full-load output of the 220-volt, three-phase induction motor shown in Fig. 208 was found by the Prony brake test to be 35 h.p. Under these conditions the efficiency was 88 per cent., and the motor took 88 amp. in each of the three-phase wires. What was its

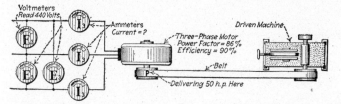

FIG. 207.—Example in computing current taken by three-phase motor.

power-factor under these conditions? SOLUTION.—Substitute in equation (66): $p.f. = (h.p._o \times 430.7) \div (I_3 \times E_3 \times \mathbf{E}) = (35 \times 430.7) \div (88 \times 220 \times 0.88) = 15,074.5 \div 17,036.8 = 0.884$. Hence, the power-factor of this motor at 35 h.p. is 88.4 per cent.

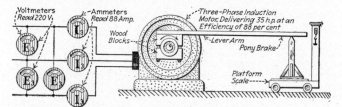
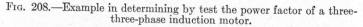

FIG. 208.—Example in determining by test the power factor of a three-three-phase induction motor.

320. To Compute Either the Horse-power Output, Current, Voltage, Power-factor or Efficiency of any Two-phase Alternating-current Motor, the other quantities being known, the following formula, or one derived from it, may be used:

$$(68) \qquad h.p._o = \frac{E_2 \times I_2 \times p.f. \times \mathbf{E}}{373} \qquad \text{(horse-power)}$$

Wherein, all of the symbols have the same meanings as in Art. 319, except that $E_2 =$ (for a four-wire, two-phase system), voltage between phase wires, and (for a three-wire, two-phase system) $= 0.707 \times$ voltage between each phase wire and the neutral.

321. Classification of Commercial Single-phase Motors

General type	Sub-classification	Commutator	Rotor	Speed characteristic	Examples
1. Induction..	(a) Straight induction or non-compensated (Fig. 211).	No commutator.	Squirrel-cage.	Constant speed.	Nearly all fan motors.
	(b) Compensated induction (Fig. 218).	Commutator in use for starting and running.	Combination squirrel-cage and d.c. armature type.	Constant speed.	Wagner Type BK.
2. Repulsion..	(c) Straight repulsion (Fig. 220).	Commutator in use for starting and running.	D.c. armature type.	Variable speed.	Wagner Type BH.
	(d) Repulsion induction (Fig. 221).	Commutator in use for starting and running.	D.c. armature type.	May be either constant or variable speed.	Genl Elec. RI = Constant speed Gen. Elec. BSS = Variable speed.
3. Repulsion, starting and induction running.	(Fig. 228).	Commutator in use during starting period only.	D.c. armature type.	Constant speed.	Wagner Type B.A. Gen. Elec. RSA. Century Type P. Peerless.
4. Series......	Unneutralized (Fig. 233).	Commutator in use whenever machine is in operation.	D.c. armature type.	Variable speed.	All *universal* motors, that is, a.c., d.c. Emerson, Westinghouse, etc.
	Neutralized (Fig. 226)	Commutator in use whenever machine in in operation.	D.c. armature type.	Variable speed.	Kimble.

322. Single-phase Motors of the types ordinarily manufactured and used in power practice may be arbitrarily classified into four different groups as shown in Table 321.   No attempt is made herein to consider single-phase railway motors. Other classifications can be made which may, for some purposes, be preferable to the one shown.   No generally adopted standard of classification is available at present.   However, it is understood that the Electric Power Club and other electrical societies coöperating in an endeavor to compile a classification of single-phase power motors which will, doubtless, ultimately be adopted as a standard classification in this country.

323. A Single-phase Induction Motor pure and simple (classification 1a in 321) develops no starting torque when its rotor *is* not revolving.   However, if the revolution of the motor is started by some means or other, there is a certain interaction of magnetic fields whereby there is exerted on the shaft a continuous turning effort.   While a single-phase induction motor may be started by hand by giving the rotor a twist, obviously, such a method of starting a motor is not feasible for commercial machines; hence others, whereby the motor can be started automatically, are adopted in practice. All of these methods of automatic starting (except that using a shading coil, Art. 330) involve electromagnetic interactions of some sort which occur—with the so-called straight induction motors—only during the starting period.   In this discussion, when a straight single-phase induction motor is referred to, the term is used to designate one with a squirrel-cage rotor.   After the motor is started it then operates as a single-phase induction motor, pure and simple.   These methods of starting may be classified thus: (1) split-phase method; (2) shading coil.

324. In the Split-phase Method of Starting a Single-phase Induction Motor, the motor (Figs. 209, 210, 211 and 212) is, in practice, provided with two distinct windings called the starting and the running windings (A and W, respectively, Fig. 211).   The starting winding circuit is so arranged that it has considerably more inductance, resistance or capacity—usually resistance—than had the running winding. Furthermore, the starting winding is displaced in the stator by 90 electrical degrees, as shown in Fig. 211, from the running winding. Due to the excess of inductance, resistance or capacity the current

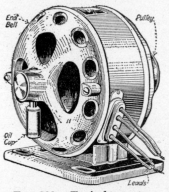

in the starting winding will differ considerably in phase from the current in the running winding. Because of this condition, and of the relative positions of the two windings, a rotating field is produced in the motor during the starting period, somewhat similar to the rotating field produced in a two-phase induction motor.

325. In Practice the Running Winding, Figs. 211 and 212, usually consist of a considerable number of turns of large wire, well distributed over the stator.

Fig. 209.—Typical construction of a split-phase-starting, single-phase motor.

Practically all of the split-phase motors on the market use a starting-winding circuit of high resistance. Hence, the starting winding, ordinarily consists of fine wire, thus giving this winding a high resistance. In fan motors of some designs an in-

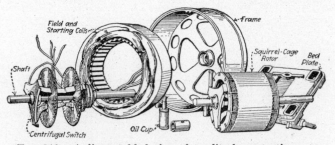

Fig. 210.—A disassembled view of a split-phase-starting motor.

ductance coil mounted in the base of the motor is connected in series with the starting winding to provide the necessary inductance. The running winding remains in circuit at all times when the motor is not in operation. But the starting winding remains in circuit only until the speed of the rotor approaches synchronous speed.   When this speed is attained then the rotor winding should be cut out, an automatic centrifugal switch (Fig. 212 and Fig. 211, S_1, S_2) operates.   This opens the starting cir-

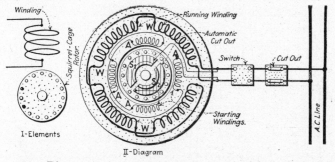

Fig. 211.—Diagrammatic representations of "straight" single-phase induction motor.

cuit and then the motor continues to operate as a squirrel-cage induction motor, solely by virtue of its running winding and circuit and its squirrel-cage rotor.   In small single-phase induction motors of certain manufacture, the squirrel-cage

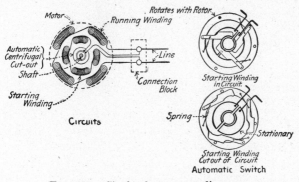

Fig. 212.—Single-phase-motor diagram.

element is arranged in the stator and the running and starting windings are arranged on the rotor.

326. The Principle of the Split-phase Method of Starting is illustrated in Fig. 213, which shows an explanatory diagram

14

and not a commercial motor.   In starting one of these motors,
first the main switch, M, is closed, which excites the running
winding, W.   However, with only this running winding excited, the motor will not, of itself, start, but if now the starting switch S is closed, which energizes the starting winding,
A, which has in series with it the resistance, R, the rotating-
field effect referred to above is thereby produced in the machine
and the rotor will commence to
revolve.   When the motor
attains a speed which approaches
synchronous speed, the switch
S may then be opened and the
motor will continue to operate as
an induction motor.

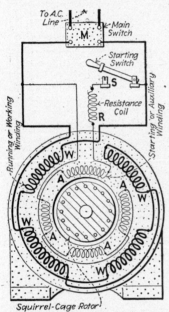

Fig. 213.—"Straight" single-
phase motor with an external
starting reactance.

**327. The Split-phase Method
of Starting Induction Motors is
Used Only for Motors of Small
Capacity.**—Most of the induction
fan motors and the fractional
horse-power motors employ this
method of starting.   However,
the repulsion method of starting
(Art. 336) is now being used to
some extent for starting fractional horse-power motors because of the more desirable starting characteristics which it
affords.

**328. As to the Starting
Torque, Starting Current and
Speed Regulation of Single-phase, Phase-splitting-starting Induction Motors**, they are suitable for applications for which the
starting torque required is not over 150 per cent. of full-load
torque.   The starting current for a motor designed to develop
150 per cent. full-load torque is approximately 550 per cent.
of full-load current.   The maximum torque is from 200 to 250
per cent. of the full-load torque.   The speed regulation
from no-load to full-load is good—better than with the

polyphase motor.   In general, however, the efficiency, power-factor and maximum torque are not as good as in corresponding polyphase motors.   They are suited only for driving machinery requiring relatively small starting torque.

329. The Condenser-compensator Method of Starting Single-phase Induction Motors (Fig. 214) is an example of the split-phase method of starting whereby permittance or capacity (capacitance) is introduced in the starting circuit. The rotor is of the squirrel-cage type.   Two terminals (Fig.

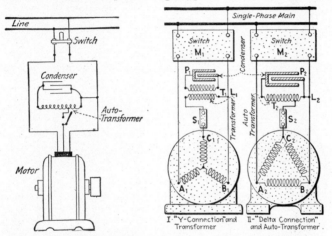

Fig.   214.—A   single-phase, self-starting induction motor with a condenser starting arrangement.

Fig. 215.—Diagrams of split-phase-starting single-phase motors ultilizing capacity in the starting circuit.

215), A_1 and B_1 of the stator winding, which is esentially similar to a standard three-phase winding are connected to the supply mains.   The third terminal, C_1, of the stator winding is connected to the line through a transformer as shown in I or through an auto-transformer (or compensator), as shown in II.   The main to which the lead, L_1 or L_2, from the transformer or auto-transformer is connected is determined by the direction of rotation desired.   A condenser or permitter, P_1, is also connected across the auto-transformer, as shown in the illustration, to provide permittance or capacity. The motor is started with both switches, M and S, closed, but

when it has attained a speed approaching synchronism,
the starting winding is cut out (by operating the switch, S)
and the motor then continues to operate on the running winding only. This method, which is due to Steinmetz, is seldom,
if ever, now used commercially but is of theoretical interest.

**330. The Shading-coil Method of Starting Induction Mo-
tors** is illustrated in Figs. 216 and 217. The face of each
pole of a machine which has been designed to be started by
this method has arranged in it a small short-circuited copper-

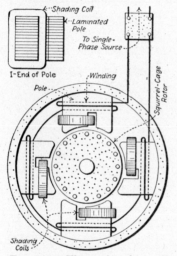

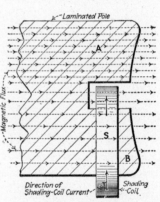

Fig. 216.—Illustrating the application of shading coils in single-phase
motors.

Fig. 217.—Illustrating the
principle of the shading coil.

bar winding called a shading coil, which encircles a portion of
the pole. When the alternating flux passes through the pole,
it induces a current in the shading soil, S, Fig. 217, which, by
virtue of Lenz's law, tends to oppose the flux in portion B,
which produces it. The result is that the flux in the "un-
shaded" portion of the pole, A, Fig. 217, attains its maximum at
a different time than does the flux in the "shaded" portion B.
Furthermore, as A and B are also space displaced against each
other, the result is that a field, which approximates in its effect
the rotating field of a polyphase motor, is produced, but this

"shifting" field is not as effective as that developed in split-phase machines. The method has the further disadvantage that the shading coil is always in position on the pole and that it involves an energy loss so long as the motor is in operation. However, the method is applied only in machines of very small capacity, such as fan motors, so that the energy loss is not a matter of great consequence. The use of this method is constantly decreasing.

331. Performance Data for Single-phase Induction Motors of capacities of from 1 to 50 h.p. will be found tabulated in the author's AMERICAN ELECTRICIANS' HANDBOOK. The

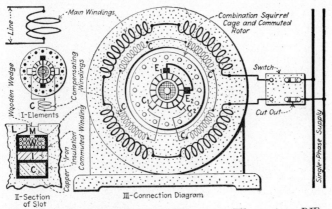

FIG. 218.—The compensated induction motor (Wagner type *BK*).

efficiencies, per cent. slip, pull-out torque and also the efficiencies and power-factors at various loads are there given.

332. A Compensating Winding on an alternating-current motor (*C*, Fig. 218) is, as the term is used herein, a winding the function of which is only to improve the power-factor of the current taken by the machine. Thus, the power-factor of an alternating-current motor, may, by the addition of a sufficiently powerful compensating winding be raised from lagging to unity power factor or to leading power factor, if desirable. All uncompensated alternating-current motors draw lagging current from the line. This means that they require greater currents than are actually necessary for the production of power which they develop.   But by using a suitably-designed compensating winding it is possible to raise the power-factor of the motor current to unity and thereby proportionately decrease the current required for the production of the power.

333. A Neutralizing Winding, as the term is here used, is one the main function of which is to neutralize armature reaction.   Hence, if a neutralizing winding is placed on a machine it will increase its output over that of the same machine without the neutralizing winding and incidentally it will improve the commutation.

Fɪɢ. 219.—A Wagner compensated induction single-phase motor.

334. The Compensated Induction Motor (classification 1*b*, Table 321) Figs. 218 and 219, is essentially a squirrel-cage-rotor induction machine to which have been added, on the stator, a compensating winding and, on the rotor, a direct-current armature winding and commutator.   Brushes and connections for the compensating winding are provided as shown in Fig. 218 and also there are provided a pair of short-circuited brushes, E_1 and E_2, which contribute partly to the mechanical output of the machine.   These brushes E_1 and

E_2 and the connecting bar between are not essential to the machine's operation, but they increase its efficiency. The feature of machines of this type that has brought them into use is that they operate with good power-factor under all load conditions. They have the further advantage that, except in starting, practically all of the work is done by virtue of the squirrel-cage winding; hence, the brushes and commutator carry little load current, commutation difficulties are minimized, the life of the commutator is increased and its size decreased.

The squirrel-cage winding consists of copper bars, C (Fig. 218, II) wedged in the bottoms of the slots in the rotor. A "magnetic bridge," I, of iron, is arranged above the squirrel-cage-bar winding and then the commutating winding—similar to a direct-current armature winding—is placed in the slot above the bridge. Fig. 218 shows the connections as they exist after the machine has attained running speed. While the machine is starting, the compensating winding is not in use because its circuit is then held open by a centrifugal switch which is located within the casing S, Fig. 219. These machines as manufactured by the Wagner Electric Manufacturing Company have a starting torque equal to $1\frac{1}{2}$ to 2 times full-load torque. Their starting current is about 3 times full-load current. When the machine is in running connection, the full-load power-factor is about unity. The adjustment of the compensating winding is so made that at full-load the power-factor is approximately unity, while at no-load it is usually appreciably leading.

335. The Straight Repulsion Motor (classification 2c, Table 321) has, as illustrated in Fig. 220, an armature which is like that of a direct-current machine. Short-circuiting brushes, E_1 and E_2, inclined at an angle to the axis of the stator winding are provided. A machine of this type has in general the same speed torque characteristics as a direct-current series motor, that is, high-starting torque with a very small starting current and rapidly decreasing torque with increasing speed. The power-factor of this machine increases with increasing speed and near synchronous speed attains a value which is higher

than usually obtained in straight induction motors. These
motors are used principally for constant-torque applications,
namely, for printing-press drives and also for other drives for
which series direct-current motors are adaptable, such as for
fans and blowers. They have been successfully applied for
hoist service. As with the series direct-current motor, the
speed of these machines can be varied by varying the impressed voltage or by shifting the brushes. The direction of
rotation of a straight repulsion motor can be changed by the
addition of a suitable reversing switch or reversing winding or
by shifting the brushes to the reverse side of the neutral.

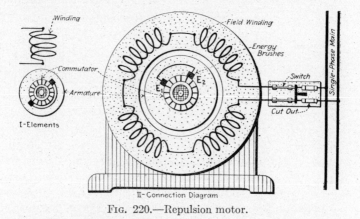

Fig. 220.—Repulsion motor.

336. The Repulsion-induction Motor (classification 2*d*,
Table 321), Figs. 221 and 222, is like the straight repulsion
machine except that in addition it has a compensating winding
as shown in the diagram. The energy brushes, E_1 and E_2,
have approximately the same angular position in relation to
the stator winding as the energy brushes of a straight repulsion motor. These machines have, in addition to the energy
brushes, a second set of brushes, C_1 and C_2, called the compensating brushes, which are connected in series with the
compensating winding. The motors have a starting torque
equal to about $2\frac{1}{2}$ to 3 times full-load torque with approximately twice full-load current. The maximum torque

is from 3 to $3\frac{1}{2}$ full-load torque. The power-factor (due to the corrective action of the compensating winding) is very

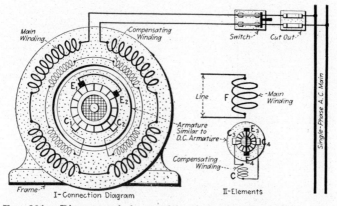

Fig. 221.—Diagrams of the repulsion induction single-phase motor. (The brushes E_3 and E_4 in *II* should be slightly inclined in the clockwise direction from the vertical, instead of being in a vertical line as shown.)

Fig. 222.—Phantom view showing construction of the General Electric Company Type *RI*, Form *C*, single-phase, repulsion-induction motor.

high at all loads but the efficiency of this machine is lower than that of the induction motor. Single-phase motors of this type are well adapted for loads involving heavy starting torque and sudden overloads.   They have the disadvantages of having commutators which carry the total armature current. They can be arranged for variable speed service as shown

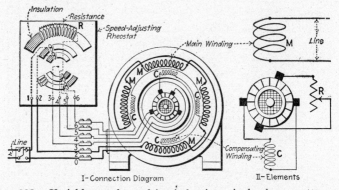

FIG. 223.—Variable-speed repulsion-induction, single-phase motor and controller.

in Fig. 223 by the insertion of a rheostat in series between the energy brushes.   They can also be arranged for reversing service as indicated in Fig. 224 by the application of a revers-

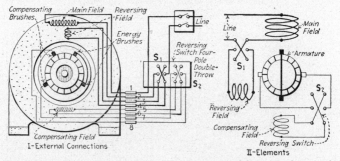

FIG. 224.—A repulsion-induction motor arranged for reversing service. (Throwing the reversing switch: (1) reverses the connection between the compensating winding and the compensating brushes, (2) reverses the connections between the reversing field winding and the main winding.)

ing field and a suitable reversing switch.   The characteristic performance graphs of machines of this type are shown in Fig. 225.

337. If a Variable-speed Single-phase Motor is Required, some modified form of repulsion-induction motor (Fig. 223) can be used. Also, the series motor (Fig. 233) and the repulsion motor (Fig. 220) may be applied for this service by using a rheostat or an auto-transformer in the line for varying the voltage impressed on the motor terminals. The behavior of such motors is similar to that of the variable-speed wound-rotor multiphase-induction motor with resistance in series with the rotor. They are consequently, owing to their unstable speed characteristics, suited only to such applications

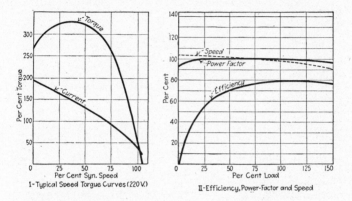

I-Typical Speed Torque Curves (220 V.)

II-Efficiency, Power-Factor and Speed

Fig. 225.—Typical performance graphs for a single-phase, repulsion-induction motor. (General Electric Co., Type *RI*, Form *C*.)

as require a steady horse-power at given speeds. Their characteristics as regards starting torque, etc., are unchanged when used for variable speeds. The speed-regulating resistance (R, Fig. 223) is in one type of motor inserted in series with the brushes which are normally short-circuited and the insertion of additional resistance decreases the speed.

338. Repulsion-starting-and-Induction-running, Single-phase Motors (classification 3, Table 321), Fig. 227, are now probably used for power service to a greater extent than those of any other type. As would be inferred from its name (Fig. 228) the motor starts as a repulsion but operates as an induction machine. The rotor, Fig. 229, is exactly the same

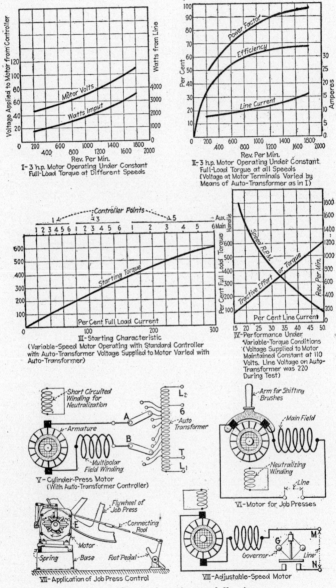

FIG. 226.—See explanation on following page.

as the armature of a direct-current motor. It is provided
with form-wound coils and a commutator. The number of
brushes used is the same as would be used with the corresponding direct-current motor with the same number of poles,

Fig. 227.—Showing the external appearance of the Wagner, Type *BA*,
repulsion-starting-and-induction-running motor.

Fig. 226.—Kimble single-phase motors. In *V* on preceding page
is shown the control used for the cylinder-printing-press motors. By
using two control handles and an auto-transformer, 30 over-lapping
speed steps are obtained. The handles, as shown in the picture, are in
the position of maximum speed, impressing 110 volts on the motor.
By utilizing the auto-transformer control, the same outfit can be used
either on 110 or 220-volt circuits.   On a 220-volt circuit, the line wires
are connected to terminals L_1 and L_2 and on a 110-volt circuit to *T*
and 6.   This motor (and also that shown in *VIII* use a fixed-brush
setting.   That is, the brushes are not shifted for speed control.   The
motor of *V* and also that of *VI* can be used only on constant-torque
loads.   In *VI* is shown the ideal diagram for the job-printing-press motors,
while in *VII* is illustrated the method of their application.   Speed control is obtained by shifting the brushes.   In *VIII* the adjustable-speed
motor is shown.   The speed is controlled with an auto-transformer
whereby the e.m.f. impressed on the line terminals *M* and *N* is varied.
The speed is maintained constant at any given speed within the range of
the motor by the action of the centrifugal governor *G* which opens and
closes the main circuit, motors of this type are made in capacities of 1.6
to 2.5 h.p.   All of the Kimble-Company motors are of the compensated-
series type and employ a neutralizing winding to neutralize armature
reaction *N*. This winding also improves the power-factor.

but in the alternating-current machines all of the brushes are
connected together electrically by the metal rocker arm which
supports them.   The stator, which has only one winding, is

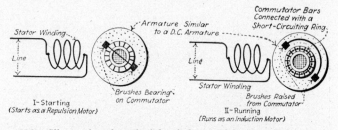

Fig. 228.—Illustrating the principle of the repulsion-starting, induction-
running, single-phase motor.

supplied with single-phase current.   There is no electrical
connection (Fig. 228) between the stator and the rotor.   The

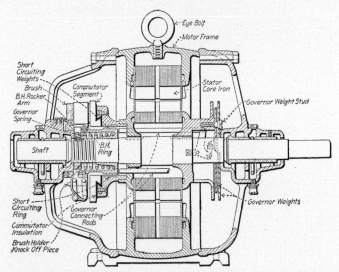

Fig. 229.—Sectional elevation of the Wagner Type *BA* repulsion-starting-and-induction-running motor.

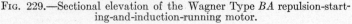

currents in the stator create an alternating flux which reacts
on the rotor and induces its rotation.   When the speed of the
rotor approaches synchronous speed, a centrifugal device of

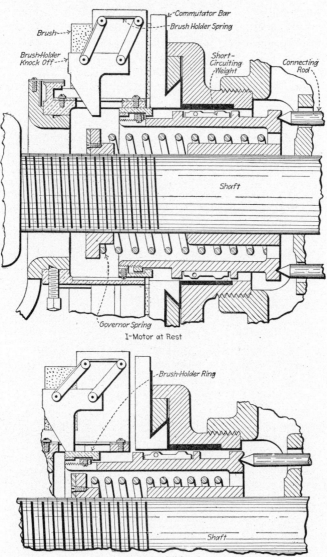

Fig. 230.—Illustrating the mechanism of the brush-lifting and commutator short-circuiting device of the Wagner repulsion-starting-and-induction-running motor.

some description short-circuits the commutator bars (Fig. 228, *II* and Fig. 230) and simultaneously pushes the brushes away from the commutator. Thus the motor is transformed into an induction machine having what is essentially a squirrel-cage rotor. Typical performance graphs are shown in Fig. 231. The machine is inherently a constant-speed motor. The applications of the repulsion-starting-and-induction-running motor are about the same as those for which a direct-current constant-speed shunt motor is ordinarily used with the exception that the repulsion induction motor has a much greater

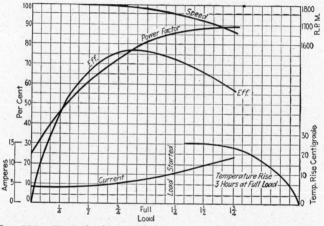

Fig. 231.—Typical characteristic curves of the repulsion-starting, induction-running motor of the general type illustrated in Fig. 228 (Peerless Electric Co.).

starting torque (Fig. 232) than the corresponding shunt motor and that it is not adaptable for adjustable-speed service.

339. The Series Single-phase Motor (classification 4, Table 321) comprises, Fig. 233, merely an armature of the same construction as any direct-current armature in series with a field winding. In fact, any direct-current series motor will operate on single-phase alternating current but if the machine is of such a capacity that it requires considerable current, commutation difficulties will be encountered. Furthermore, for alternating-current work the stator core should be lami-

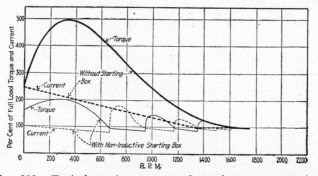

Fig. 232.—Typical starting torque and starting current graphs for repulsion-starting, induction-running, single-phase motors (Century Elec. Co.).   Note.—Motors of standard construction and rating will be found capable, when the voltage and frequency for which they are wound and adjusted is maintained, of bringing a load up to speed equal to at least $1\frac{1}{8}$ of their rated capacity.   When connected directly across the line (which is the usual manner of making the installation), they will develop, at the moment of starting, approximately two and one-half times full-load torque and take approximately two and one-half times full-load current.   By the time the motor has reached one-quarter speed, the torque will have increased to approximately five times full-load torque and the current decreased to double full-load current; from that speed both torque and current gradually drop to normal as the motor increases in speed.   By the use of a resistance starter, full-load starting torque may be secured with approximately one and one-quarter times full-load current under the most favorable conditions.   In commercial practice the starting current may be expected to be around one and one-half times full-load current.

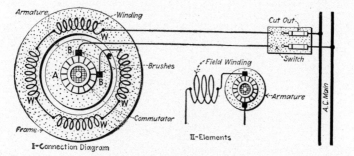

Fig. 233.—Diagrams of the series, single-phase induction motor.   (The so-called "universal" motor.)

nated. However, for motors of small capacity where the currents are of low intensity, the commutation difficulties are not unsurmountable, hence small single-phase series motors are being manufactured and used successfully in capacities of less than 1 h.p. The important commercial example of this type of motor is the so-called "universal" motor which will operate on either direct- or alternating-current circuits. It

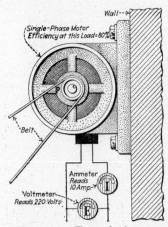

is used for fans and small appliance motors and electric drills, where the manufacturers in sending out the motor may not know whether the ultimate purchaser will have available either alternating or direct current. These are variable-speed machines, that is, they have (approximately) the speed-torque characteristics of a direct-current series motor.

340. To Compute Either the Horse-power, Current, Voltage, Power-factor or Efficiency of any Single-phase Alternating-current Motor, the other quanti-

FIG. 234.—Example in computing the horsepower output of a single-phase motor.

ties being known, one of the following formulas may be used:

$$(69) \qquad h.p._o = \frac{E \times I_1 \times p.f. \times \mathbf{E}}{746} \qquad \text{(horse-power)}$$

$$(70) \qquad E = \frac{h.p._o \times 746}{I_1 \times p.f. \times \mathbf{E}} \qquad \text{(volts)}$$

$$(71) \qquad I_1 = \frac{h.p._o \times 746}{E \times p.f. \times \mathbf{E}} \qquad \text{(amperes)}$$

$$(72) \qquad p.f. = \frac{h.p._o \times 746}{E \times I_1 \times \mathbf{E}} \qquad \text{(power-factor)}$$

$$(73) \qquad \mathbf{E} = \frac{h.p._o \times 746}{p.f. \times E \times I_1} \qquad \text{(efficiency)}$$

Wherein, $h.p._o$ = power output of the motor, in horse-power.
E = alternating voltage impressed between the wires on motor

terminals, in volts. I_1 = current in each of the two wires of the motor in amperes.   *p.f.* = power-factor of the motor, expressed decimally.   **E** = efficiency of the motor, expressed decimally.

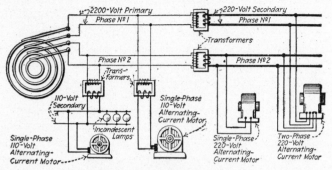

FIG. 235.—Diagram illustrating methods of feeding motors from a two-phase line.

EXAMPLE.—What will be the horse-power output of the pulley, *P*, of the single-phase motor shown in Fig. 234, when: the impressed voltage is 220, the current is 10 amp., the power-factor is 84 per cent. and the efficiency is 80 per cent.?   SOLUTION.—Substitute in the formula (69):

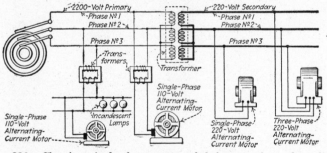

FIG. 236.—Showing single-phase motors fed from a three-phase line.

$h.p._o = (E \times I_1 \times p.f. \times E) \div 746 = (220 \times 10 \times 0.84 \times 0.80) \div 746 = 1{,}478.4 \div 746 = 1.98 \ h.p.$, or, say, 2 *h.p.*

EXAMPLE.—What will be the full-load current taken by a 10-h.p. single-phase, 220-volt induction motor, which, at its rated horse-power has a power-factor of 80 per cent., and an efficiency of 84 per cent.?   SOLUTION.—Substitute in equation (71): $I_1 = (h.p._o \times 746) \div (E \times p.f. \times E) = (10 \times 746) \div (220 \times 0.80 \times 0.84) = 7{,}460 \div 147.84 = 50.4$ amp.

341. That Single-phase Motors may be Operated from any Alternating-current Circuit is Their Principal Advantageous Feature.—Obviously they may be operated from a single-phase circuit and can also be operated from two-phase and three-phase circuits, as diagrammed, respectively, in Figs. 235 and 236. Frequently utility companys do not extend poly-phase circuits to certain outlying districts. Where a motor is to be installed in such a territory and the extension of the polyphase circuit is not economically desirable, a single-phase motor offers a solution to the problem.

SECTION 9

SYNCHRONOUS MOTORS AND CONDENSERS

342. Synchronous Motors* (Fig. 237 and 238).—Generally speaking, any modern alternating-current generator will oper-

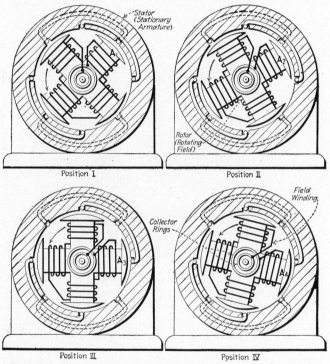

Fig. 237.—The operating principle of the synchronous motor.

ate with more or less satisfaction as a synchronous motor, and unless special operating features must be provided for, the two are often identical in construction. There are two

* Carl C. Knight in PRACTICAL ENGINEER, June 1, 1912.

advantages of the synchronous motor, namely: it operates at a constant speed at all loads, provided the driving alternator runs at a constant speed, and its power-factor is at all times under the control of the attendant. It can be used to correct low power-factor of the system that feeds it, in addition to driving a mechanical load, provided it has sufficient capacity.

The latter characteristic is often of considerable importance. It is well known that the power-factor of the induction motor, even under full-load conditions, is seldom greater

FIG. 238.—A Westinghouse Type *C* belt-drive synchronous motor with a direct-connected exciter.

than 95 per cent., and it often falls as low as 50 or 60 per cent. at light-load. The result is that an alternating-current generator driving a considerable number of induction motors ordinarily operates at a comparatively low power-factor. If this alternator is loaded to its full kilowatt capacity at such a low power-factor, overheating will result. If the alternator is not loaded beyond its normal current capacity it operates at a low energy load but with the same heating losses as at full-load, on account of the reduced power-factor. The advantage of the synchronous motor on such a system is, that by proper adjustment of its field current it may be made to draw from the line a current which is leading with respect to the voltage. This current which will "neutralize" the lagging current taken by the induction motors. The current in the alternating-current generator can thereby be *brought into phase* with the voltage and the generator will operate under its normal conditions. When used in this manner as a compensator for lagging current, the synchronous motor must be of larger size than required by its mechanical power output, on account of the excess current which it draws from the line.

343. A Synchronous Condenser is a synchronous motor that operates to correct power-factor only and does not pull any mechanical load.

344. Disadvantages of the Synchronous Motor.—To offset its advantages, the synchronous motor has disadvantages which ordinarily limit its application to relatively large capacities, and to installations where it can be used as a "neutralizer" for lagging current. The chief disadvantage is that the motor has relatively small starting torque even at full-load current. The motor also requires direct current for its field excitation.

345. The Uses of Synchronous Motors.†—Due to the fact that synchronous motors require more care than induction motors, that they are not self-exciting and are started with some difficulty, they are seldom employed where induction motors can be used. Where an induction motor would be objectionable on account of its lagging "wattless" currents which affect the voltage regulation, a synchronous motor may be used to advantage. It is also used as a "synchronous condenser" in connection with induction-motor loads for power-factor correction as noted above.

346. The Steps in Starting a Synchronous Motor are about as follows:

1. See that motor is clean, that bearings are well supplied with oil, and that oil rings are free to turn.

2. See that all switches are open.

3. Close the double-throw field switch, cutting in the field rheostat with its resistance all in.

† STANDARD HANDBOOK.

4. Close the main-line switch (if any) in the circuit and throw in the double-throw switch, throwing it in the starting position. The motor should start and speed up to synchronism in from 30 to 60 sec.

5. When motor is up to speed, throw field switch over to the other (running) position with rheostat all in.

6. Throw double-throw main switch over to running position, putting motor on full-line voltage.

7. Adjust field rheostat for minimum armature current.

Fig. 239 shows the method of connecting a three-phase, self-starting synchronous motor to its exciter. This diagram shows a double-throw switch in the field circuit. This switch, however, may (where the exciter is connected to the same shaft as the synchronous motor) be single-throw and the field connected direct through the exciter armature with the rheostat in the circuit. The field is thus short-circuited at standstill and is gradually charged as the motor speeds up.

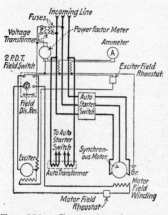

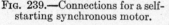

FIG. 239.—Connections for a self-starting synchronous motor.

347. Starting Synchronous Motors.*—Practically any polyphase synchronous motor may be started by applying full-load voltage to the armature, leaving the field open until the motor has reached its normal speed. Such a procedure would require, however, 2 or more times the full-load current of the machine. Since the power taken by a synchronous motor starting in this manner is of very low power-factor, the line disturbances might be considerable. Starting at full-line voltage is also liable to induce in the field windings an excessively high voltage, often resulting in breaking down the insulation.

348. To Limit the Starting Current to a Reasonable Value, Auto-starters or Compensators are Often Used.—These are

* PRACTICAL ENGINEER.

similar and used in exactly the same manner as the starting compensators used with induction motors (Art. 371).   When starting with a compensator, the field-winding circuit is opened by a switch provided for the purpose or the field circuit may be closed through a resistance until the motor has attained its normal speed.   This arrangement does not provide a great starting torque, and in most modern synchronous motors the revolving field of the motor is provided with a special auxiliary winding (Fig. 240) similar to the winding on the rotor of a squirrel-cage induction motor.   It has been possible to construct motors having nearly 30 per cent. of full-load torque at approximately 1½ times full-load current.   Beside improv-

Fig. 240.—Rotating element of a synchronous motor showing the squirrel-cage starting winding.

ing the starting torque this squirrel-cage winding also has a tendency to reduce the hunting or pumping effect which is sometimes encountered in the operation of synchronous motors.

349. Where the Capacity of the Motor Which is to be Started is Comparable with the Capacity of the Generator which feeds it, it is often necessary to connect a small induction motor to the synchronous motor to bring it up to speed. When approximately normal speed has been reached the synchronous motor is thrown on the line as before, and the field closed immediately.

350. When a Large Starting Torque is Required, as, for example, in driving a considerable amount of shafting, it is often impractical to start the load and the motor from rest simultaneously. In such instances it is customary to install a friction clutch or similar device between the motor and its load, so that the motor may attain its normal speed before any load is imposed upon it.

351. Occasional Installations are Encountered Where the Motor is the Only Load on the Driving Generator.—In such cases it is possible to connect the synchronous motor to the line before starting the alternator. On starting the alternator, both will come up to speed together. Cases have been known in which the motor was a small part of the load on the driving alternator, that is, the alternator was larger compared with the motor, when an auto-starter was used to raise the voltage at start instead of to reduce it. This method gives a fairly good torque, but requires large current, and the operator must be certain that the motor windings will not be damaged before trying such a method.

352. In Cases Where it is Desired to Use an Alternating-current Generator as a Motor and no Compensator is Available, water rheostats can be used to good advantage, one being placed in series with each phase. They are short-circuited when the motor has attained normal speed.

353. General Summary of Synchronous-motor Troubles.—Failure of a synchronous motor to start is often due to faulty connections in the auxiliary apparatus. These should be carefully inspected for open circuits or poor connections. An open circuit in one phase of the motor itself, or a short-circuit will prevent the motor from starting. Most synchronous motors are provided with an ammeter in each phase, so that the last two causes can be determined from their indications—no current in one phase in case of an open circuit, and excessive current in case of a short-circuit. Either condition will usually be accompanied by a decided buzzing noise, and in case of a short-circuited coil, it will often be quickly burned out. The effect of a short-circuit is sometimes caused by two grounds on the machine. Starting troubles should never be assumed until a trial has been made to start the motor light, that is, with no load except its own friction. It may be that the starting load is too great for the motor.

354. If the Motor Starts but Fails to Develop Sufficient Torque to Carry its Load when the field circuit has been closed, the trouble will usually be found in the field circuit. First, determine whether or not the exciter is developing its normal voltage. Assuming the exciter voltage to be correct, the trouble will probably be due to one of the following causes. (1) Open circuit in the field winding or rheostat or (2) short-circuit or reversal of one or more of the field spools. Open circuit can often be located by inspection or by use of the magneto.

355. The Majority of Field Troubles are caused by excessive induced voltage at start, or by the field circuit being broken. This excessive voltage may break down the insulation between field winding and frame or between turns on any one field spool, thus short-circuiting one or more turns, or it may even burn the field conductor off, causing an open circuit.

356. Causes of Overheating in Synchronous Motors are about the same as those in alternating-current generators. Probably the most common cause of overheating is excessive armature current due to an attempt to make the motor carry its rated load, and at the same time compensate for a power-factor lower than that for which it was designed. If the motor is not correcting low power-factor, but doing mechanical work only, the field current should be adjusted so that the armature field is a minimum for the average load that the motor carries.

357. Difficulties in Starting Synchronous Motors.*—A synchronous motor is "weaker" in starting than is an induction motor. In general, however, a synchronous motor will start itself and perhaps a very light load. Starting requires no field current as the flux which tends to start the motor is not the flux that operates it when it is up to speed. In starting, the field current is lagging, and a lagging current tends to pull down the voltage on the supply circuit, hence tends to lower the applied voltage. The starting torque, as in an induction motor, is proportional to the square of the applied voltage. For example, if the voltage is halved, the starting effort is quartered. When a synchronous motor will not start, it may

---

* Based largely on Raymond's Motor Troubles.

be because the voltage on the line has been pulled down below the value necessary for starting.

In general, at least half voltage is required to start a synchronous motor. Difficulty in starting may also be caused by an open circuit in one of the lines to the motor. Assume the motor to be three-phase. If one of the lines is open the motor becomes single-phase, and no single-phase synchronous motor, as such, is self-starting. The motor will, therefore, not start, and will soon get hot. The same condition is true of a two-phase motor, if one of the phases is open-circuited.

Difficulty in starting may also be due to a rather slight increase in static friction. It may be that the bearings are too tight, perhaps from cutting during the previous run. Excessive belt tension, in case the synchronous motor is belted to its load, or any cause which increases starting friction will probably give trouble. Difficulty in starting may be due to field excitation being on the motor. After excitation exceeds one-quarter normal value, the starting torque is influenced. With full field on, most synchronous motors will not start at all. If the proper voltage is applied to a motor, and the circuits are all closed except the field circuit and the friction is a minimum, and still the motor will not start, the fault is probably with the manufacturer. Pole-pieces often receive extra starting windings or conducting bridges are provided between the pole-pieces to assist in starting. Possibly the manufacturer in shipping may have omitted these devices. In such cases one must refer to the factory.

Usually, as above suggested, compensators are used for starting synchronous motors. If there is a reversed phase in a compensator, or, if the windings of the armature of the synchronous motor are connected incorrectly, there will be little starting torque. Incorrect connection can be located by noting the unbalanced entering currents. Readings to determine this unbalancing should be taken with the armature revolving slowly. The revolving can be effected by any mechanical means. While the motor is standing still, even with correct connections, the armature currents of the three phases usually differ somewhat. This is due to the position of the poles in relation to the armature, but when revolving slowly, the currents should average up. If the rotor cannot be revolved mechanically, similar points on each phase of the armature must be found. Then, when the rotor is set successively at these points, the currents at each setting should be the same. Each phase when located in a certain specific position as related to a pole, should, with right connections, take a certain specific current. With wrong connections, the currents will not be the same.

358. Open Circuit in the Field of a Synchronous Motor.— If in the operation of a synchronous motor the field current breaks for any reason, the armature current will largely increase, causing either a shutdown or excessive heat. It becomes important, therefore, in synchronous motors to have the field circuit permanently established.

359. A Short-circuit in an Armature Coil of a Synchronous Motor burns it out completely, charring it down to the bare copper. When this occurs, the symptoms are so evident that there is no difficulty in identifying the trouble. Such a coil may under ordinary circumstances be cut out and operation continued. In an induction motor, the current in the short-circuited coil rises only to a certain value, but heats it many times more than normal. It is not necessarily burned out immediately, and perhaps it may not be burned out at all.

360. Hunting of Synchronous Motors.—Synchronous motors, served by certain primary sources of energy, tend to "hunt." The periodicity of the swinging is determined by properties of the armature and the circuit. It may reach a certain magnitude and there stick, or the swinging may increase until finally the motor breaks down altogether. This trouble usually occurs on long lines having considerable resistance between the source of energy and the synchronous motor. Sometimes it occurs under the most favorable conditions. Irregular rotation of a prime mover (Art. 289), such as a single-cylinder steam engine, is often responsible for the trouble. The usual remedy is to apply to the poles, bridges (Fig. 240) of copper or brass in which currents are induced by the wavering of the armature. These currents tend to stop the motion. Different companies use different forms of bridges. When hunting or pulsating occurs, and the motor is not already equipped wiht bridges, it is best to consult the manufacturer. In general, the weaker the field on a synchronous motor, the less the pulsation. Sometimes pulsation may be so reduced that no trouble results by simply running with a somewhat weaker field current.

361. Improper Armature Connections in Synchronous Motors.—This trouble usually manifests itself by unbalanced entering currents and by a negligible or very low starting torque. The circuits should be traced out and the connections remade until the three entering currents for three-phase, or the two entering currents for two-phase, are approximately equal. These currents will not be equal even with correct connection when the armature is standing still.

362. Polarity of Synchronous Motors.—Since the winding of a synchronous motor armature is in series all the way around the circumference and under all of the poles, except in exceedingly rare cases, the trouble from a reversed pole is much less serious than with an induction motor or direct-current machine. With a reversed pole everything operates fairly well. The only trouble is that the fields require more current than they should because of the pole that is opposing the field. If, therefore, excessive field current is required for minimum input to a motor, it is a good plan to test the polarity of all the spools with a compass.

363. Bearing Troubles of Synchronous Motors are similar to those of induction motors (Art. 402). A difference is that, with a synchronous motor, the air gap between the revolving element and the poles is relatively large, so that the wearing of the bearing, which throws the armature out of center, is not so serious as with an induction motor. End play should be treated the same as with an induction motor (Art. 416).

MANAGEMENT OF, AND STARTING AND CONTROLLING DEVICES FOR ALTERNATINGCURRENT MOTORS

364. The National Electrical Code Requirements Relating to the Installation of Alternating-current-motor Control Equipment are essentially the same as those governing the installation of direct-current control equipment which are discussed briefly in Art. 120. For further information in regard to wiring requirements for motors, see author's WIRING FOR LIGHT AND POWER.

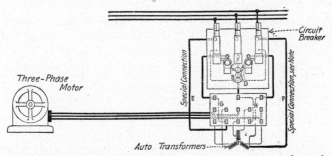

FIG. 241.—Connections for a circuit breaker protecting a three-phase motor.

365. Connecting a Circuit-breaker for Polyphase Induction Motor Protection.*—Terminals A and B are connected as shown in Fig. 241 for three-wire systems, two- or three-phase. The circuit-breaker should be so located in the circuit that the no-voltage coils will be subjected to the full voltage of the circuit, irrespective of the position of the starting switch. Where it is desired to have the overload of the circuit-breaker in-

* The Cutter Co.

operative with the auto-starter switch in starting position, the connections G and H within the starter should be removed and the special connections E and F made instead.

366. The Methods of Starting Induction Motors may be listed as follows:

1. *By Connecting Directly to the Line.*—This method is ordinarily used only for small motors—those of less than 10 h.p. output—because on starting the motor takes an excessive current and the voltage regulation will be disturbed unless there is ample generating capacity and the conductors are of a generous cross-section.

2. *By Inserting Internal Resistance in the Rotor Circuit.*—This method is used only with wound-rotor machines. The resistance is cut in or out of the circuit by the operation of a switch on the motor shaft so arranged that the handle of the switch is stationary when the rotor is turning.

3. *By Introducing External Resistance in the Rotor Circuit.*—This method can be used only with a wound-rotor machine having collector rings upon which brushes bear that connect with the resistance. The resistance is cut in or out of the rotor circuit by a controller somewhat similar to the ordinary direct-current motor controller.

4. *By Using a Transformer having Low-voltage Taps.*—A low voltage can be impressed on the motor at starting by connecting it with a suitable switch to the low-voltage taps.

5. *With a Starting Compensator or Auto-transformer.*—This is the usual method for motors of ordinary capacity and is similar to the transformer method in that low voltage from the compensator taps are impressed on the motor at starting.

6. *By Connecting the Armature Coils in Star for Starting and in Delta for Running.*—This method is described in detail in following Art. 383.

367. A Small Induction Motor can be Started by Throwing it Directly on the Line (Fig. 242).—This method is, as a general thing, not used for motors of capacities exceeding 5 h.p. Two sets of fuses should be provided, one for starting and one for running, with a double-throw switch to connect the motor to either set. A switch, having a spring so arranged that the

blades will not remain in the starting position unless manually
held there, should be used.   The starting current of an in-

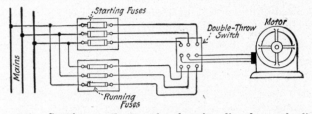

Fig. 242.—Starting small motor by throwing directly on the line.

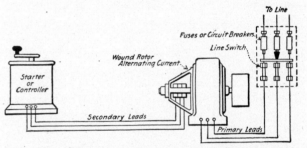

Fig. 243.—Connections of starter to wound-rotor motor.

duction motor thrown directly on the line will be something
between 3 and 8 times the full-load running current.   If only
one set of fuses is used for a polyphase
motor and they are of sufficient capacity to carry the starting current, one
fuse may open but the motor will continue to operate on one phase, drawing
a current considerably above normal.
The probable result is a burnt-out
motor.

**368. Self-contained Starters for
Wound-rotor Induction Motors of Relatively Small Capacity** (Figs. 243 and
244) can be purchased.   The resistors

Fig.   244.—Enclosed
starter for a phase-wound
motor.

for these are mounted within the enclosing case that carries the
switching mechanism that increases or decreases the amount

16

of effective resistance in the rotor circuit. As a rule, the resistors in these starters are designed only for starting service, hence they can be used only where starts are infrequent and starting conditions are not severe. They are not usually designed for speed control for which service drum-type controllers with externally mounted resistances are used. In the usual designs a set of resistors is connected in series with each phase of the motor (Fig. 245) secondary and all three are interconnected in star by the frame of the starter which is grounded, protecting the operator against shocks.

369. In Operating a Self-contained Starter for a Wound-rotor Motor (Figs. 243 and 244) before closing the primary line switch or breaker, the handle of the starter must be in the starting position, where all the starting resistance is in

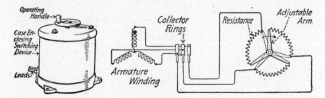

Fig. 245.—Method of varying rotor resistance of a wound-rotor induction motor.

circuit. If the connections are correct, and the load is not too great, the motor should start as soon as the line switch is closed; on failure to start, open the primary circuit, and examine the load conditions and the connections. With some starters the handle may have to be advanced slightly beyond the starting position before the motor starts. As the motor speed accelerates the starter handle should be moved gradually to the running position, bringing the motor to full speed within the time which is usually specified by the manufacturer of the starter. In the running position all starting resistance is, in starters of most designs, short-circuited.

370. Starting a Coil-wound Rotor Motor.*—With the coil-wound rotor, high and variable starting torque can be obtained by inserting a variable ohmic resistance directly in the rotor

---

* Southern Electrician.

circuit.   The rotor circuit is connected to a non-inductive resistance, which can be varied and gradually cut out as the motor attains speed.   Figs. 245 and 246 illustrate the connections.   When the rheostat handle is in the extreme left-hand position, the resistance is all out of circuit.   To start the motor, current is first switched on to the stator circuit by closing a triple-pole switch.   The three-pole contact blades of the starting rheostat are now moved over from the off position on to the resistance studs, the first contacts of which place the whole of the resistance in circuit with the respective three-phase windings of the rotor.   This prevents the current induced in the rotor windings by the stator circuit from reaching an excessive intensity.   The switch handle on being further rotated

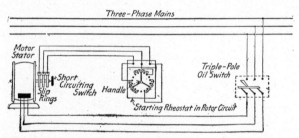

Fig. 246.—Starting arrangement for three-phase coil-wound rotor motor.

in a right-hand direction gradually cuts out the resistance until all the resistance is out of circuit.   In this position the rotor windings are short-circuited.

371. Commercial Starting Compensators for Squirrel-cage Induction Motors usually have three positions at which the starting lever will come to rest—an "off" position, a "starting" position, and a "running" position.   The lever is so arranged that the switch which it controls cannot come to rest in any other positions unless forcibly restrained.   The connections of a two-phase and of a three-phase compensator are shown in connection with the material on auto-transformers in Sec. V of the author's AMERICAN ELECTRICIANS' HANDBOOK.   Connection arrangements for compensators of other types are shown on pages adjacent hereto.

In starting compensators, as usually arranged, when in the "off" position the switch is open and the motor and auto-transformer are entirely disconnected from the source of energy. When in the "starting" position, the source of energy is directly connected by the switch to the auto-transformer terminals and the low-voltage taps of the auto-transformer are connected to the motor. Usually there are no fuses inserted in the starting leads at the compensator.

When thrown to the "running" position the switch connects the motor through fuses to the source of energy and the auto-transformer is entirely disconnected from the source of energy. The fuses provided in the running leads are for the protection of the motor against overload while it is in normal operation. The fuses protecting the tap circuit to the compensator where the tap circuit branches from the main are

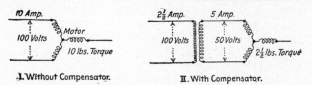

I. Without Compensator.　　　　II. With Compensator.

Fig. 247.—Starting with and without compensator.

usually depended upon to protect the motor while it is starting.

372. Starting With and Without Compensators.—The starting current taken by a squirrel-cage induction motor at the instant of starting is equal to the applied electromotive force divided by the impedance of the motor. Only the duration of this current, and not its value, is affected by the torque against which the motor is required to start. The effect of starting without and with a compensator is illustrated by diagrams *I* and *II* in Fig. 247. In this diagram, motor *I* is thrown directly on a 100-volt line. The impedance of the motor is 5.77 ohms per phase, the starting torque 10 lb. at 1-ft. radius and the current taken 10 amp. In diagram *II* a compensator is inserted, stepping down the line pressure from 100 to 50 volts. This reduces the starting current of motor one-half and the starting torque becomes one-quarter its previous value or $2\frac{1}{2}$ lb. at 1-ft. radius.   The current in the line is reduced inversely as the ratio of transformation in the compensator and becomes $2\frac{1}{2}$ amp.

373. When a Compensator is Used the Starting Torque of the Motor can be Reduced to Approximately the Value Required by the Load and the current taken from the line correspondingly decreased.   Where a compensator is not used, an increase of rotor resistance results in a proportional increase in the starting torque of the motor with a very slight decrease in the starting current drawn from the line.   Where a compensator is used with a motor having a high-resistance rotor the voltage can be reduced to a lower value than would

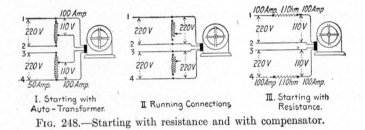

I. Starting with Auto-Transformer.   II. Running Connections   III. Starting with Resistance.

Fig. 248.—Starting with resistance and with compensator.

be required with a low-resistance rotor for the same starting torque.   Standard compensators are provided with several taps from which various combinations can be obtained.

374. Comparison of Auto-transformer and Resistance for Decreasing Voltage for Starting Squirrel-cage Motors.—The motor in Fig. 248 is supposed to require 100 amp. to start it; that is, to provide the energy, which will produce the necessary starting torque.   At *I*, where an auto-transformer is used to lower the voltage to 110, a current of 100 amp. is produced in the motor primary with a current in the line of 50 amp.   This condition is due to the transformer action of the auto-transformer.   At *II* the running connections are shown wherein the autotransformer is entirely disconnected from the circuit.   At *III* are illustrated the conditions that would obtain were the voltage lowered for starting by inserting resistance in series with the line. Obviously 100 amp. must flow in all portions of the line even though the resistance of 1.1 ohms reduces the line voltage of 220 to a voltage of 110 which is impressed on the motor. There is a loss of energy (watts) in the resistance. Evidently the auto-starter method is preferable because with it the line current is reduced and there is practically no loss of energy. Although the example illustrated is for a two-phase motor the principle is the same for a three-phase motor.

375. Approximate Starting Currents and Starting Torques of Squirrel-cage Induction Motors with Different Impressed Voltages Obtained by Using a Compensator Starter.—Starting current and starting torque are expressed in terms of normal full-load current and full-load torque, and impressed voltage is expressed in terms of normal voltage:

Voltage impressed on motor, per cent.	Starting current taken from line, per cent.	Starting torque, per cent.
40	112	32
60	250	72
80	450	128
100	700	200

376. Taps of a Starting Compensator.*—Compensators are usually shipped by their manufacturers connected to the auto-transformer tap giving the lowest torque. If the motor will not start its load with this tap connected the next higher voltage tap should be tried, and so on, until the tap is found that provides the required torque. Compensators for use with motors of 15 h.p. and under sometimes have three taps giving voltages of 40 per cent., 60 per cent. and 80 per cent. of full-line impressed voltage. For motors above 15 h.p., four taps are frequently provided giving 40, 58, 70 and 85 per cent. of full-line voltage. The proper tap for giving the maximum starting torque without causing an inconvenient voltage disturbance in the supply circuit, can best be ascertained by experiment.

* Southern Electrician.

One make of compensator has for motors of from 5 to 18
h.p., taps starting the motor at 50, 65 and 80 per cent. of the
full impressed line voltage, with respective line currents equal
to 25, 42 and 65 per cent. of the current that would be taken
by the motor if no compensator were used. For motors larger
than 18 h.p., compensator-voltage taps are provided giving
voltages equal to 40, 58, 70 and 85 per cent. of the full impressed line voltage, and respective currents approximately
equal to 16, 34, 50 and 72 per cent. of the current that would
be taken by the motor if it were started directly from the
supply line.

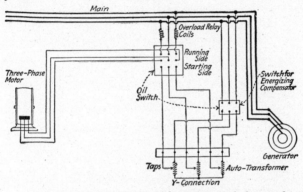

FIG. 249.—Starting compensator with separate switches, and auto-
transformer for high-voltage or large capacity motor.

**377. Starting Compensators for Motors of High-voltage or
Large Current Capacity** are arranged with the switches separate from the auto-transformer (Fig. 249). The equipment
usually consists of one double-throw or two interlocked single-
throw oil switches for the motor and a single-throw oil switch
for energizing the auto-transformer. In the running leads to
the motor may be inserted overload relays which will open the
oil switches in the case of over-draught of current. The oil
switches are usually mounted on a switchboard panel while
the auto-transformer may or may not be mounted on the panel.
The construction indicated in the other compensator diagrams
is used by certain manufacturers for motors of capacities up
to and including 550 volts when the normal current does not

exceed 300 amp. per phase and for motors of from 1,040 to 2,500 volts with currents not greater than 125 amp. per phase. Where motors take greater normal currents or are of higher voltage the arrangement of Fig. 249 is applied.

378. When No-voltage Release Compensator Starters are Used for High-voltage Motors a small voltage transformer is

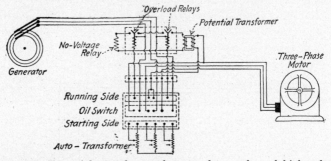

FIG. 250.—Potential transformer for no-voltage relay of high-voltage motor.

usually arranged as in Fig. 250 to energize the no-voltage coil. This arrangement is used by certain manufacturers for compensators, with the no-voltage release attachment, for voltages

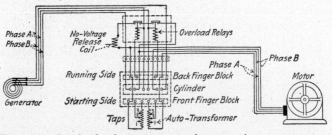
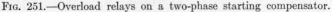

FIG. 251.—Overload relays on a two-phase starting compensator.

of from 1,040 to 2,500. The secondary of the transformer furnishes 110 volts for which the no-voltage relay is wound.

379. Overload Release Coils on Compensators are arranged Essentially as Shown in Figs. 251 and 252.—When there is an overload on either phase the iron plunger of the overload relay is drawn up which opens the no-voltage release-coil circuit. This de-energizes the no-voltage release coil and the compensator circuit is automatically opened as described in

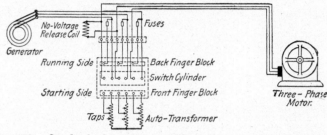

FIG. 252.—Overload release coils on a three-phase starting compensator.

the paragraph on the no-voltage release. The overload relays are usually arranged so that they can be adjusted, to operate at different currents, just as a circuit-breaker can be adjusted. An inverse-time-element feature is usually incorporated whereby the relay will operate almost instantly on very heavy overloads but will not operate until a certain interval of time has elapsed (the length of the interval being approximately inversely proportional to the amount of overload) on lesser overloads. It will be noted from the diagrams that fuses are not necessary where the overload relays are used. A decided advantage of the overload relays is that they can be adjusted to protect a motor against running single-phase. If one phase opens, sufficient additional current will be drawn through the others to operate a relay which will open the circuit to the compensator. An installation of a Westing-

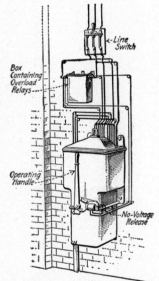

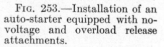

FIG. 253.—Installation of an auto-starter equipped with no-voltage and overload release attachments.

house compensator having no-voltage and overload relays is shown in Fig. 253.

380. A No-voltage Release can be Provided on Starting Compensators.—The connection diagram is shown in Fig. 254 for a three-phase compensator and that for a two-phase compensator is similar. When a condition of no-voltage exists on

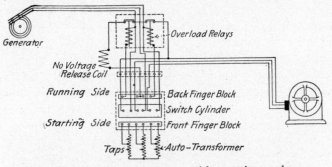

FIG. 254.—Starting compensator with no-voltage release.

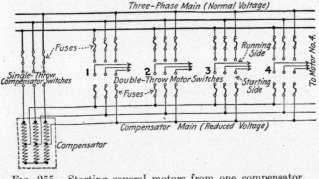

FIG. 255.—Starting several motors from one compensator.

the line, the *no-voltage release coil* is de-energized which permits the iron armature or core of the no-voltage coil to drop, automatically releasing the compensator handle, which is returned to the off position by its spring. This opens the circuit through the compensator.

381. A Method of Starting Several Polyphase Induction Motors from One Compensator is shown in Fig. 255. This can frequently be employed to advantage where there are a number of motors situated close together or where a number of motors must be started from one location. A double-throw switch is necessary for each motor to be started, and there should be a switch for the compensator. If all of the starting switches are located close together, so that one operator can open or close them consecutively, the compensator need have a capacity only sufficient for serving the largest motor in the group. If the starting switches are so located that several can be operated at once by different men, the compensator must have a sufficient margin of capacity to provide for this. After all of the motors are started the compensator switch is opened, eliminating compensator

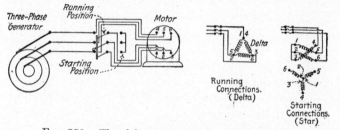

Fig. 256.—The delta-star method of starting.

losses. Where motors exceed possibly 7 h.p. in capacity, oil switches should be used for the starting switches.

382. Fuses for Use in Connection with Compensator Starters.—*National Code* standard fuses carried in holders mounted on slate bases are usually used for compensators for voltages up to 600 volts. For voltages of from 1,040 to 2,500, if fuses are used, the expulsion type is preferable. A table of fuse sizes for induction motors is given in the author's American Electricians' Handbook, but where not otherwise specified, fuses of a capacity corresponding to $1\frac{1}{4}$ times the full-load current of the motor are supplied.

383. The Delta-star Method of Starting Three-phase, Squirrel-cage Induction Motors is sometimes used (Fig. 256). The stator-coil terminals are brought out from the frame and connected to a double-throw switch as shown. In starting,

the coils are connected in star and the current is $1 \div 1.73$ or
0.58 of what it would be with the coils connected in delta.
After the rotor has attained full speed the switch is thrown
to the running position, which connects the coils in delta and
normal voltage is thereby impressed on them. Motors must
be specially constructed for this method of starting as it is
not extensively used by the principal manufacturers.

384. Speed Control of Polyphase Motors.*—The speed of
polyphase induction motors can be controlled by a number of
different methods, of which the following are the most important. I. Adjusting the resistance of the secondary circuit.
II. Adjusting the primary voltage. III. Using two motor
primaries, one of which is capable of being rotated. IV.
Changing the number of motor poles. V. Operating two or
more motors connected in cascade. VI. Adjusting the frequency of the primary current. VII. Changing the number
of phases of the secondary windings.

The results obtained by the use of these various methods
differ widely, so that in selecting a variable-speed alternating-
current motor careful consideration must be given to the
characteristics of the method of control in order to determine
its suitability for the service. In many cases a combination
of methods is required in order to produce the desired speed
changes.

**385. Speed Control of a Polyphase Motor by Adjusting
the Resistance of the Secondary Circuit.**—With constant
torque, the speed of the motor increases regularly as each step
of the resistor is short-circuited and remains constant on any
given notch. But with varying torque the motor speed varies
also; that is, an alternating-current motor when operating
with auxiliary resistance in the rotor circuit is properly classified as a *varying-speed motor*. This method of speed control
is, therefore, not suitable for service requiring several constant
speeds with varying torque, such as machine-tool work, etc.

Speed control by means of adjustable secondary resistance
is, however, very useful where constant speeds are not essential, for example, in operating cranes, hoists, elevators, and

* B. G. Lamme.

dredges, and also for service in which the torque remains constant at each speed, as in driving fans, blowers, and centrifugal pumps. In service where reduced speeds are required only occasionally and where small speed variation is not objectionable, this method of control can also be used to good advantage. On account of energy loss in the resistors, the efficiency is reduced when operating at reduced speeds, this reduction being greatest at the slowest speeds. The circuits are essentially the same as for starting by varying resistance in the rotor circuit, as shown in Figs. 245 and 246.

386. With Secondary Speed Control the rotor usually has a Y-connected winding to which is connected, in series in each phase, an external resistance, Figs. 245 and 246. By moving the adjustable arm the amount of resistance in series in each phase can be varied from a maximum to zero and the speed varied from the highest speed to the lowest speed. This form of control is in general preferable to the primary-control method and is used where a larger number of speeds is required and it is not necessary for the motor to run at any considerable period at reduced speed.

387. Speed-torque Graphs of a Secondary Speed-control Induction Motor (see Fig. 257).—To determine the speed of such a motor on any point of the controller when operating against a given torque and to find the current taken at that speed and torque, refer to graphs which show the speed, torque and current for phase-wound variable-speed motors. Those of Fig. 257 are typical of ordinary capacities. For any given torque, follow along the abscissa corresponding to this value to its point of intersection with the torque curve for that particular notch of controller. Then follow up the ordinate until it intersects the current curve corresponding to the same controller notch and the value so obtained is the current taken by the motor.

EXAMPLE.—Suppose it is desired to determine the current taken on the various points of the controller when starting a 25-h.p. 220-volt motor and bringing it from rest to full speed against full-load torque —the first point (Fig. 257) at which more than full-load torque can be obtained is the third notch and following the line upward to the current curve we see that the current taken is 150 per cent. full-load current. This value drops until about 45 per cent. synchronous speed is reached, when in order to hold up the torque it is necessary to throw to the fourth notch.

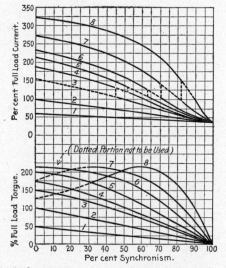

Fig. 257.—Typical current, torque and speed curves for an induction motor with secondary speed control.

The current rises correspondingly to 130 per cent. full-load, then drops until 53 per cent. synchronous speed is reached. Then the controller must be moved to the fifth notch, thence it drops until 65 per

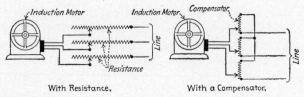
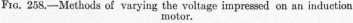

With Resistance.   With a Compensator.

Fig. 258.—Methods of varying the voltage impressed on an induction motor.

cent. synchronous speed is reached, etc. The dotted line indicates the variation in current.

388. Speed Control of a Polyphase Motor by Adjusting the Primary Voltage (Fig. 258).—Adjusting the primary voltage of a motor causes speed changes that are similar to those produced by adjusting the resistance of the motor secondary. The voltage variations can be obtained by means of adjustable resistors, auto-transformers, or choke coils in series with the primary. This method has the disadvantages of poor speed regulation, low efficiency, and unsatisfactory control, especially when the primary voltage is high; it is not in general commercial use. Squirrel-cage induction motors are, however, almost invariably started with reduced primary voltage obtained by means of auto-transformers. Fig. 259 indicates the external appearance of a variable-resistance starter for such service.

389. Primary Speed Control (Fig. 258).—Where a compensator is used, contactors, connected by conductors to the stator, are arranged to slide over the compensator taps, in a manner similar to that in which the lever arm slides over the segments of a rheostat, and thereby vary the voltage impressed on the motor. The speed regulation of a motor controlled by this method is very poor and the power-factor and efficiency decrease with the speed. Where a

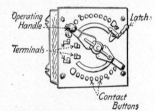

Fig. 259.—Primary resistance starter for a squirrel-cage motor.

resistance is used for varying the voltage impressed on the stator, the regulation and efficiency of the machine are not as good as when a compensator is used.

390. Speed Control of a Polyphase Motor with a Double Primary Arrangement.—The double primary motor resembles an ordinary squirrel-cage induction motor in construction except that the primary is divided vertically into halves, each with separate core and windings. One-half can be rotated around the rotor by means of a worm-screw and rack device. Fig. 260 shows this construction. When the two halves of the primary are placed so that like poles are in line, the rotor windings are subjected to maximum magnetic flux from the primary, and the motor will run with minimum slip and therefore at its maximum speed. By turning the movable half of the primary, the flux acting on each rotor bar is gradually reduced, causing increased slip and a corresponding reduction of the motor speed for a given torque.

This operation is equivalent to varying the primary voltage and therefore cannot be used with advantage where constant speed with varying torque is desired. The mechanism is, however, self-contained; the speed changes are effected without opening circuits; and the motor, having no brushes, operates without sparking.

391. Speed Control of a Polyphase Motor by Changing the Number of Motor Poles.—The synchronous speed of a polyphase motor is inversely proportional to the number of its poles. Thus on a 60-cycle circuit a two-pole induction motor

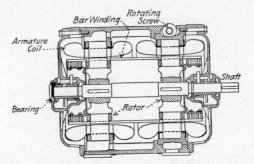

Fig. 260.—Longitudinal section of a double primary motor.

has a synchronous speed of approximately 3,600 r.p.m., a four-pole motor 1,800 r.p.m., an eight-pole motor 900 r.p.m., etc. It is therefore possible to alter the speed of a motor by changing the number of its poles.

This can be accomplished by using two or more separate primary windings, each having a different number of poles, or by using a single winding which can be connected so as to form different numbers of poles. In general only two speeds are possible without great complication, the preferable ratio being 1:2. The rotor should be of the squirrel-cage type as this is adapted to any number of poles, whereas the windings of a wound rotor must be reconnected for the different speeds.

With very few exceptions these motors are squirrel-cage

machines with special stator windings. They are designed
to operate at full and half speed, the different speeds being
obtained by changing the connection of the coils so as to halve
or double the number of poles. Usually motors with the lower
speed other than half speed require more complicated connections and necessitate bringing out a large number of leads
from the motor. The motors can be designed for three or
four speeds, but such will require two distinct stator windings.
Obviously, these motors are very special and their use is not
advocated except when absolutely necessary.

The efficiency is approximately the same at each speed and
the power-factor which is lower at full speed than that of
the normal motor is reduced very greatly at the lower speed.
Also the output is proportional to the speed, while the percentage slip remains approximately the same for each speed,

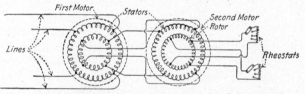

FIG. 261.—Two polyphase motors connected in cascade.

and the starting torque per ampere varies approximately inversely as the speed.

**392. Speed Control of Polyphase Motors by Operating
Two or More Motors Connected in Cascade** offers, under
some conditions of service, the most convenient and economical method of speed variation. In this arrangement all the
rotors are mounted on one shaft or the several shafts are
rigidly connected. The primary of the first motor is connected to the line, its secondary, which must be of the
phase-wound slip-ring type, to the primary of the second
motor and so on. The secondary of the last motor can be
either of the squirrel-cage or of the phase-wound type. In
practice more than two motors are rarely used. The
arrangement is shown in Fig. 261.

Speed changes are obtained by varying the connections of

17

the motors, the following combinations being possible with two motors: Each motor can be operated separately at its normal speed with its primary connected to the line, the other motor running idle; the motors can be connected in cascade so that the rotors tend to start in the same direction (direct concatenation); or the motors can be connected so that the rotors tend to start in opposite directions (differential concatenation). If the first motor has 12 poles and the second 4, the following synchronous speeds can be obtained on a 25-cycle circuit.

(1) Motor *II* (4 poles) running single, 750 r.p.m.; (2) motors in differential cancatenation (equivalent of 8 poles), 375 r.p.m.; (3) motor *I* (12 poles) running single, 250 r.p.m.; (4) motors in direct concatenation (equivalent of 16 poles), 187.5 r.p.m. By the use of adjustable resistance in the secondary circuits, changes from one speed to the next can be made with uniform gradations.

A great number of speed combinations are possible by the use of this method; the control is simple and safe, as few leads are required and main circuits are not opened for most of the speeds. The rotors can be made with smaller diameters than is possible with other multispeed motors, hence the flywheel effect is reduced to a minimum. In general, a cascade set is applicable where speed changes must be frequently made with high horse-power output and primary voltage, and where the speed ratios are other than 1:2.

393. Speed Control of a Polyphase Motor by Adjusting the Frequency of the Primary Current.—Since the synchronous speed of an induction motor is equal to the alternations of the supply circuit divided by the number of poles in each circuit, a change in speed can be effected by changing the frequency of the circuit.

Fig. 262 shows the speed-torque and other curves of a motor when operated at 7,200, 3,600, 1,800, and 720 alternations per minute, or at 100, 50, 25, and 10 per cent. of the normal alternations. The speed-torque curves corresponding to the above alternations are *a*, *b*, *c*, and *d*. The current curves are *A*, *B*, *C*, and *D*. This figure shows that for the rated torque *T*, the current is practically constant for all speeds, but the electromotive force varies with the alternations. Consequently, the apparent power supplied, represented by the product of the current by electromotive force, varies with

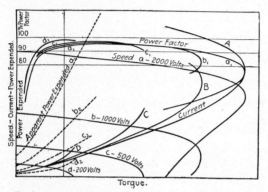

Fig. 262.—Performance curves of a polyphase induction motor with different applied frequencies and different applied electromotive forces.

the speed of the motor, and is practically proportionate to the power developed.

In a few cases, where only one motor is operated, the generator speed can be varied. If the generator is driven by a waterwheel, its speed can be varied over a wide range, and

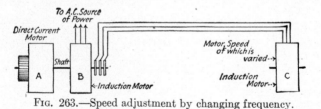

Fig. 263.—Speed adjustment by changing frequency.

the motor speed will also vary. If the generator field is held at practically constant strength, then the motor speed can be varied from zero to a maximum at constant torque with a practically constant current.

Another method of accomplishing this result is by the use of a frequency changer. Fig. 263 shows the arrangement.

B and C are induction motors of the ordinary type; A is a direct-current motor directly connected to the rotor of B. C is the driving motor and B the frequency changer. The primary of B is connected to the line, its secondary to the

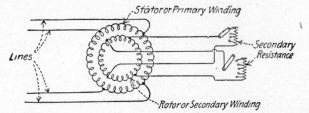

Fig. 264.—One secondary circuit closed (changing the number of phases of the secondary winding).

primary of C. The frequency of the current delivered to C depends on the relation of the speed of the rotor B to the synchronous speed of B; the slower the rotation of the rotor

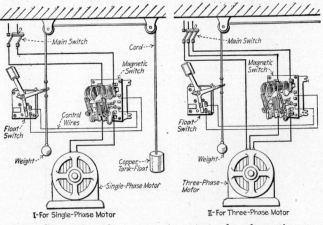

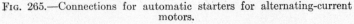

Fig. 265.—Connections for automatic starters for alternating-current motors.

the higher the frequency delivered to C and the higher the speed of C. The speed of the rotor B is controlled by adjusting the field of motor A. Motor B must be practically the same size as C; but motor A can generally be relatively smaller, the exact size depending on the maximum and minimum frequency and the power required for motor *C*. This method can be applied with special advantage where direct-current motor drive is not desirable.

394. Speed Control of a Polyphase Motor by Changing the Number of Phases of the Secondary Winding.—If only one of the secondary circuits is closed the motor will run at about half speed, with very low power-factor and poor

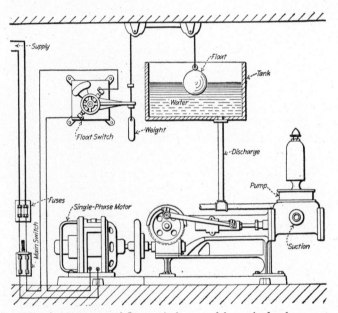

Fig. 266.—Arrangement of float switch control for a single-phase motor.

efficiency. This method of speed adjustment (Fig. 264) is frequently used in experimental work, but has no extensive commercial applications.

395. The Methods of Connecting Float-control Automatic Starters for Alternating-current Pump Motors are illustrated by the typical diagrams of Fig. 265. Fig. 266 shows the wiring of a non-automatic float switch used with a single-phase motor of the type which does not require an automatic starter.

The principle of operation of this float switch is shown in Fig. 114.   Where the pump motor is controlled by a pressure regulator, the connections for an alternating-current motor are essentially the same as those for a direct-current motor and are illustrated in Fig. 115.

396. To Reverse the Direction of Rotation of a Polyphase Induction Motor.—For a two-phase, four-wire motor, interchange the connections of the two leads of either phase.   For a two-phase, three-wire motor, interchange the two outside leads.   For a three-phase motor, interchange the connections of any two motor leads.

SECTION 11

TROUBLES OF ALTERNATING-CURRENT GENERATORS AND MOTORS

397. The Troubles of Alternating-current Generators and Motors are in some respects similar to those encountered with direct-circuit machines, and the methods of rectifying them are, in some cases, similar. However, since the construction of the alternating- is radically different from that of the direct-current apparatus, it follows that each type (a.c. and d.c.) will be subject to certain troubles peculiar to itself. The reader is advised to review carefully Sec. 4, "Troubles of Direct-current Generators and Motors" because such portions of that section as may apply to alternating-current machines will not be repeated in this section. The methods there (Sec. 4) described of locating field-coil (Art. 223) and insulation-resistance (245) troubles can, with obvious modifications, be applied for alternating-current revolving fields. Considerable of the material in this section is based on that in the book, MOTOR TROUBLES by E. B. Raymond.

398. Bearing Troubles of Alternating-current Machinery are due to the same causes that originate difficulties with bearings in direct-current units. Hence, for information on this subject see Art. 230 and following articles in Sec. 4, "Troubles of Direct-current Generators and Motors." See following Art. 402 for discussion of induction-motor bearing troubles.

399. Troubles of Alternating-current Generators.*—The following causes may prevent alternating-current generators from developing their normal e.m.f.:

(1) The speed of the generator may be below normal. (2) The switchboard instruments may be incorrect and the voltage

* WESTINGHOUSE INSTRUCTION BOOK.

may be higher than that indicated, or the current may be greater than is shown by the readings. (3) The voltage of the exciter may be low because its speed is below normal, or its series field reversed, or part of its shunt field reversed or short-circuited. (4) The brushes of the exciter may be incorrectly set. (5) A part of the field rheostat or other unnecessary resistance may be in the field circuit. (6) The power-factor of the load may be abnormally low.

400. Induction Motor Troubles.[*]—The unsatisfactory operation of an induction motor may be due to either external or internal conditions. The voltage or the frequency may be wrong, or there may be an overload on the machine. Low voltage is the most frequent cause of trouble. The starting current is sometimes twice the running current, with the result that the voltage is particularly low at starting. The best remedy for this disorder is larger transformers and larger motor leads, one or both. The troubles that occur most frequently within the motor itself are caused by faulty insulation, and by uneven air gap due to the springing of the motor shaft or to excessive wear in the bearings. If a wound-rotor machine refuses to start, the trouble may be due to an open circuit in the rotor winding. A short-circuited coil in the motor will make its existence known by local heating in the latter. Most motors designed to employ a starting resistance will not start at all if the resistance is omitted from the secondary circuit.

401. Causes of Shutdowns of Induction Motors.—Sometimes there is trouble from blowing fuses. Or possibly, and more serious, the fuses do not blow and the motor, perhaps humming loudly, comes to a standstill. Under these conditions, the current may be 10 times normal, so that the heating effect, being increased as the square of the current, or 100 fold, causes the machine to burn out its insulation. Since the torque or turning power of an induction motor is proportional to the square of the applied voltage (one-half voltage produces only one-quarter torque), it is evident that lowering the voltage has a decided effect upon the ability of the motor to

[*] H. M. Nichols, POWER AND THE ENGINEER.

carry load, and may be the cause of its stopping, Another cause may be that the load on the motor is more than equal to its maximum output.

402. Bearing Troubles in Induction Motors.—The bearings may have become worn, so that the air gap (which ordinarily is not much over 0.040 in. and on small motors as small as 0.015 in.) has been gradually reduced at the lower side of the rotor to practically zero. The rotor commences to rub on the stator. The friction soon becomes so great that it is more than the motor can "pull." The result is that it shuts down. A shutdown may be due to bearings introducing excessive friction. Hot bearings, in turn, may be due to excess of belt tension, dirt in the oil, oil rings not turning, or to improper alignment of the motor to the machine that it drives. Hence, under such conditions, it should be ascertained whether the voltage has been normal, whether the air-gap is such that the rotor is free from the stator, and whether the load imposed upon the motor is more than that for which it was designed. In any installation a system should be arranged whereby an inspector will examine the gap, bearings, etc., periodically. See Art. 233 for information relating to ball bearings for motors.

403. Starting Switch Troubles in Wound-rotor Motors.— Rarely, shutting down may be due to the working out of the starting switch, which may be located within the armature. Such a switch is operated by a lever engaging a collar which bears on contacts which, as they move inward, cut out the resistance in series with the rotor winding and located within it. If the short-circuiting brushes work back, introducing resistance into the armature circuit while the machine is trying to carry load, it will at once slow down in speed and probably stop, usually burning out the starting resistance. Of course, this can occur only from faulty construction. The remedy is to fit the brushes properly, so that they will not work out.

404. Low Torque while Starting Induction Motors.—Although the circuit to the motor be closed, sometimes it does not start. The same general laws of voltage, etc., apply to the motor at starting as when running. Hence, the points

mentioned under "shutdowns" (Art. 401) should be investigated and if necessary corrected. The resistance, which is
frequently inserted in the armature, may be short-circuited,
thus giving a low starting torque. Unless a starting compensator is used for starting, it is necessary, in order to
obtain a proper starting torque with a reasonable current, that
a resistance be inserted in the rotor circuit. The resistance
not only limits the current, which would, with the motor
standing still, be large, but it causes the current of the armature to assume a more effective phase relation, so that with
the same current a far larger torque is obtained. A partial
or complete short-circuit of the resistance partially or wholly
ruins the starting torque.

405. Low Maximum Output of Induction Motors.—The
maximum load which a motor can carry may be less than
desired, or less than the nameplate indicates. If the voltage, air gap, load, etc., are right, it may be possible that a
mistake has been made in connections. It is then easiest to
return the motor to the factory, but if immediate operation
is essential, the armature connections can readily be changed
so as to give a large increase in output. To ascertain what to
do, remove the bracket on the side of the motor which covers
the connections between the coils. Pick out one phase, and
find out how many groups of coils are connected up. From
this, the number of poles can be determined. A better way
is to calculate this from the speed of the motor and the frequency of the circuit on which it is running. See 315.

From an examination of the connections it can be easily
determined whether the poles in any place are connected in
series or in multiple, or in series-multiple. Thus, in a motor
the connections may be as shown at the left in Fig. 267,
which indicates the windings of one phase of a four-pole motor
If the connections be changed to those shown at the right
in Fig. 267, each coil will then receive double its former voltage and the motor will give 4 times the output. Before making a change in connections such as that indicated here one
must ascertain to a certainty that the increased current that
will result will not injure the windings.

It should be borne in mind, however, that this renders the motor less efficient, increasing the exciting current, and thus lowering the power-factor. If conditions demand it, this method may be followed. The temperature under the new conditions should be carefully observed to insure that there is no undue heating. The only change in connections

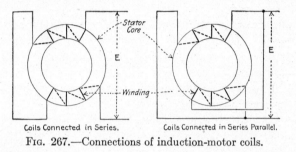

Coils Connected in Series.   Coils Connected in Series Parallel.

Fig. 267.—Connections of induction-motor coils.

that can be used for quarter-phase motors is of the type of the one just described.

With three-phase motors the poles can be grouped not only as previously suggested, but a variation of connections from delta to star, or the reverse, can be made. A delta-connected,

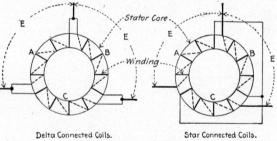

Delta Connected Coils.   Star Connected Coils.

Fig. 268.—Three-phase motor coil connections.

two-pole motor is shown at the left in Fig. 268, where the three phases are indicated by the letters, A, B and C. Any one of these phases may have poles connected in either series or multiple. In a delta connection with the coils spaced 120 deg. apart, as shown in Fig. 268, each phase has the line voltage E.

In the star connection the phases are joined as shown at the right in Fig. 268. In this case, as with the delta connection each phase may have poles in series or in multiple. In the star connection of Fig. 268, each coil has a voltage of 0.58 $\times E$.

406. Winding Faults of Induction Motors.—When a new induction motor is received, it sometimes happens that in attempting to operate the machine, although it will start, the currents are excessive and unbalanced, undue heating appears or a peculiar noise is emitted and accompanied possibly by dimming of the lights on the same circuit and the lowering of speed with perhaps actual shutdown of other induction motors thereon. If, after examination, there is found to be no difficulty with the air gap, belt tension, starting resistance or bearings, the probabilities are that the coils of the motor have been wrongly connected or that the winding has been damaged during transportation. Certain indications of these conditions are shown by instrument readings. The winding faults in a three-phase motor may be:

(1) One coil of the rotor may be open-circuited. The armature or rotor may have a defective winding just as may the field. (A coil-wound rotor construction is used only when a starting resistance is used. When a compensator is used no starting resistance is required, and the winding consists simply of bars connected at the ends by a ring.) (2) Two coils or phases of the armature may be open-circuited. (3) Armature may be connected properly but field coil or phase may be reversed. (4) Part of field may be short-circuited. (5) One phase of field may be open-circuited.

407. With an Open Circuit in Field or Stator in a three-phase motor, current would flow only in two legs. There would be no current in the other leg and the motor would not start from rest with all switches closed. However, a three-phase motor or a two-phase motor will run and do work single-phase if it is assisted in starting. The starting torque is zero, but as the speed increased the torque increases. With a small motor, giving a pull on the belt will introduce enough torque so that it will pick up its load. Therefore, while an open circuit in the field winding should be found and repaired, if there is not time for repairs, the motor can be operated single-phase to about two-thirds of normal load.   The power-factor conditions and effects on the rest of the circuit are practically no worse than when the motor is running three-phase. The torque graph of a 1-h.p., three-phase induction motor from rest to synchronism, when running single-phase, is indicated in Fig. 203.   The torque curve of a 20-h.p., three-phase motor is given in Fig. 204, and of a 1-h.p., three-phase motor in Fig. 205.

408. Balking of Induction Motors.—With induction motors having certain slot relations between armature and field, at one certain percentage of speed, the torque will decrease to almost zero.   The motor will start its load properly, but will suddenly lose its torque at some slow speed, perhaps one-tenth normal.   Such trouble may be caused by a magnetic locking effect of the teeth of the armature with the poles of the field. This phenomenon cannot easily be measured with ordinary measuring instruments and facilities.   But with special torque measuring instruments the peculiar synchronous locking can be measured and exactly located.   If all other investigations show no cause of weak torque during the rise of the speed from rest to synchronism, the relation between the number of poles and slots in the rotor may account for the trouble. This is an unusual condition, but on squirrel-cage motors it has existed.   There is no remedy but a change in design, so that the manufacturer must take action for correction.

409. Squirrel-cage Armature or Rotor Troubles.—Unusual operation due to reversals of phase, phases open-circuited, and other causes, occur with squirrel-cage armatures as well as with wound armatures.   Poor soldering of the armature bars may be the cause.   Sometimes a solder flux may be used that will insure proper operation for a while, but time will develop poor electrical contacts due to chemical action at the joints.   If the resistances of all of the squirrel-cage joints are uniformly high, the effect is simply like that of an armature having a high resistance, which causes a lowering of the speed and local heating at the joints.   If some of the joints are perfect, but some bad, the motor may not have the ability to come up to speed and there will be unbalanced currents.

410. Effects of Unbalanced Voltages on Induction Motors. —The maximum output of a polyphase induction motor may be materially decreased if the voltages impressed on the different phases are unequal. On a three-phase system, the three voltages between the legs 1–2, 2–3 and 1–3 should be approximately equal. Also on a two-phase the voltage 1–2 should equal 3–4. If these voltages, impressed on the induction motor, are not equal the maximum output of the motor as well as the current in the various legs is proportionately affected.

EXAMPLES.—With a two-phase motor, if the voltages in the two legs differ by 20 per cent., a condition sometimes encountered in normal practice, the output of the motor may be reduced 25 per cent. Then, instead of being able to give its maximum output of, say, 150 per cent. for a few moments, it will give but 112 per cent. The varying loads which the motor may have to carry may shut it down. In cases of low maximum output, the relative voltages on the various legs should always be investigated. If they vary, the trouble may be due to this variation.

In addition to the effect on the maximum output, the unequal distribution of current in a two-phase motor under such conditions may be quite serious. Consider a specific case of a 15-h.p., 6-pole, 1,200-r.p.m., 220-volt motor, with the voltage on one leg 220 and the voltage on the other leg 180; current in leg No. 1 was 60 amp. and in leg No. 2, 35 amp. at full-load. The normal current at full-load was 35 amp. Thus the fuse might blow in the phase carrying the high current, causing the motor to run single-phase. If an attempt is made to start the motor, the blown fuse not being noticed, there would be no starting torque.

Consider the specific case of a six-pole, 10-h.p., 1,200-r.p.m., 160-volt, three-phase motor. The motor on normal voltage, at full-load, took 110 amp. in each leg. With unbalanced voltages of 161, 196 and 168, only full-load could be carried, although the average of these voltages is such that it might be assumed that 25 per cent. overload should be carried.

411. Induction Motor Starting Compensator Troubles.— Sometimes a mistake is made in the connections to the compensator, so that full voltage is used at starting and the lesser voltage after throwing over the switch. Then the motor

at starting takes excessive current, and, since the maximum
output is in proportion to the square of the voltage, the motor
capacity is much reduced when it is apparently running on
the operating position.   Such action, therefore, can usually be
accounted for by a wrong connection in the compensator.
Sometimes a motor connected to a compensator takes more
current at starting than it should, under which conditions a
lower tap should be tried.   Compensators are usually supplied with various taps and the one should be selected which
produces the least disturbance on the line, giving at the same
time the desired starting torque on the motor.

**412. When a Motor, Having Been Connected to a Com-
pensator, Will Not Start,** the cause may be entirely in the
compensator.   The compensator may have become open-circuited, due to a flash within.   The switch may have become
deranged, so that it will not close, or a connection within
the compensator may have become loosened.   Possibly, when
a motor will not start when connected to a compensator just
installed, a secondary coil may be "bucked" against another
secondary coil within the compensator so that on voltage is
produced by the compensator at the motor.   This results in
no appreciable excess heating and in no apparent phenomenon
which would account for the motor not starting.   An ammeter in the motor leads will indicate the absence of current,
or a voltmeter will indicate the absence of voltage.

413. Induction-motor Collector-ring Troubles.—It is essential that the contact of the brushes on the collector rings
be good, else the contact resistance will be so great as to slow
the motor down and to cause heating of the collector itself.
This effect is particularly noticeable when carbon brushes are
used.   The contact resistance of a carbon brush under normal
operation pressure and carrying its usual density of current
(40 amp. per sq. in.) is 0.04 ohm per sq. in.   Thus, under
normal conditions, the drop is 0.04×40, which equals 1.6
volts.   If the contact is only one-quarter the surface, this
drop would be 6.4 volts, and might materially affect the speed
of the motor.   Thus, if the speed is below synchronous speed
more than it should be (normally it should not be over 4 per

cent. below), an investigation of the fit of the brush upon the collector may show up the trouble.

If copper brushes are used, this trouble is much less liable to occur, since the drop of voltage, due to contact resistance when running at normal density (150 amp. per sq. in.), is only one-tenth that of carbon. The same trouble may occur due to the pigtail, which is usually used with carbon brushes, making poor contact with the carbon, which gives the same effect as a poor contact with the collector itself.

414. Hunting of Induction Motors.—In very rare cases an induction motor will hunt and cause much trouble. The phenomenon appears as a speed variation of 1 or 2 per cent. each side of the normal speed, with a period of vibration depending upon the conditions. It may be anywhere from 10 to 500 swings a minute. This rare phenomenon of induction motors depends upon the drop in the line between the generator operating the induction motor and the motor itself, and upon the design and slot relations of field and armature. It will cease if the line resistance be cut out between the motor and the generator. If this is not possible, it can sometimes be stopped on at three-phase motor by changing from delta to Y connection, or possibly the grouping of the poles may be changed. In any case, the flux in the motor is altered.

415. The Period of Motor Hunting Has Nothing Whatever To Do with the Hunting of the Generator.—Hunting of a motor may occur even though the generator speed is exactly uniform. This action is entirely distinct from a variation of the uniformity of the speed of the generator due to the engine driving (Art. 289) which lack of uniformity is repeated by the motor itself. It is more vicious and usually results in a gradual increase of amplitude of swing until the motor finally gets swinging so badly that it finally breaks down and stops entirely. Ordinarily, the manufacturer is responsible, but a change of connections will often cure the trouble and keep the apparatus in operation until a permanent correction can be effected.

416. Improper End Play in Induction Motors.—Induction motors are so designed that the revolving parts will play endwise in the bearing; $\frac{1}{16}$ in. or so. If in setting up the machine the bearings so limit this end action that the rotor does not lie exactly in the middle of the stator, there is a strong magnetic pull tending to center the rotor. If the bearings will not permit this centering, the thrust collars must take the extra thrust which, in an induction motor, is considerable. If in addition to the magnetic thrust the belt pull is such as to also draw in the same direction, the trouble is aggravated. The end force may be such as to heat the bearing excessively and to cause cutting, soon rendering the motor inoperative.

417. In Case of Trouble with Bearings, the end play should be tested by pushing against the shaft with a·small piece of wood, placed on the shaft center. With the machine operating and rotating under normal conditions there should be no particular difficulty in pushing the shaft first one way from one side, and then the other way from the other side. If it is found that the revolving part is hugging closely against one side, the trouble can be corrected either by pressing the spider along the shaft in a direction toward which the hugging is occurring, or by driving the tops of the lamination teeth in the same direction. With a wooden wedge, the tops of the teeth can often without any difficulty be driven over $\frac{1}{8}$ to $\frac{3}{16}$ in. This movement will usually correct the trouble. Driving the teeth of the stator $\frac{1}{8}$ in. or so in the opposite direction to that of the end thrust will usually accomplish the same result. It is best to choose the teeth (stator or rotor) which are most easily driven over. The thin long ones move easier than do the short broad ones.

418. Oil Leakage of Induction Motor Bearings.—Sometimes a bearing will permit oil to be drawn out, perhaps a very little at a time. Ultimately enough will accumulate to show on the outside or on the windings of the machine. While a motor will run for a period with its windings wet with ordinary lubricating oil without being apparently injured, insulation soaked with oil will deteriorate and eventually fail. One of the principal causes is a suction of the oil due to the drafts of air from the rotor, and one of the best methods of stopping the trouble, under ordinary conditions, is to cut grooves in the babbitt lining as shown in Fig. 269 at B and D. These

18

grooves on a 50-h.p. motor may be ⅛ in. deep and 3⁄16 in. wide.   Each groove has three holes drilled through the bearing shell to convey the oil collected by the grooves into the oil well. These grooves are just as effective with a split as with a solid bearing.   It is impossible here to go into the various causes of oil leakage.   The grooves as suggested are a general remedy and may correct many oil-leakage difficulties.   See Art. 233 for information relating to ball bearings for electrical machinery.

419. To Locate a Short-circuited Coil in an Alternating-current Motor or Generator there are several methods which may be used.   Which one is most applicable is determined by the conditions of the case.   Frequently a short-circuited coil

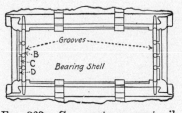

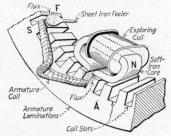

Fig. 269.—Grooves to prevent oil leakage.

Fig. 270.—An "inducer" or exploring-coil for locating short-circuited coils.

will "burn out," that is, the insulation will be charred completely from it, in which case the identification is obvious. When this occurs it is usually possible to cut out the short-circuited coil, to close the circuit and continue operation. Often such a coil will not become sufficiently heated to burn out, but can be located by feeling with the hand because of its excess temperature above that of the adjacent coils.   Where a motor is under consideration, the machine can be operated for a time until the short-circuited coil heats so that it can be located with the hand and then it should be marked with a piece of chalk for future identification.

420. An "Inducer" for Locating Short-circuited Coils* is illustrated in Fig. 270.   This device, the principle of operation

* ELECTRICAL REVIEW, Aug. 29, 1914, p. 425.

of which is similar to that of the one described in Art. 270, has been used successfully for locating short-circuited coils. A C-shaped soft-iron core, N (preferably laminated) is provided with a winding having sufficient reactance so that when the coil is connected across the available (a 110-volt line will do) alternating-current line, it will not overheat. The coil may otherwise be of any reasonable proportions. When this exploring coil is placed over the core laminations, A, and rests over a slot in which one side of a short-circuited coil lies, the exploring coil will induce sufficient current in this short-circuited coil to set up a magnetic flux across the slot, S (Fig. 270), which can be detected with a soft sheet-iron feeler, F. Hence, to use an exploring coil of this type, shift the energized coil around the entire interior circumference of the state, at the same time holding the feeler at a distance from the gap of the exploring coil, equal to the pitch of the coils.

TESTING OF ALTERNATING-CURRENT GENERATORS AND MOTORS

421. An Alternating-current Generator Excitation or Magnetization Test is diagrammed in Fig. 271. The object of this test is to determine the change of the armature voltage, due to the variation of the field current, when the external circuit is open. As shown in Fig. 271 the field circuit is connected with an ammeter, I, and a rheostat, R, in series with a direct-current source of supply. The resistance of the rheostat is varied, and readings of the voltmeters across the armature coils and of the ammeter, are recorded. The generator speed must be kept constant, preferably at the normal speed

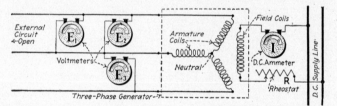

FIG. 271.—Arrangement of apparatus for determining data for plotting a magnetization graph of a three-phase, alternating-current generator.

which is specified on the nameplate. By plotting the current and the voltage values thus obtained on squared paper the excitation or magnetization graph of the machine will be the result.

422. A Synchronous-impedance Test of an Alternating-current Generator may be made as indicated in Fig. 272. In determining the regulation of an alternating-current generator, it is necessary to obtain what is called the "synchronous impedance" of the machine. To do this, the field is connected, as shown. The voltmeters (E_1, E_2 and E_3) are removed and the armature short-circuited with the ammeters (I_1, I_2, and I_3) in circuit. The field current, I_f, is then varied, the armature driven at synchronous speed, and the armature current measured by the ammeters. The relation between field and armature amperes is then plotted on squared paper. A combination of the results of this test, with those obtained from the test shown in Fig. 271, is used in the determination of the regulation of a generator. Engineers differ, however, as to application of the values obtained as above to the determination of regulation. Methods of combining the results will not, therefore, be discussed here.

423. A Load Test of a Three-phase, Alternating-current Generator may be made by means of the connection shown

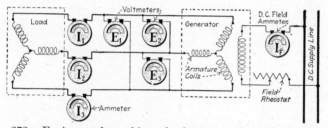

Fig. 272.—Equipment for making a load test on a three-phase alternating current generator.

in Fig. 272. Readings of armature current and field amperes are obtained at any desired load. The field current, I_f, can be varied also so as to maintain constant armature voltage irrespective of load, or the field current may be kept constant and the armature voltage allowed to vary as the load increases. The connections may also be used to make a temperature test on the generator by loading it with an artificial load. In some cases after the generator is installed the arrangement shown may be used to make a temperature test, loading the machine with the actual commercial load the generator is serving.

424. In Testing Alternating-current Generators for Insulation Resistance, the same general methods (Art. 245) may be followed as with direct-current machines.

425. For Determining the Brake Horse-power Output and the Torque of Alternating-current Motors the same Prony-brake methods (See Art. 237) that are used with direct-current motors are employed. Refer to Sec. 5, "Testing of Direct-current Motors and Generators," for further information.

426. With Very Large Machines Under Test, it is inadvisable to use the above method as it is sometimes difficult to so adjust the pulleys and belt tension that the belt slip will be just right to compensate for the difference in the diameters of the pulleys, and very violent flapping of the belt results. To meet such conditions various other methods have been devised. One which gives consistent results is the following:

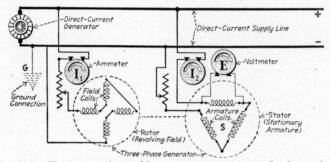

Fig. 273.—Equipment for making a temperature test of a large three-phase generator or synchronous motor.

Supply the rotor with normal field current. The stator, S, is connected in open delta (Fig. 273) and full-load current sent through it from an external source of direct current. Care should be taken to ground one terminal of the direct-current generator, as at G, so as to eliminate danger of shock, to attendants, due to the voltage on the stator winding. The rotor is then driven at synchronous speed.

If the stator is designed for 2,300-volt star connection, the voltage generated in each leg of the delta will be 1,330 volts, and unless one leg of the direct-current generator were grounded, the tester might receive a severe shock by contacting with the direct-current circuit. The insulation of the direct-current machine will also be subjected to abnormal strain unless one terminal is grounded.

By the above method the rotor is subjected to its full copper loss and the stator to full copper loss and core loss. Temperature readings are taken as recommended in the STANDARDIZATION RULES OF THE A. I. E. E. This method may also be used with satisfactory results on large three-phase motors of the wound-rotor type.

427. The Method of Measuring the Input of a Single-phase Motor of any type is shown in Fig. 274, the ammeter, voltmeter and wattmeter being connected as indicated. The ammeter, A, measures the current flowing through the motor, the voltmeter, C, the e.m.f. across the terminals of the motor, and the wattmeter, B, the total power which flows through

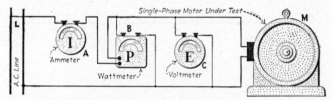

FIG. 274.—Instruments and connections for measuring the input of a single phase motor.

the motor circuit. With the connections as shown, the watt-meter would also measure the slight losses in the voltmeter and the potential coil of the wattmeter, but for motors of $\frac{1}{4}$ h.p. and larger, this loss is so small that it may be neglected. *The power-factor may be calculated* by dividing the true watts as indicated by the wattmeter, by the product of the volts and amperes.

428. A Three-phase Generator or Synchronous-motor Temperature Test may be made as diagrammed in Fig. 275, which shows the arrangement usually employed in shop temperature tests of these machines. The two generators or synchronous motors of same size and type are belted together, one, M, to be driven as a synchronous motor and the other, G, as an alternating-current generator. The method employed is to synchronize the synchronous motor, M, with the generator or generators on the three-phase circuit, L, and then connect it to the line by means of a three-pole, single-throw switch. The alternating-current generator, G, is then similarly synchronized with the generator of the three-phase circuit and thrown on the line. By varying the field of the generator it can be made to carry approximately full-load. The motor will then also be approximately fully loaded. The usual method is to have the motor carry slightly in excess of full-load, and the generator slightly less than full-load. Under these conditions the motor will run a little warmer than it should with normal load, while the generator will run slightly

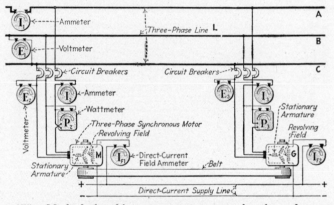

Fig. 275.—Method of making a temperature test of a three-phase generator or motor.

cooler. Temperature measurements are then made in the same way as discussed under three-phase motors. The necessary ammeters, voltmeters and wattmeters for adjusting the loads on the motors and generator are shown in the illustration.

If the pulleys are of sufficient size to transmit the full-load with, say, 1 per cent. slip, the pulley on the motor should be 1 per cent. larger in diameter than the pulley on the generator, so that the generator will remain in synchronism and, at the same time, deliver power to the circuit, L.

429. To Determine the Approximate Input Load on a Three-phase Motor by the Voltmeter and Ammeter Method the ar-

rangement shown in Fig. 276 may be used. The current
through one of the three lines and the voltage across one phase
is measured. If the voltage is approximately the rated voltage
of the motor and the amperes the rated current of the motor
(as noted on the nameplate), it may be assumed that the
motor is carrying approximately full-load. If, on the other
hand, the amperes are much in excess of full-load rating, it is
evident that the motor is carrying an overload. The heat
generated in the copper varies as the square of the current.
That generated in the iron varies anywhere from the 1.6 power
to the square of the current. This method is exceedingly
convenient if a wattmeter is not available, although it is, of
course, of no value for the determination of the efficiency or
power-factor of the apparatus. This method gives fairly

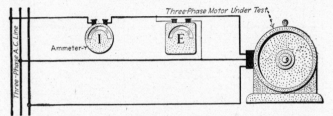

Fig. 276.—Connections for determining the load on a three-phase motor
by the approximate "voltmeter-and-ammeter" method.

accurate results, providing the load is fairly well balanced on
all three of the phases of the motor. If there is much difference
in the voltages across the three phases, the ammeter should be
switched from one circuit to another, and the current measured
in each phase. If the motor is very lightly loaded and the
voltage of the different phases varies by 2 or 3 per cent., the
current in the three legs of the circuit will vary 20 to 30 per
cent.

**430. Where an Accurate Input Test of a Three-phase
Motor is Desired the "Two-wattmeter" Method is Used.—**
This is illustrated in Fig. 277. Assume that the motor is
loaded with a Prony brake so that its output can be determined. This method gives correct results even with considerable unbalancing in the voltages of the three phases. With

the connections as shown, the sum of the two wattmeter readings gives the total power in the circuit. Neither meter by itself measures the power in any one of the three phases. In fact, with light-load one of the meters will probably give a negative reading, and it will then be necessary to either reverse its current or potential leads in order that the deflection may be noted. In such cases the algebraic sums of the two readings must be taken. In other words, if one reads + 500 watts and the other − 300 watts, the total power in the circuit will be: 500 − 300 = 200 *watts.*

As the load comes on, the readings of the instrument which gave the negative deflection will decrease until they drop to zero, and it will then be necessary to again reverse the po-

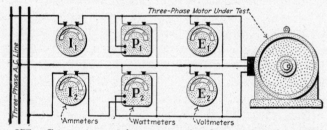

Fig. 277.—Connections of instruments for determining the load on a three-phase induction motor by the "two-wattmeter" method.

tential leads on this wattmeter. Thereafter, the readings of both instruments will be positive, and the numerical sum of the two should be taken as the measurement of the load. If one set of the instruments is removed from the circuit, the reading of the remaining wattmeter will have absolutely no meaning. As suggested above, it will not indicate the power under these conditions in any one phase of the circuit. The power-factor is obtained by *dividing the actual watts input by the product of the average of the voltmeter readings* × *the average of the ampere readings* × 1.73.

431. The Three-phase-motor Input Test, Polyphase-watt-meter Method is identical with that described above except that the polyphase wattmeter itself combines the movements of the two wattmeters. Otherwise the method of making the measurements is identical.   If the power-factor is known to be less than 50 per cent., connect one of the wattmeter movements so as to give a positive deflection; then disconnect movement 1 and connect movement 2 so as to give a positive deflection.   Then reverse either the potential or current leads of the movement giving the smaller deflection, leaving the remaining movement with the original connection.   The readings now obtained will be the correct total watts delivered to the motor.

If the power-factor is known to be over 50 per cent., the same method should be employed, except that both movements should be independently connected to give positive readings. An unloaded induction motor has a power-factor of less than 50 per cent., and may, therefore be used as above for determining the correct connections.   For a better understanding of the reasons for the above method of procedure, it is suggested that the discussion of power measurement by the two-wattmeter method (Art. 430) be read.

The power-factor may be calculated as under the test previously described in Art. 427.   Connect as per Fig. 277.   The following check on the connections may be made.   Let the polyphase induction motor run idle, that is, with no load. The motor will then operate with a power-factor less than 50 per cent.   The polyphase meter should give a positive indication, but if each movement is tried independently one will be found to give a negative reading, the other movement will give a positive reading.   The movements can be tried independently by disconnecting one of the potential leads from the binding post of one movement.   When the power-factor is above 50 per cent. then both movements will give positive deflection.

432. The "One-wattmeter-method," Three-phase-motor Input Test is equivalent to the two-wattmeter method with the following difference.   A single voltmeter (Fig. 278) with a switch, *A*, can be used to connect the voltmeter across either one of two phases.   Three switches, *B*, *C* and *D*, are employed for changing the connection of the ammeter and wattmeter in either one of the two lines.   With the switches *B* and *D* in the position shown, the ammeter and wattmeter series coils are connected in the upper line. The switch *C* must be closed under these conditions to close the middle line. Another reading should then be taken before any change of load has occurred, with switch *A* thrown down, switch *B* closed, switch *D* thrown down and switch *C* open. The ammeter and the current coil of the wattmeter will then be connected to the middle line of the motor.

To prevent any interruption of the circuit, the switches *B*, *D* and *C* should be operated in the order given above. With very light load on the motor, the wattmeter will probably give a negative deflection in one phase or the other, and it will be necessary to reverse its connections before

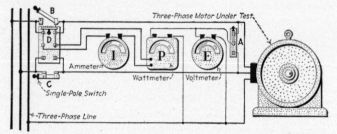

Fig. 278.—Arrangement of circuits for testing a three-phase motor by the "one-wattmeter" method.

taking the readings. For this purpose a double-pole, double-throw switch is sometimes inserted in the circuit of the potential coil of the wattmeter so that the indications can be reversed without disturbing any of the connections. It is suggested, that, before undertaking this test, the instructions for test by the two-wattmeter (Art. 430) and by the polyphase-wattmeter (Art. 431) methods be read.

433. The "One-wattmeter-and-Y-box" Method of Testing the Input of a Three-phase Motor, a diagram for which is shown in Fig. 279, is of service, only, where the voltages of the three phases are the same. A slight variation in the voltages of the different phases may result in a very large error in the readings of the wattmeter, and inasmuch as the voltages of all commercial three-phase circuits are more or

less unbalanced, this method is not to be recommended for
motor testing.   With balanced voltages in all three phases,
the power is: *that indicated by the wattmeter, multiplied by*
3.   Power-factor may be calculated as described above.

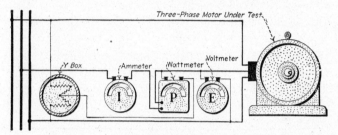

Fig. 279.—Method of testing a three-phase motor with one wattmeter
and a Y box.   (To be used on balanced circuits only.)

**434. The Method of Testing for the Input of a Three-
phase Motor Where the Neutral of the Motor has Been
Brought Out** is diagrammed in Fig. 280.   Some star-con-
nected motors have a connection from the neutral point
brought outside of the motor frame of the stator or armature

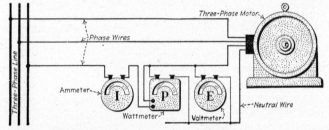

Fig. 280.—"Single-wattmeter" method of testing a three-phase motor
which has the neutral brought outside the frame.

winding.   In this case the testing circuit may be connected
as shown.   The voltmeter, E, measures voltage between the
neutral and one of the lines, and the wattmeter, P, the power
in one of the three phases of the motor.   Therefore, the total
power taken by the motor will be 3 times the wattmeter readings.   By this method, as accurate results may be obtained
as with the two-wattmeter method.   The power factor will

be: *the indicated watts divided by the product of the indicated amperes and volts.*

435. The Temperature Test of a Three-phase Induction Motor may be conducted as delineated in Fig. 281. Temperature tests are usually made on small induction motors by belting the motor to a generator and loading the generator with a lamp-bank or resistance until the motor input is equal to full-load input. If, however, the motor is of considerable size so that the cost of the energy expended in making the test becomes a large item in the expense of testing, the method shown in Fig. 206 may be employed. Two motors, preferably

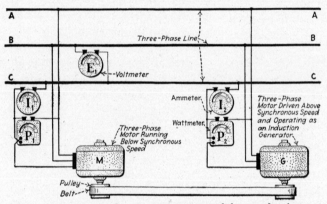

Fig. 281.—Apparatus and arrangement thereof for conducting a temperature test of a large three-phase induction motor.

of size the same and type, are required. One, *M*, is driven as a motor and runs slightly below synchronism, due to its slip when operating under load. This motor is belted to the second machine, *G*. If the pulley of the second machine is smaller than the pulley of the first the second will then operate as an induction generator, and will return to the line as much power as the first motor draws from the line, less the losses of the second machine.

By selecting the ratio of pulleys properly, the first machine can be caused to draw full-load current and full-load energy from the line. In this way, the total energy consumed is equivalent to the total of the losses of both machines, which is approximately twice the losses of a single machine.   Fig. 277 shows the connection of the wattmeters (without necessary switches) for reading the total energy by the two-wattmeter method.   Detailed connections for the wattmeter are shown in Fig. 278.   It is usual, in making temperature tests, to insert one or more thermometers in what is presumed to be the hottest part of the winding, one on the surface of the laminæ and one in the air duct between the iron laminæ.   The test should be continued until the difference in temperature between any part of the motor and the air reaches a steady value.   The motor should then be stopped and the temperature of the rotor also measured.   For the method of testing wound-rotor type induction motors of very large size, see Fig. 273.   For the approved procedure in taking temperature readings and interpreting results, see the STANDARDIZATION RULES OF THE A. I. E. E.

TEST DETERMINATION OF MOTOR-DRIVE POWER REQUIREMENTS

436. It is Important That a Reasonably Accurate Determination of the Power Required to drive a certain machine or a group of machines be made before the motor for the drive is purchased or ordered. Money expended in this direction is always well spent. The reason for this is that the tendency is usually to select a motor considerably larger than is actually necessary for a certain drive. Hence, the difference in cost between a motor that is selected on the basis of an actual test and the one that probably would have been selected had the test not been made, often represents a very material saving in capital expenditure. Such a test is particularly desirable where a motor to pull a group drive is to be installed, because the power requirement of a group of machines is a quantity that is difficult, if not impossible, of accurate estimation. It is the purpose of this article to describe some simple methods and apparatus whereby the power requirements of ordinary group or machine-tool drives can be economically ascertained with sufficient precision for commercial purposes.

437. Machine-tool Builders and Motor Manufacturers Often Over-estimate the Horsepower Required of a motor because their tendency is, obviously, to "be on the safe side." This is particularly true of the tool builders. These concerns are often requested to advise as to the proper horse-power rating of a motor to drive a given machine. Where a motor that is larger than is necessary is recommended and installed the result is that it may operate most of the time at a fraction of full load at correspondingly reduced efficiency. In a large installation, the unnecessary electrical losses and the interest and depreciation on the unjustified extra investment may total to a very considerable annual charge.

438. To Determine the Actual Power Required to drive a given machine or load, probably the best and simplest method is to arrange a temporary motor belt-drive to the tool or load in question (Fig. 282) and then measure the input to this temporary motor. To determine the actual power required to drive the load there should be subtracted from the input of the motor (as measured with a wattmeter or with a voltmeter and an ammeter) the power losses in the motor, because motors are rated on the basis of their brake horse-power outputs.

439. To Determine the Losses of the Testing Motor at various loads arrange the motor for a Prony-brake test (Art. 238) and thereby ascertain its input and output at various loads. From these data, a graph indicating the efficiency at any load can be plotted. Then, the values from this graph can be used in making the correction for motor efficiency suggested in the preceding paragraph. That is, where it is necessary that the power input of a machine or a drive be determined quite accurately it is essential that the testing motor be calibrated—its efficiency at different loads must

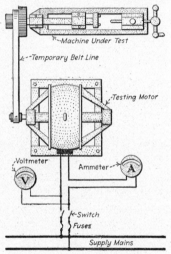

Fig. 282.—Arrangement of apparatus for testing power input to machine tools.

be known. It is often possible to obtain an efficiency curve of a testing motor from the manufacturer to the machine. If such a graph is not attainable this efficiency data may be ascertained by testing as suggested above. The power output of a motor at any instant is equal to: *the power input at the same instant multiplied by the efficiency of the motor, at the load which it is carrying at that instant.*

440. Frequently Such Refinements as Corrections for Efficiency are Considered Unnecessary because the purchaser will buy a motor of a rating which is standard with some manu-

19

facturer. Hence, with small motors—because it is always desirable to have a motor for any drive at least large enough—corrections for the efficiency of the test motor may prove an undesirable refinement.

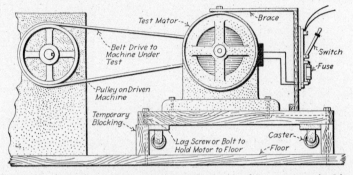

Fig. 283.—Portable motor arranged to determine the power required by machine tools.

441. There are Many Workable Arrangements for Test Motors.—Figs. 283 to 286 show some that have been applied in practice. It is usually desirable, if several determinations of power requirements are to be made, to mount the test motor

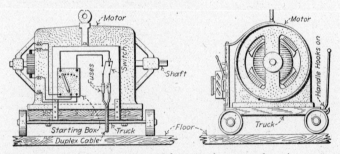
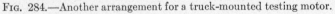

Fig. 284.—Another arrangement for a truck-mounted testing motor.

on a truck so that it can be transported to any part of the plant with a minimum expenditure of time and labor. After the portable test motor has been drawn to the machine or group which it is to drive, it, or the platform on which it rests, should be securely bolted (Fig. 283) or braced in position. In many cases it is desirable to arrange a step pulley or counter shaft on the platform of the test motor (Figs. 285 and 286) to insure that the arrangement can be used to drive a machine or shaft rotating at any reasonable speed.

442. In Making a Test of the Power Required the motor is drawn to a convenient location near the machine, tool or shaft and a temporary belt drive arranged (Figs. 282 and 283) between the driven device and the motor. Then the machine or group to be driven is subjected to its normal cycle of operations and in the meantime the power input of the motor is measured.

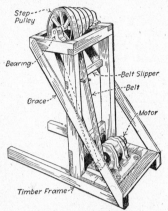

Fig. 285.—A portable test motor equipped with a counter shaft.

443. In Connecting the Test Instruments in the Motor Circuit it is desirable that provision be made which will render it unnecessary to unsolder lugs or disconnect leads. This

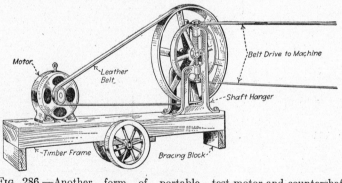

Fig. 286.—Another form of portable test-motor-and-countershaft equipment.

feature is particularly important where it is necessary to determine the power input of some motor which is already installed and in operation.   Often the most expensive and tedious part of the work of making such a power-input test of an

existing motor is that involved in connecting the instruments
into the motor circuit. As suggested in Fig. 287 the most
convenient and economical method of connecting the instrument in such a circuit appears to be that involving the application of "dummy"—fuse-connectors, the construction of certain types of which are detailed
in Figs. 288 to 291. In Fig. 287
a direct-current testing motor
is shown but the general scheme
suggested is quite as applicable
for three-phase-motors. However, for testing a three-phase
motor two "dummy" fuse-connectors will be required whereas
for direct-current tests only one
is necessary.

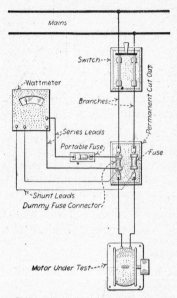

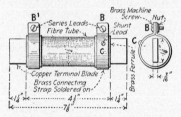

FIG. 287.—Connections for
motor testing. (Note that placing
the switch in the circuit ahead of
the permanent cut-out is in viola-
tion of *National Electric Code* Rule
23a, Par. *II*.)

FIG. 288.—"Dummy-fuse" connector for a 101–200 amp. National-
electrical-code-standard. Knife-
blade-contact, fuse block.

**444. In Connecting Any Instrument with Dummy-fuse-
connectors** instead of disconnecting one of the leads to the
motor, the series coil leads of the wattmeter or ammeter may
be inserted at the cut-out by means of the dummy-fuse-connector. The connection is effected as shown at Fig. 287.
One of the fuses is removed from the cut-out and in its stead
is inserted (Fig. 288) a dummy-fuse-connector. The leads of
the wattmeter or ammeter are connected—frequently permanently—to the binding post B and B^1 (Fig. 288) of the con-

nector.   There is no electrical path directly through the dummy-fuse-connector because the old "blown" fuse from which it was made was taken apart and the portions of the fusible conductor which it originally contained have been removed.   The circuit of the motor must, therefore, be completed through the watt-meter—or an ammeter if an ammeter is used.   Where a test is being conducted, as indicated in Fig. 287, a portable fuse is often inserted in the circuit which contains the dummy-fuse-connector so that the motor and the instruments will be pro-tected against over-load while the test is being made.   Such a fuse is not always used, but to insure against accident should be.

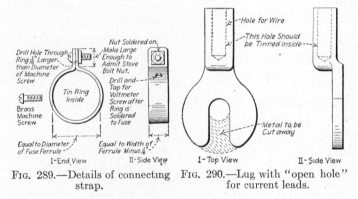

FIG. 289.—Details of connecting   FIG. 290.—Lug with "open hole"
strap.   for current leads.

445. A Dummy-fuse-connector for 61- to 600-Ampere N. E. C. Standard Fuse Blocks is indicated in general construc-tion in Fig. 288.   However, this illustration is dimensioned for a 101–200-ampere fuse.   Connecting straps, which are de-tailed in Fig. 289, are soldered to the ferrules of what was a fuse.   The terminals or binding posts may be arranged by soldering on to each of the connecting straps a nut, through which a brass machine screw, B and B^1, turns.   Wattmeter or ammeter leads may be connected either by clamping them under the heads of the binding post (B and B^1) or they may be soldered into lugs of the type suggested in Fig. 290.   For con-necting the voltage lead, a small brass machine screw, C, is ar-ranged to turn in a tapped hole in one of the connecting straps.

This hole should be drilled or tapped after the strips have been soldered to the ferrules. The other voltage lead can be connected to its side of the circuit by inserting its thin metal terminal lug or its bared end between the fuse knife blade and the corresponding contact clip.

446. A "Forked" or "Open Hole" Lug of this type is desir-

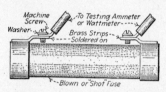

Fig. 291.—"Dummy-fuse" connector for a small capacity national-electrical-code-standard (10–30 and 30–60) ferrule-contact fuse block.

able in that it may be clamped under the machine screw head on the connector without removing the screw entirely from its hole. The lug (Fig. 290) may be made by filing away from an ordinary lug the portion enclosed in the dotted lines in the illustration.

447. A Dummy-fuse-connector for Ferrule-contact Fuse Blocks may be arranged as detailed in Fig. 291. A brass strip constituting a terminal is soldered to each of the ferrules. Machine screws, provided with washers, turning in tapped holes in these strips provide for the connection of the ammeter or wattmeter leads.

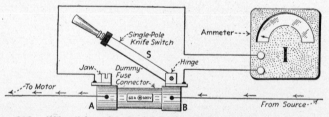

Fig. 292.—"Shot" fuse fitted with knife switch for shunting out ammeter

448. A Shunting-out Switch may be arranged on a dummy-fuse-connector as diagramed in Fig. 292. When the switch, *S*, is closed the ammeter or wattmeter connected across the dummy-fuse-connector, at *A* and *B*, is shunted out of circuit. As indicated in the illustration, the hinge and the jaw of a knife switch are respectively soldered to each of the ferrules of the "blown" fuse. The lead from each of the ferrules to an ammeter or wattmeter may be soldered to the ferrules or connected thereto as detailed in Fig. 288. When inserting a dummy-fuse-connector of the type shown in Fig. 292 in a live circuit, arrange a shunted circuit around one of the fuses by placing a jumper between its terminal clips; then, pull out the fuse and insert the dummy-fuse-connector. Then, when the switch, *S*, is opened the current taken by the machine under test will flow through the ammeter or wattmeter. Hence, the operation of the motor continues uninterruptedly and production is not blocked. When the test has been completed the terminals of the cut-out are again shunted, the dummy-fuse-connector withdrawn and the intact fuse replaced before the shunted jumper is removed.

449. Graphic Instruments are Very Desirable for Recording Motor Power Input Tests. —A graphic wattmeter of one of the types which has been satisfactory for work of this character is illustrated in Figs. 293 and 294. A graphic watt-meter will record on a strip of paper (Fig. 295) a graphic record of the power taken by the motor driving the machine, tool or group being tested at the dif-

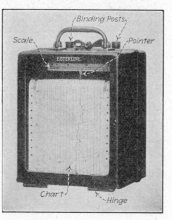

Fig. 293.—A portable graphic meter.

ferent instants of its operation. Such a curve constitutes a valuable permanent record and provides information which is difficult to obtain by any other method. Furthermore, where a curve-drawing instrument is used, it can be connected in the test-motor circuit and left there for a day or several days or for a month, during which period it will be automatically recording a graph of the performance and of the power taken by the motor. The graph indicates clearly just what are the maximum average and minimum power inputs to the motor and it shows the time relation between them. Where a company is purchasing a considerable number of motors, a graphic instrument will usually pay for itself in less than a year by enabling its owner to select motors of the smallest capacity which will do the work.

FIG. 294.—Disassembled view of an Esterline graphic instrument.

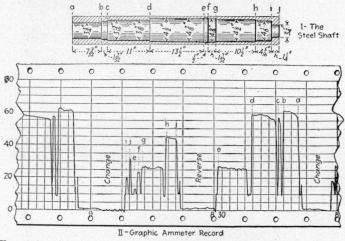

FIG. 295.—Graphic-ammeter record indicating the power required to "rough out" the steel shaft illustrated.

450. Graphic Ammeters are sometimes used instead of graphic wattmeters for motor test work and on direct-current circuits where the voltage regulation is reasonably good they may, in certain cases, be preferred to graphic wattmeters. The reason for this is that the ammeter is simpler than the wattmeter and more readily connected by inexperienced men than is the wattmeter. Such a direct-current, graphic ammeter will draw graphs which, by taking into account the voltage (which is assumed to be constant) can be calibrated in watts or horse-power. However, for alternating-current work, particularly where low power-factors are encountered and where, therefore, the current taken by a motor may not be

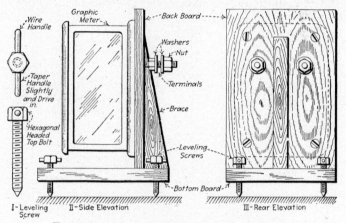

Fig. 296.—Portable stand for graphic wattmeter.

at all proportional of the actual power consumed, a wattmeter must be used.

451. One Graphic Instrument Can be Used to Record the Inputs to Motors of Various Capacities by providing suitable shunts and multipliers for the direct-current instruments and series and shunt transformers for the alternating-current instruments. It frequently occurs that the electrical manufacturers do not regularly list these "wide-range" outfits but will usually furnish data concerning them on application.

452. A Stand for a Graphic Instrument, originally designed for switch-board mounting, can be constructed as shown in Fig. 296. Portable, graphic instruments (Fig. 293) are regularly manufactured but it is sometimes necessary, for one reason or other, to use those of the switch-board type. The stand of Fig. 296 can be made of straight grained wood. The actual thickness of the backboard should be determined by the thickness of the switch-board panel for which the terminals and supporting studs of the instrument were designed. Fig. 297 details the method of holding the nuts for the leveling screws.

453. An Example of the Record of a Graphic Ammeter* connected in a machine-tool-drive motor circuit is represented in Fig. 295. This graph indicates the power consumption at different instants in "roughing out" the steel shaft shown at Fig. 295*I*. The graph reads continuously from the right to

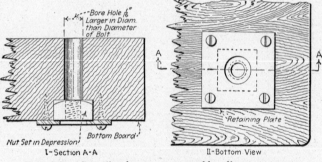

FIG. 297.—Details of arrangement of leveling-screw nut.

the left in accordance with the sequence of the time intervals shown along the lower line of the chart. The reference letters on the graph correspond with those indicated on the sectional view of the shaft. Hence, although the shaft was reversed in position while it was being measured the power and time required to make the various cuts (shown by the cross-hatched portion in *I*) can easily be ascertained.

454. To Ascertain the Energy Represented by a Graphic Power Record, the area included within the graph of the record can be ascertained with a planimeter. This area will be proportional to the energy (kwh) consumed during the period represented by the graph.

* Westinghouse Elec. & Manfg. Co.

455. The Practical Determination of the Torque Required to Drive or Start a Given Load may be effected as suggested in Figs. 298 and 299. With the method of Fig. 299 a wooden clamp is bolted on the belt driving the load and the actual torque measured by pulling on a spring balance fastened to the clamp. The force, in pounds, which the spring balance measures will be the force required to start the load at the radius, L. The torque is obtained by multiplying this force by the length of the lever arm, L. In

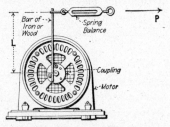

Fig. 298.—Ascertaining by test the torque required by measuring it at the motor coupling.

pulling on the balance, it should be held parallel to the belt. By applying the torque formulas given in Art. 237—the speed and diameter of the driven pulley being known—the horse-power re-

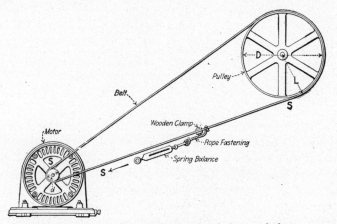

Fig. 299.—The determination with a spring balance of the torque required for a belt drive.

quired by the drive may be readily computed. Where the driving motor transmits its power to the load through a coupling, the scheme suggested in Fig. 298 may be utilized. The direction of the pull on the spring balance must be at right angles to an imaginary line passing through the center of the shaft and through the point where the balance is attached to the testing lever. Where a machine is gear-driven, the torque may be ascertained by placing the hook of a spring balance over one of the arms of the gear and pulling thereon, noting the pounds force required to start and to move the load.

SECTION 14

MOTOR GENERATORS AND FREQUENCY CHANGES

456. A Motor-generator Set* is Defined thus: "A transforming device consisting of a motor mechanically coupled to one or more generators."

457. A Motor-generator Set Comprises two electrically distinct elements, a motor and a generator coupled mechanically together and usually mounted on the same bed plate. The motor and the generator may each be of any commercial type. See Fig. 300. A motor-generator converts electrical energy

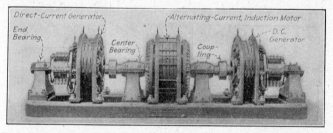

Fig. 300.—A "Ridgway" motor-generator set. The 210-h.p., 2200-volt, 3-phase, 60-cycle, induction motor drives two 70-kw., 125-volt, 700-r.p.m. direct-current generators.

from one voltage or frequency to some other voltage or frequency or from alternating to direct current. Where the motor is operated by alternating current, a synchronous motor is frequently used because of its ability to correct low power-factor, but an induction motor may be used. The motor or generator may be either alternating current or direct current. Figs. 111, 112 and 113 show a motor-generator mine-hoist outfit; refer to the text accompanying these illustrations for information relative to this application.

*STANDARDIZATION RULE 104, A. I. E. E., June 28, 1916.

458. Alternating-current Motor, Direct-current Generator Sets (Fig. 301) are used to obtain a direct e.m.f. where the source of energy is an alternating one. The alternating-current motor may be of either the induction or the synchronous type, each of which has its advantages for certain applications, as suggested below.

459. An Induction-motor Drive for a Motor-generator Set has in its favor the features of low first cost and simplicity. Induction motors may be wound for high pressures—as great as 13,000 volts—which, in many cases, will render the use of transformers unnecessary. Because of the fact that induction motors have a lower speed at full-load than at no-load (Art. 316), where it is desired that the direct-current generator driven by such a motor maintain a constant voltage, the gen-

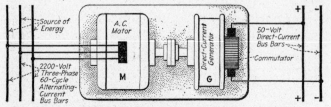

Fig. 301.—Illustrating the application of a motor generator.

erator must be suitably over-compounded to maintain close voltage regulation.

460. A Synchronous-motor Drive for a Motor-generator Set is probably the more frequently used, particularly for sets of considerable output. An important advantage of the synchronous-motor drive is that an over-excited synchronous motor acts as a synchronous condenser (Art. 342) and hence may be utilized in improving the power-factor of the supplying system. Due to the fact that the synchronous motor (Art. 342) is inherently a constant-speed motor, where a direct-current generator is driven by one, the voltage on the direct-current circuit can be maintained practically constant at all loads regardless of the alternating-current voltage and of the distance of the motor-generator set from the energy-supplying station.

461. A Frequency Changer motor generator set is one consisting of an alternating-current motor and an alternating-current generator each of a different frequency. For illustration (Fig. 302) a 25-cycle motor may drive a 60-cycle generator.   The motor must be of the synchronous type if it is necessary that the frequency of the supplied circuit be maintained constant because (Art. 316) the speed of an induction motor decreases with the load.   Frequency changers are used when the frequency of the supplied circuit must be different from that of the supply circuit.   In other words, they must be installed where it is necessary to interchange power between two circuits or systems of different frequencies.

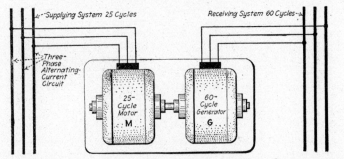

FIG. 302.—Illustrating the application of a frequency-changer, motor generator.

EXAMPLE.—Electrical energy is developed at the Keokuk hydroelectric plant at 25 cycles and transmitted at that frequency to St. Louis and to other localities.   However, inasmuch as a frequency of 60 cycles is, in general, more desirable for lighting—because the "flicker" of incandescent lamps which occurs with 25 cycles is not visible with 60 cycles— and furthermore, since 60-cycle motors of given outputs and speeds cost less than do equivalent 25-cycle motors, a frequency of 60 cycles is used in St. Louis and in most of the other communities supplied from this plant.   Hence, at each of these localities where 60-cycle energy is utilized, a frequency changer—a 25-cycle synchronous motor driving a 60-cycle generator—has been installed.

462. The Two Machines of a Frequency Changer are Mechanically Coupled Together hence the speed of both machines must be one which will, considering the number of poles of each, provide the correct frequency. Where the ratio of the two frequencies is an even number, the result is readily obtained. For instance, for converting from 25 to 50 cycles the generator should have twice as many poles as the motor. Often the frequencies involved are 25 and 60. The following tables show some synchronous speeds for 25- and 60-cycle machines.

Number of poles	Synchronous speed	
	25 cycles	60 cycles
2 poles..............................	1,500	3,600
4 poles..............................	750	1,800
6 poles..............................	500	1,200
8 poles..............................	375	900
10 poles.............................	300	720
14 poles.............................	214.27+	514
18 poles.............................	166.6+	400
20 poles.............................	150	360
24 poles.............................	125	300

Note.—From the table it is evident that the only pole combinations that give precisely the same speed are 10 poles for 25 cycles and 24 poles for 60 cycles. Each gives 300 r.p.m. This is a low speed and the cost of a set of such a speed is relatively high. For practical purposes a frequency of $62\frac{1}{2}$ cycles can often be used instead of 60. A four-pole, 750-r.p.m., 25-cycle motor driving a ten-pole generator will provide $62\frac{1}{2}$ cycles.

INDEX

A

Adjustable-speed motors, d.c., classification................................ 47
   reliance..................... 42
Air gap of d.c. generators, variation in flux distribution in, illustration.. 17
Alternating-current generators, see *Generators, a.c.*
   motors, see *Motors, a.c.*
Alternators, see *Generators, a.c.*
Ambient temperature, a.c. generator guarantees.................. 166
   definition.................. 30, 166
   d.c. generator guarantees....... 28
   motor guarantees............ 29
Ammeter, for compound, d.c. generator..................... 56
   graphic, example of record..... 298
   used instead of wattmeters... 296
   knife switch for shunting out... 294
   shunt, mounting on generator... 58
Arc-light (constant-current) d.c., generator regulated by field variation.. 5
Armature, a.c. generator, three-phase, methods of connecting..... 168
   two-phase, methods of connecting.................. 168
   or stator turbo generator, illustration................... 161
   three-phase generator, connecting, diagram.......... 170
   circuit, open, sparking may be due to..................... 128
   circuit, see *Circuit, armature.*
   coil, d.c., grounded, test........ 138
   hot, cause.................. 140
   reversed, test............... 139
   connection, d.c., shunted, series motor..................... 77
   control, d.c., objections........ 94
   regulator, d.c., construction... 93
   speed regulators, d.c......... 93
   operation, d.c.............. 94
   d.c., balancing................ 147
   rack for..................... 147
   series-wound, number of brush sets in................... 15
   to insure proper balance...... 146
   tested for common troubles.. 130
   handling, 67
   heating, causes................ 140
   short-circuits, test.............. 138
   stand, description.............. 147
   synchronous motor, improper connections................. 238
   testing where only a.c. or low-voltage cells are available.... 132
   testing, with high-voltage a.c.... 132
   unbalance, noise caused by..... 146
   windings, d.c., flying grounds, short-circuits and open circuits..................... 140
Automatic regulation of d.c., constant-current generator...... 3
   starter, see *Starter, automatic.*

B

Auto-starters, to limit starting current, synchronous motors, a.c..... 232
Auto transformer for starting induction motors, see *Compensator.*

Balking, a.c., induction motors...... 269
Ball bearings, examples............ 144
   vertical motors................ 146
Bar and coil leads, poor connection between........................ 137
Bearing, bearings.
   hot, correction................ 144
   troubles, motors and generators. 143
   a.c. generators and motors... 263
   induction motor........... 273
   motors................. 265
   synchronous a.c. motors...... 238
   warm, causes.................. 144
   a.c., induction motor, oil leakage. 273
   cleanliness essential............ 144
   motor, grooves to prevent oil leakage...................... 274
Bipolar machine, definition......... 15
Blackening, commutator........... 116
Blow holes in frame castings sometimes cause sparking............. 126
Brake, prony, different forms....... 149
   motor horsepower determined with..................... 149
   torque concept basis for........ 149
Braking, dynamic, connections...... 98
   d.c. motors, method........... 97
   heating...................... 97
   principal advantages........... 97
   when used.................... 97
Brush, carbon, pressure............ 124
   contact resistance............. 124
   fine grain, soft; possibility of using with slotted commutator 121
   position of commutating-pole machine................... 20
   sets in d.c. machines, number of. 15
   shifting, regulation of constant-current generator by........ 4
   trouble, glowing and pitting.... 114
Brushes, adjustment and care...... 122
   carbon, glowing and pitting.... 126
   chattering.................... 127
   copper, reversal of current must be accurately effected........ 113
   d.c. generators, management.... 66
   effect of shifting on speed...... 41
   should be fitted to commutator.. 123
   sparking, causes............... 125
Building up, shunt d.c. generator.... 7
Buses, equalizer, required for three-wire machines................... 58

C

Capacity, overload, commutating-pole motors.................. 34
   normally rated generators...... 33
   steam engines................. 33

Carbon brush, see *Brush carbon.*
Cascade, speed control, a.c., poly-
    phase, induction motors......... 257
Characteristics, principles and con-
    struction, induction and repul-
    sion a.c. motors.......... 190
    speed, compound-wound, d.c.
        motors.................. 44
    d. c. motors, series, shunt and
        compound............... 34
    shunt motor.............. 40–42
    series and compound-wound
        motors, graphic compari-
        sion.................... 46
    speed-torque, series d.c. motor.. 37
Chattering of brushes............. 127
Circuit, armature, open, sparking
    due to................... 128
    symptoms of trouble due to.... 128
Circuit-breaker, polyphase a.c. in-
    duction motor, protection.. 236
    vs. fuses, advantages and dis-
        advantages................ 76
Circuit, field, open, locating........ 142
    open armature, tests.......... 137
    three-phase, phasing out...... 180
Classification, single-phase a.c. mo-
    tors.......................... 206
Coil, armature, grounded, test...... 138
    hot, causes................. 140
    open-circuited, test.......... 137
    reversed, test.............. 139
    field, grounded, low located..... 140
        heating causes.............. 142
        open-circuited, locating...... 141
    inducing, a.c., for localizing
        armature troubles........... 133
    leads, crossed, test.............. 139
Coils, balance of three-wire genera-
    tor, connecting requirements
    for...................... 26
    series, three-wire, compound-
        wound generator, division.... 25
    short-circuited, a.c. motor or
        generator, to locate....... 274
Collector-ring troubles, a.c., induc-
    tion motor...................... 271
Commutating pole d.c., generator,
    correct polarity at full-load
    and incorrect at no-load.... 66
    shunt motor, speed regulation. 41
    generators and motors, see *Gen-
    erators, commutating pole or
    motors, commutating pole.*
    machines, see *Motors* or *genera-
    tors, commutating pole.*
    poles, effect on speed regulation,
        d.c. motors................ 46
        object..................... 17
        winding of................. 20
    three-wire generator connec-
        tions.................... 27
    windings, determining polari-
        ties..................... 66
Commutation, d.c. motors, deter-
    mines overload capacity...... 34
    process..................... 113
Commutator, all brushes should be
    fitted..................... 123
    bar, loose, sparking............ 118
    blackening..................... 116
    commutators.................. 115
    heating...................... 115
    high mica.................... 121
    high-mica, roughened, to remedy 122
    hot............................. 115

Commutator, loose, to correct...... 119
    management.................. 67
    methods of slotting............ 121
    reason for slotting............. 120
    roughness, correcting........... 116
    due to loose bar............. 118
    rough, sparking............... 114
    sandpaper to smooth........... 118
    segments, loose............... 115
    slotted, care.................. 121
        possibility of using fine grain,
            soft brush.................. 121
    slotting...................... 119
    to smooth with grindstone...... 117
    trouble, glowing and pitting.... 114
    truing with file.............. 118
    what is accomplished by slotting. 120
Compensated d.c. generator....... 21
    conductors for.............. 16
    induction a.c. motor, see *Motor,
    a.c., compensated induction.*
Compensating winding, a.c. motor... 213
Compensator, a.c., induction motor
    connected to, will not start... 271
    for starting squirrel-cage a.c.
        motors.................... 245
    method of starting several poly-
        phase a.c., induction motors
        from one.................. 250
    starter, starting currents and
        starting torques of squirrel-
        cage induction a.c. motors,
        with different impressed vol-
        tages by using.............. 246
    starters, fuses used with...... 251
        high-voltage motors, a.c., with
            no-voltage release........ 248
    starting, overload release coils,
        arrangement.............. 248
        for a.c. motors, high voltage
            large capacity.............. 247
        no-voltage release can be pro-
            vided.................. 250
        for squirrel-cage induction
            a.c. motors............... 243
        induction motors with and
            without.................. 244
        several motors from one...... 250
        taps...................... 246
    to limit starting current, a.c.
        synchronous motors.......... 232
    troubles, a.c., induction motor.. 270
    when used starting torque re-
        duced to value required by
        load...................... 245
Compounding d.c. generator, effect
    on voltage.................. 154
    over, voltage increase due to... 13
Compound dynamo, see *Generator,
    compound.*
Compound motor, see *Motors, d.c.,
    compound wound.*
Compound-wound d.c. generators, see
    Generators, d.c., compound wound.
Condensers a.c., synchronous....... 229
    definition...................... 231
Conductors for d.c., compensated
    generators...................... 16
Connecting leads, d.c., compound
    generators...................... 56
Connection, field-spool, reversed.... 142
    d.c., shunt generators for parallel
        operation.............. 51
        motors, illustration........ 39
    switchboard, synchronous, a.c.
        motor...................... 232

Constant-current d.c. generators, see *Generators d.c., constant current.*
Construction of commutating-pole d.c. generators............. 18
principles and characteristics, induction and repulsion a.c. motors.................... 190
Contact, brush, resistance.......... 124
Continuous rating, definition....... 29
Control, armature, objections....... 94
regulator, construction....... 93
speed regulators, operation... 94
d.c. motors with flywheel motor-generator................... 99
definition..................... 1
equipment, motor, a.c., National Electrical Code installation requirements................ 239
float, automatic starters, a.c. pump motors, connecting.. 261
switch. a.c.,single-phase motor. 261
speed, a.c. polyphase, induction motor, by adjusting frequency.......... 258
by adjusting primary voltage............ 254
by changing number of poles.......... 256
of secondary phases. 261
with double primary... 255
motors................. 252
by adjusting resistance of secondary circuit. 252
cascade 257
compound d.c. motor........ 78
primary, a.c., polyphase induction motor............ 255
secondary, a.c. motor........ 253
shunt d.c. motors.......... 77
Controller, drum, rotary or machine-tool type, d.c. motors...... 78
type, advantages............ 80
operation................. 80
magnet-switch, d.c. motors..... 85
regulating, connections, compound-wound d.c. motor... 83
d.c. series motor............. 82
rheostatic.................... 72
Controllers, crane, d.c. motors, arrangement.................... 95
Controlling, devices for a.c. motors.. 239
Copper brushes, reversal of current must be accurately effected....... 113
Crane controllers, d.c. motors, arrangement..................... 95
Cumulative-compound windings for d.c. motors and generators.... 14
-wound d.c. motors, description.. 45
Current, computation, single-phase a.c. motor................ 226
two-phase motor a.c......... 205
cross, a.c. generators, parallel operation................... 184
d.c. motor, to compute........ 48
or voltage, a.c., single-phase generator, kilovolt-amperes output, computation.......... 174
three-phase generator, kilovolt amperes output, computation...................... 174
reversal must be accurately effected, with copper brushes.. 113
starting, a.c. motors........... 200
squirrel-cage inductions a.c. motors, with different impressed voltages using compensator starter. 246

Current, voltage, efficiency, power-factor, a.c. generator, horse-power required to drive, computation............... 172
three-phase generator...... 176–204
Curves, see *Graphs.*

D

Data, performance, d.c. motors..... 34
Delta-star method of starting three-phase, squirrel-cage induction a.c. motors........................ 251
Detector, telephone receiver, used with inducer................... 135
Differential compound-wound d.c. motors, description.......... 45
-compound windings for d.c. motors and generators....... 14
Direct-current generators, see *Generators, d.c.*
power and lighting, compound-wound d.c., generators used for........................... 10
Division, load, compound generators. 13
Drum controllers.................. 80
rotary or machine-tool type, d.c. motors............... 78
Drying out motors and generators... 68
Dummy-fuse connectors........... 292
Dynamic braking, see *Braking dynamic.*
Dynamo, definition................ 1
Dynamos, see *Generators.*

E

Efficiency, computation, single-phase a.c. motor................. 226
two-phase motor, a.c......... 205
d.c. generator, average value.... 32
motor, to compute.......... 48
computation of three-phase motor.................... 204
loss with a.c. induction motor at reduced speeds............ 195
or power factor, kilowatt-ampere output, horse-power required, a.c., three-phase generator, computation................. 175
power factor, voltage or current, a.c., three-phase generator, horse-power required, computation.................... 176
voltage, current, power factor, a.c. generator, horse-power required to drive, computation 172
Electric motor, see *Motor.*
Electromotive force, a.c. generator, how generated.................. 164
Energy ascertained from graphic power record with a planimeter.... 298
Engine, size required to drive a.c. generator................ 177
d.c. generator............ 32
steam, overload capacity....... 33
Equalizer buses, required for three-wire machines............... 58
or equalizer connection, d.c. generator................... 55
Esterline graphic instrument........ 296
Excitation of generator fields....... 2
test, a.c. generator............ 276
Exciter, belt-driven, for vertical water-wheel generator........ 171

Exciter, belt-driven, capacity required examples............ 171
should be ample............. 170
drives......................... 170
Exciters, a.c. generators, characteristics....................... 169
separately-driven, preferable.... 169
Exploring terminal and test lamp, convenient arrangement......... 136

F

Field, a.c., turbo generator......... 161
circuit, open, locating......... 142
coil, d.c. generators or motors, placing................... 65
grounded, how located....... 140
heating causes.............. 142
open-circuited, locating...... 141
d.c. generator, to excite from outside source.............. 60
-discharge switches and resistors. 102
for automatically discharging field circuits, a.c. generators. 171
flux, d.c. motor, test........... 142
generator, excitation of......... 2
magnetic, a.c. induction motor.. 191
polarity, testing.............. 62
relay switches................. 88
rheostat, compound-wound d.c., generators................... 10
shunting, series d.c. motor..... 77
-spool connection, reversed... 142
series, equalizer buses required for three-wire machines...... 58
troubles, a.c. synchronous motor. 235
variation, arc-light, d.c. (constant-current) generator regulated by.................... 5
windings on d.c. generator frames, direction of, illustration...... 15
File for tuning commutator......... 117
Flashing, commutator, sparking.... 130
Flat-compounded compound-wound d.c. generator, definition.......... 9
Float-control automatic starters, a.c. pump motors, connecting..... 261
switch........................ 101
control, a.c. single-phase motor. 261
Flux, action of in commutating-pole d.c. generator.............. 21
distribution in air gap of d.c. generator, variation, illustration of..................... 17
field, d.c. motor, test.......... 142
Flywheel motor-generator control of d.c. motors.............. 99
function...................... 101
Frames, d.c. generator, direction of field windings on, illustration..... 15
Frequencies a.c., polyphase induction motor, performance graph 259
and voltages, different, a.c., polyphase induction motor, performance graph............. 259
a.c. motor operation, effect of changes.................... 196
changer, motor generators...... 301
motor generator, construction. 303
ratio of frequencies........... 304
speed and number of poles, a.c. generator, relation between, formulas..... 164
synchronous induction motor................. 201

Fuse, dummy, connectors........... 292
used with compensator starters. 251
vs. circuit-breaker, advantages and disadvantages........... 76

G

General Electric Co., repulsion induction motor...................... 217
Generator, generators, alternating current.
bearing troubles............. 263
characteristics of exciters..... 169
different types.............. 157
direct-connected, engine-type, illustration............... 159
electromotive force, how generated.................... 164
excitation or magnetization test...................... 276
exciters compound-wound.... 169
field discharge switches and resistors for automatically discharging field circuits... 171
general construction and definition of parts............ 157
horse-power required to drive, voltage, current, efficiency, power factor, computation. 172
how rated.................. 166
hunting.................... 186
prevents parallel operation. 182
inductor, definition.......... 157
insulation resistance test.... 277
kilowatt output, voltage current or power factor, computation.................... 176
locating short-circuited coil... 274
management................. 178
maximum temperature rise... 166
operating in parallel, switchboard diagram............. 184
parallel operation, adjustment of field current.......... 183
cross current.............. 184
division of load........... 182
performance guarantees...... 166
principles, construction and characteristics............. 157
relation between speed, frequency and number of poles, formulas.................. 164
revolving-armature, definition. 157
illustration............... 159
revolving-field, definition..... 157
short-circuited armature coils, "inducer" for locating..... 274
single-phase, current or voltage, kilovolt-amperes output, computation........ 174
elements................. 158
horse-power required to drive based on kilovolt-ampere output, computation.................... 172
kilowatt output, computation.................... 173
principle.................. 165
six-phase, grouping of coils... 167
size engine required to drive.. 177
steam-turbine, illustration.... 160
successful parallel operation, requirements.............. 182
surging..................... 186
synchronizing requirements... 178
synchronous-impedance test.. 276

Generator, generators, alternating
   currnet, testing............ 276
   three-phase................ 167
     armature, methods of con-
       necting................. 168
     connecting armature, dia-
       gram................... 170
     current or voltage, kilovolt-
       amperes output, compu-
       tation 174
     horse-power required to
       drive, kilowatt-ampere
       output, power factor or
       efficiency, computation.. 175
     horse-power required, vol-
       tage, current efficiency or
       power factor, computa-
       tion.................... 176
     large, temperature test..... 278
     load test................. 277
     synchronizing connection for
       more than two.......... 180
     temperature test.......... 279
     to start a single............. 188
     to run in parallel.......... 188
     troubles.................... 263
     turbo, construction.......... 160
       illustration................ 160
       rotor or field.............. 161
       speeds................... 162
       stator or armature, illus-
        tration................. 161
       ventilation................ 162
     two-phase, armature, method
       of connecting............. 168
       diagram.................. 167
       principle................. 166
     vertical waterwheel, belt-
       driven exciter for........ 171
       construction.............. 163
     which is running in parallel,
       to cut out................ 188
     Y-connected, diagram........ 169
   bearing troubles................ 143
   classification of, by poles....... 16
   definition...................... 1
   direct current.
     armature, handling.......... 68
     bipolar, definition........... 15
     commutating-pole, action of
       flux in................. 21
     and compensated, compari-
       son.................... 22
     construction and operation
       of..................... 18
     correct polarity at full-load,
       incorrect polarity at light
       load.................... 66
     operation in multiple....... 59
     principal advantage of...... 16
     to reverse direction of rota-
       tion.................... 60
     commutators, management... 67
     compensated................. 21
     conductors for............ 16
     compound................... 8, 9
       ammeters for.............. 56
       commutating pole, perform-
        ance data.............. 44
       connecting leads for....... 56
       determination of external
        characteristic........... 153
       directions for starting...... 51
       effect on voltage.......... 154
       field rheostat.............. 10
       for power and lighting..... 10

Generator, generators, direct current, compound, getting
     to "pick up".......... 61
   magnetization graph deter-
     mines voltage regulation. 13
   parallel operation of....... 53
   series shunt for components
     of..................... 15
   shutting down when operat-
     ing in parallel........... 52
   to adjust division of load
     between two 56
   constant-current............. 2
     arc-light, regulated by field
       variation............... 5
     automatic regulation....... 3
     regulation of, by brush
       shifting................ 4
   definition...................... 2
   differential and cumulative-
     compound windings....... 14
   drying out.................. 68
   efficiency average value...... 32
   equalizer or equalizer con-
     nection.................... 55
   failure to excite............. 62
     when starting............. 60
   fields, excitation of.......... 2
   flat-compounded compound-
     wound, definition.......... 9
   frame castings, blow holes
     sometimes cause sparking 126
     direction of field windings
       on, illustration.......... 15
   how to reverse direction of
     rotation.................. 59
   long-shunt.................. 11
   magnetization-graph test, how
     conducted................ 151
   management................. 50
     brushes.................... 66
   motor generator, a.c. motor... 302
   multipolar, definition........ 15
     number of brush sets in.... 15
   normally rated, usual overload
     capacity.................. 33
   number of poles............. 15
   operating at different speeds,
     voltage regulation....... 12
     below normal speed........ 14
   operation of shunt and com-
     pound in parallel.......... 57
   over-compounded............ 9
   performance guarantee....... 28
   placing field coils............ 65
   poor connection between com-
     mutator bar and coil leads.. 137
   separately-excited............ 4
   series, application........... 2
     shunt on, form of......... 15
     wound 2
   short-shunt compound-wound. 11
   shunt....................... 6
     exciting current........... 7
     external characteristic test. 154
     operation at constant speed, 7
     parallel operation.......... 50
       connections.............. 51
     -wound, directions for shut-
       ting down.............. 50
     wound for starting...... 50
     voltage of............... 8
   size engine required......... 32
   sources of losses............. 27
   temperature of, effected by
     speed changes........... **14**

Generator, generators, direct current,
    test, loading back method .. 152
    terminal voltage, increase
      due to over-compounding... 13
    testing...................... 148
      for polarity.............. 54
    three-wire, ammeter shunt on. 58
    compound-wound, division
      of series coils........... 25
    connecting balance coils, re-
      quirements of........... 26
    connections, commutating-
      pole.................... 27
    definition................. 22
    equalizer buses required for. 58
    operation in multiple...... 57
    starting and shutting down,
      method................. 53
    switchboard connections.... 58
    time required for building
      up..................... 7
    to compute horse-power input,
      kilowatt output, efficiency 30
    kilowatt output, current, or
      voltage................. 30
    troubles.......,........ 105–112
    two-wire, connections to feed
      three-wire system........ 58
    variation in flux distribution
      in air gap of, illustration of.. 17
    when refuses to excite, pro-
      cedure.................. 61
    windings, danger of over-heat-
      ing when drying.......... 68
  frequency-changer............. 301
  insulation resistance, measure-
    ment...................... 155
  performance specifications for... 1
Glowing and pitting of carbon brushes 126
  brush, causes................. 126
Graph, definition................. 4
  motor, a.c. induction, char-
    acteristic 198
  performance, d.c. series-wound
    method of reading......... 38
  a.c., polyphase induction mo-
    tor, with different frequen-
    cies and voltages.......... 259
    d.c. series motor............ 36
  speed-torque, secondary speed-
    control a.c., induction motor.. 253
Graphic ammeter, example of record. 298
  instrument, one, can be used to
    record inputs to motors of
    various capacities......... 297
  for recording motor power in-
    put tests................. 295
  portable stand for........... 297
  power record, energy ascertained
    with a planimeter.......... 298
Grindstone, to smooth commutator.. 117
Grounded armature coil, test........ 138
  field coil, how located........ 140
Grounds, flying, in d.c. armature
  windings....................... 140
Guarantees, performances, a.c. gen-
    erators................. 166
  motors.................... 197
  d.c. generators............. 28
  temperature rise, a.c. motors.... 197

H

Heating, armature, causes.......... 140
  commutator.................. 115
  field coils, causes.............. 142
  dynamic braking.............. 97

Horse-power, computation, single-
    phase a.c. motor........... 226
  current, voltage, power-factor,
    efficiency three-phase motor. 204
  two-phase motor a.c.......... 205
  formulas, motors.............. 148
  of d.c. motors, effect of torque
    and speed................. 34
  output a.c. motors, test to deter-
    mine..................... 278
    d.c. motor, to compute...... 48
  required, a.c., three-phase gen-
    erator, voltage, current,
    efficiency or power factor,
    computation.............. 176
  of motor, often over-estimated. 288
  to drive a.c. generator, voltage,
    current, efficiency, power
    factor, computation..... 172
  single-phase generator based
    on kilovolt-ampere out-
    put, computation........ 172
  three-phase generator, kilo-
    watt-ampere output,
    power factor or efficiency,
    computation............. 175
Hot box, causes.................... 144
Hunting, a.c. generators........... 186
  induction motors............ 272
  prevention.................. 187
  prevents parallel operation.... 182
  synchronous, a.c. motors....... 237

I

Inducer for locating short-circuited
    a.c. motor or generator arma-
    ture coils................. 274
  principle.................... 133
  telephone receiver detector used
    with.................... 135
Inducing coil, a.c. for localizing arma-
    ture troubles.................... 133
Induction motors, see *Motors, A.C.,
  Induction.*
Input, a.c., single-phase motor,
    measuring................. 279
  to motors of various capacities,
    one graphic instrument can be
    used to record.............. 297
  test, a.c., three-phase motor,
    "two-wattmeter" accu-
    rate method............. 281
    "one-wattmeter" method.. 283
    "one-wattmeter-and-Y-box"
    method................ 284
    polyphase-wattmeter meth-
    od..................... 282
    method where neutral motor
    is brought out........... 285
  motor power, graphic instru-
    ments for recording........ 295
Instruments, graphic, for recording
    motor power input tests.... 295
  portable stand for........... 297
Insulation resistance, see *Resistance,
  Insulation.*
Interpoles, see "*Commutating Poles.*"

K

Kilowatt input, d.c. motor, to compute........................... 48
Kimble single-phase a.c. motors..... 221

L

Lamps, synchronizing.............. 181

Leads, bar and coil, poor connection
    between...................... 137
  coil, crossed, test.............. 139
Lighting compound-wound genera-
    tors used for................... 10
Load, adjustable, d.c. compound gen-
    erator, determination of ex-
    ternal characteristic......... 153
  division, compound generators.. 13
  to adjust between two d.c.,
    compound-wound generators, 56
  power required to drive, to deter-
    mine by test................ 289
  test, d.c. shunt motor.......... 152
  three-phase, a.c. generator.... 277
Long-shunt d.c., generator.......... 11
Losses, d.c. motors and generators,
    sources..................... 27
  testing motor.................. 289
Lug, testing, "forked"............. 294
  test with open hole............ 293

M

Machine-tool, rotary or drum type
    controllers, d.c. motor............ 78
Magnetic field, a.c. induction motor.. 191
  flux, action of, in commutating-
    pole d.c. generator.......... 21
Magnetism, residual, permits shunt
    generator to build up.......... 7
Magnetization, field, determining
    direction................... 63
  graph determines generator vol-
    tage regulation............
  test d.c. motor or generator,
    how conducted............ 151
  test a.c. generator............ 276
Magnet-switch controllers, d.c.
    motors...................... 85
Management, a.c. generators........ 178
  d.c. generators................ 50
  motors, a.c.................... 239
  d.c........................... 70
Mica, actual raising rare occurrence.. 122
  high, identified................ 122
  in commutators.............. 121
Motor, motors, alternating current
    automatic starters, connec-
    tions...................... 260
  bearing troubles.............. 263
  compensating winding......... 213
  compensated induction....... 214
  compensator vs. resistance for
    starting squirrel-cage, a.c.
    motors.................... 245
  control equipment, National
    Electrical Code installation
    requirements.............. 239
  high-voltage, when no-voltage
    release compensator starters
    used for.................. 248
  induction and repulsion, prin-
    ciples, construction and
    characteristics............ 190
  induction, see also *Motors, a.c.
    polyphase, induction.*
  balking.................... 269
  bearings, oil leakage....... 273
  bearing troubles....... 265, 273
  collector-ring troubles...... 271
  connected to compensator,
    will not start........... 271
  construction.............. 191
  current taken at instant of
    starting 194

Motor, motors, alternating current,
    induction current, when run-
    ning without load....... 194
  effects of unbalanced vol-
    tages 270
  efficiency definition........ 194
  factors affecting perform-
    ance................... 194
  hunting................. 272
  improper end play........ 272
  inherently a constant speed
    motor.................. 203
  loss of efficiency at reduced
    speeds................. 195
  low maximum output,
    causes and correction.... 266
  low torque while starting... 265
  magnetic field............ 191
  maximum output, definition 194
  open circuit in field or stator,
    effect.................. 268
  polyphase, primary speed
    control............... 255
  speed control with double
    primary.............. 255
  pull-out torque........... 200
  regenerative feature....... 203
  relation between speed, fre-
    quency number poles.... 201
  rotor, definition.......... 191
  secondary speed-control,
    speed-torque graphs..... 253
  special types............ 192
  squirrel-cage, compared with
    wound rotor.......... 197
  rotor troubles........... 269
  starting compensators... 243
  three-phase, delta-s t a r
    method of starting.... 251
  small started by throwing on
    line.................. 240
  starting compensator
    troubles.............. 270
  methods.............. 240
  stator or primary winding.. 191
  relation between speed, fre-
    quency, number poles.... 201
  winding faults............ 268
  wound rotor, self-contained
    starters.............. 241
  connections of starter.... 241
  operation on, of self-con-
    tained starter......... 242
  starting............... 242
  torque graphs.......... 199
  locating a short-c i r c u i t e d
    coil 274
  management, starting and
    controlling devices for..... 239
  neutralizing winding........ 214
  operation, effect of changes in
    voltage and frequency...... 196
  performance guarantees...... 197
  polyphase, induction, cascade,
    speed control......... 257
  causes of shutdowns..... 264
  circuit-breaker protection. 239
  electrical behavior—same
    as transformer....... 193
  method of starting several
    from one compensator. 250
  performance graph with
    different frequencies
    and voltages......... 259
  speed control by adjust-
    ing frequency..... 258

Motor, motors, alternating current, polyphase speed control, by
  adjusting primary voltage 254
  by changing number of poles 256
  by changing number of secondary phases.. 261
  to reverse direction of rotation. 262
  troubles. 264
  wound-rotor and internal-starting-resistance type, characteristics. 197
  characteristics. 198
  speed control. 252
  by adjusting resistance of secondary circuit.... 252
  squirrel-cage induction, general characteristics. 193
pump, connecting float-control automatic starters. 261
repulsion. 215
  -induction. 216
  arranged for reversing service. 218
  starting induction-running, characteristic graphs. 224
  secondary speed control. 253
short-circuited armature coils, "inducer" for locating. 274
single-phase, classification. 206
  computation of horse-power, current, voltage, power-factor and efficiency. 226
  float switch control. 261
  induction, condenser-compensator method of starting. 211
  develops no starting torque when rotor is not revolving. 207
  performance data. 213
  shading-coil method of starting. 212
  split-phase method of starting. 207
  principle. 209
  used only for small capacity motors. 210
  starting, construction. 208
  torque, starting current speed regulation, single-phase phase-splitting-starting. 210
Kimble. 221
may be operated from any circuit. 228
measuring input. 279
repulsion induction variable speed. 218
  -starting - and - induction running. 219
series. 224
  universal. 225
  variable-speed. 219
slip, speed regulation. 202
squirrel-cage induction, starting currents and starting torques with different impressed voltages using compensator. 246
starting compensators, high voltage large capacity. 247
synchronous. 229
  advantages. 230
  any a.c. generator will operate as. 229

Motor, motors, alternating current, synchronous, bearing troubles. 238
direct-connected exciter, illustration. 230
disadvantages. 231
hunting. 237
improper armature connections. 238
induction motor bring to speed. 233
relation between speed, frequency, number poles 201
limiting, starting current, auto-starters, compensators. 232
methods starting. 232
open circuit in field, effect.. 237
over-heating, causes. 235
polarity. 238
short-circuit in armature, effect. 237
starting. 231
  difficulties. 235
squirrel-cage starting winding. 233
starts but fails to develop sufficient torque procedure.. 235
switchboard connections... 232
temperature test. 278-279
troubles, summary of. 234
uses. 231
testing. 276
three-phase, accurate input test, "two-wattmeter" method 281
coil, wound rotor, starting arrangement. 243
computation of horse-power, current, voltage, power-factor, efficiency. 204
determination of input by voltmeter and ammeter method, test. 280
induction, temperature test. 286
input test, method where neutral motor is brought out. 285
polyphase-wattmeter method. 282
"one-wattmeter" method 283
"one-wattmeter- and- Y-box" method. 284
troubles. 263
two-phase, computation of horse-power, current, voltage, power-factor, efficiency 205
vertical, induction, cement-mill, construction. 192
Wagner repulsion-starting-and -induction-running. 222
wound-rotor, starting switch troubles. 265
and its starter, National Electrical Code protection rules.. 76
an inverted generator. 70
bearings, grooves to prevent oil leakage. 274
bearing troubles. 143
Motor, motors, direct current.
adjustable speed, classification 47
armature, handling. 68
automatic starter. 83
brush glowing and pitting, remedy. 114
commutating-pole, overload capacity. 34

Motor, motors, direct current.
  commutating pole, principal
    advantage of 16
  shunt, speed regulation 41
  commutation determines over-
    load capacity 34
  compound, connections of
    regulating controller 83
    speed characteristics 44
    control 78
    -wound, differential and
      cumulative, description . . 45
  construction 33
  control, armature, disadvan-
    tages 94
    rheostat 70
    with flywheel motor-genera-
      tor 99
  controller, magnet-switch 85
  crane controllers, arrangement 95
  differential and cumulative-
    compound windings 14
  directions for starting 72
    stopping 73
  drying out 68
  dynamic braking 97
  field flux, test 142
  frame castings, blow holes
    sometimes cause sparking . . 126
  horse-power output 34
  how to reverse direction of
    rotation 59
  magnetization-graph test, how
    conducted 151
  management and starting and
    controlling devices 70
    brushes and commutator . . . 66
  motor-generator with a.c.
    generators 302
  multipolar, definition 15
  multi-switch starter 84
  non-automatic-starting and
    speed-adjusting rheostat . . . 81
  performance data 29, 34
    graphs, series-wound method
      of reading 38
    guarantees 29
  placing field coils 65
  poor connection between bar
    and coil leads 137
  procedure when it will not start
    when starting box is operated 142
  pressure - regulator - control,
    automatic starter, connec-
    ting regulator, speed-arma-
    ture control 102
  reliance adjustable-speed, il-
    lustration 42
  rheostat arrangement of one
    starting and speed ad-
    justing for control of two
    motors 92
  shunt- and compound-
    wound, starting and
    speed adjusting (field-
    control) 89
  rotary, drum or machine-tool
    type controllers 78
  runs in wrong direction, pro-
    cedure 142
  series, performance graph 36
    regulating controller 82
    shunt, compound, speed
      characteristics 34
    and series-wound, start-
      ing rheostats 47

Motor, motors, direct current,
  series, shunted armature con-
    nection 77
  series and compound-wound,
    speed characteristics,
    graphic comparison 46
  shunting field 77
  speed at no-load 38
  speed-torque characteristics . 37
  speed variation with load . . . 76
  shunt, effect shifting brushes
    on speed 41
    illustration, connections 39
    speed characteristics 40
  load and speed test 152
  series and compound, con-
    nection diagrams 73
  speed characteristics 42
    control 77
  temperature test, loading
    back method 152
  speed, definition 35
    proportional to voltage 34
    regulation, effect of com-
      mutating poles 46
    variation, definition 35
  starting panels 75
    rheostat 71
    with multi-switch starter 85
  sources of losses 27
  testing 148
  to compute kilowatt input,
    horse-power, output, effi-
    ciency, impressed voltage or
    current 48
  torque, proportional to field
    conductors and current 34
  troubles 105–112
    brush glowing and pitting . . 114
Motor-drive power, test 288
Motor-generator, a.c. generator d.c.
  motor 302
  definition and construction 301
  flywheel, equalizer, control of
    d.c. motors 99
  function 101
  frequency changer, construction 303
    changes 301
  induction-motor drive 302
  synchronous-motor drive 302
Motor, horsepower determined with
  prony brake 149
  required, often over-estimated. 288
  torque and speed formulas . . . 148
  induction, computation of slip . . 202
  drive, motor generator 302
  insulation resistance, measure-
    ment 155
  nameplate 148
  output, to determine 148
  portable, arranged to determine
    power required by machines . . 290
  power input tests, graphic instru-
    ments for recording 295
  required, importance of accur-
    ate determination 288
  of various capacities, inputs, one
    graphic instrument can be used
    to record 297
  synchronous, drive for motor
    generator 302
  testing, connections 292
    losses 289
  test, portable, workable arrange-
    ments 290
  equipped with counter shaft 291

Motor, torque, function............ 101
    vertical, ball bearings. 146
Multiplolar generators d.c., number
    of brush sets................. 15
    machine, definition............ 15
Multi-switch starter, starting d.c.
    motor...................... 85
    d.c. motors.................. 84

N

Nameplate, motors................ 148
National Electrical Code require-
    ments, a.c. motor, control
    equipment, installation....... 239
Rules, protection of motor and
    starter.................... 76
Neutralizing winding a.c. motor.... 214
Noise caused by armature unbalance. 146

O

Oil leakage, a.c., induction motor
    bearings.................. 273
    motor bearings, grooves to
    prevent.................. 274
    rings, bearing, to prevent stick-
    ing...................... 144
Open-circuited field coil, locating.... 141
    circuits, flying in d.c. armature
    windings................. 140
Operation of commutating-pole, d.c.
    generators................. 18
    of non-automatic-starting and
    speed-adjusting rheostat..... 82
    parallel, a.c. generators, division
    of load.................. 182
    d.c., shunt generators........ 50
    successful, a.c. generators,
    requirements............. 182
Output, a.c. motors test to determine. 278
    kilovolt-amperes current or vol-
    tage, a.c., single-phase
    generator, computation 174
    three-phase generator,
    computation........... 174
    power factor or efficiency,
    three-phase, a.c. generator
    horse-power required, com-
    putation.............. 175
    kilowatt a.c., single-phase gen-
    erator, computation....... 173
    voltage, current or power
    factor, a.c. generators, com-
    putation............... 176
    low maximum, a.c., induction
    motors, causes and correction. 266
    of d.c. motors, effect of torque
    and speed................ 34
    of motor, to determine........ 148
Over-compounded d.c. generator.... 9

P

Panels, starting, d.c. motors......... 75
Parallel operation, a.c. generators,
    division of load............. 182
    hunting prevents............. 182
    successful, a.c. generators, re-
    quirements............. 182
Performance data, compound-wound
    d.c. commutating-pole gen-
    erators................. 28
    d.c. motors.................. 34
    single-phase a.c. induction
    motor................... 213
    graph d.c. series motors........ 36

Performance data, guarantees, a.c.
    generators................ 166
    a.c. motors................. 197
    d.c. generators.............. 28
    specifications for generators..... 1
Phasing out........................ 179
    three-phase circuits........... 180
Pitting and glowing of carbon brushes 126
Planimeter, energy ascertained from
    graphic power record............ 298
Polarity, field coil, illustration...... 63
    testing................... 62
    synchronous a.c. motors........ 238
    tester, field, inductive.......... 64
    testing for, d.c. generators...... 54
Polarities, commutating-pole wind-
    ings, determining............. 66
Pole, classification of d.c. generators. 16
    commutating, object........... 17
    windings of................. 20
    number on d.c. generators...... 15
    relation between speed and
    frequency, a.c. synchronous
    induction motors.......... 201
    speed and frequency, a.c.
    generator, relation between,
    formulas................ 164
Polyphase induction motors, see
    Motors, polyphase-induction.
Polyphase motors, see *Motors, a.c.,
    polyphase.*
Power-factor, computation single-
    phase a.c. motor.......... 226
    two-phase motor a.c.......... 205
    efficiency, horse-power, current,
    voltage, computation of,
    three-phase motor......... 204
    voltage or current, a.c. three-
    phase generator, horse-power
    required, computation..... 176
    low, results................. 230
    synchronous motor corrects... 230
    or efficiency, kilowatt-ampere
    output, horse-power required,
    a.c. three-phase generator,
    computation.............. 175
    voltage, current, efficiency, a.c.
    generator, horse-power re-
    quired to drive, computa-
    tion.................... 172
    voltage or current, kilowatt out-
    put, a.c. generator, compu-
    tation.................. 176
Power, motor-drive, test............ 288
    motor, input tests, graphic in-
    struments for recording.... 295
    required, importance of accur-
    ate determination......... 288
    record, graphic, energy ascer-
    tained with a planimeter..... 298
    required, to drive machine test
    for procedure............ 291
    to drive a load, to determine
    by test................. 289
Pressure, carbon brush............ 124
    -regulator-control, d.c. motor,
    automatic starter, connecting. 102
Primary or stator winding, a.c. in-
    duction motor................ 191
Principles, construction and char-
    acteristics, induction and repulsion
    a.c. motors................. 190
Prony brake, different forms...... 149
    motor horse-power determined
    with........................ 149
    torque concept basis........... 149

Pull-out torque, a.c. induction motor. 200

Q

Quarter-phase, see *Two-phase*.

R

Rack for d.c. armatures............ 147
Record, graphic power, energy ascertained with a planimeter......... 298
Regenerative feature, a.c. induction
  motor......................... 203
Regulating controller, see *Controller,
  regulating*.
Regulation, automatic, of d.c. constant-current generator....... 3
  of d.c. constant-current genera-
    tor by brush shifting........ 4
  speed, a.c. induction motors.... 202
  commutating-pole, d.c. shunt
    motor..................... 41
  d.c. motors, effect of commu-
    tating poles.............. 46
  definition................... 35
  how expressed.............. 35
  voltage, compound d.c. genera-
    tor magnetization graph
    determines.............. 13
  d.c., generator operating at
    different speeds.......... 12
  definition................... 1
Regulator, armature control, construction................... 93
  speed, armature c o n t r o l, 93
  operation................... 94
Reliance d.c. adjustable speed motor. 42
Repulsion, induction motor, see
  Motor, a.c. repulsion induction.
Repulsion motors, see *Motors, a.c.,
  repulsion*.
Resistance, brush contact......... 124
  for starting squirrel-cage a.c.
    motors.................... 245
  insulation, generators and motors,
    measurement............. 155
  complete machine, method of
    increasing............... 155
  measured with high-resistance
    voltmeter................ 155
  test, a.c. generators........ 277
Resistors and switches, field discharge,
  for automatically discharging
  field circuits, a.c. generators.. 171
  field-discharge............. 102
Rheostat controller............. 72
  field, compound-wound d.c.,
    generators............... 10
  non-automatic starting and
    speed-adjusting, d.c. motors. 81
  non-automatic-s t a r t i n g and
    speed-adjusting, operation... 82
  starting and speed-adjusting,
    arrangement of one for
    control of two d.c.
    motors................. 92
  construction............. 89
  (f i e l d -control, for d.c.
    shunt and compound
    motors................. 89
  operation............... 92
  starting, arcing devices....... 74
  d.c. motor............... 71
  low-voltage release device.... 74
  overload release device...... 75
  shunt-, compound- and series-
    wound d.c. motors........ 74

Ring fire, sparking................ 128
Rings, oil, to prevent sticking....... 144
Rotary, drum or machine-tool type
  controllers, d.c. motors......... 78
Rotor, a.c. induction motor, definition 191
  or field, a.c., turbo generator.... 161
  troubles, a.c., induction, squirrel-
    cage motors.................. 269

S

Sandpaper, to smooth commutators. 118
Segments, commutator, loose....... 115
Separately excited d.c. generator, see
  Generators, d.c., separately excited.. 4
Series fields, equalizer buses required
  for three-wire machines...... 58
  generators, see *Generators, d.c.,
    series wound*.
  motor, see *Motors, d.c., series
    wound*.
  shunt for compound-wound gen-
    erators, components of..... 15
  on d.c. machines, form of..... 15
  -wound d.c., armatures, number
    of brush sets in.......... 15
  generators, see *Generators,
    d.c., series wound*.
  motors, see *Motors, d.c.,
    series wound*.
Shading-coil method of starting a.c.
  induction motors............. 212
Short-circuited a.c. motor or generator armature coils, "inducer"
  for locating................. 274
  -circuits, armature, test........ 138
  flying, in d.c. armature wind-
    ings..................... 140
  -shunt d.c., compound-wound
    generator................ 11
Shunt d.c., generators, parallel operation, connections............ 51
  dynamo, see *Generator, shunt*.
  motor, see *Motors, d.c., shunt
    wound*.
  series, for compound-wound gen-
    erators, components of..... 15
  on d.c. machines, form of.... 15
Shunt-wound generators, see *Generators, d.c., shunt wound*.
Shunted armature connection, series
  d.c. motor................... 77
Shunting field, series d.c. motor..... 77
Shutdowns, causes, a.c., polyphase
  induction motors............. 264
Single-phase a.c. motors, see *Motors,
  a.c., single-phase*.
  generator, see *Generator, a.c.,
    single phase*.
Six-phase a.c. generators, grouping
  of coils..................... 167
Slip, a.c. induction motors......... 202
  computation of.............. 202
Slotted commutator, see *Commutator
  slotted*.
Slotting, commutators............. 119
  reason..................... 120
  what it accomplishes......... 120
Sparking, blow holes in frame castings sometimes cause........ 126
  brush, causes.............. 125
  due to open armature circuit.... 128
  rough commutator......... 114
  ring fire................... 128
Specifications, performance, for generators....................... 1

Speed-adjusting and starting rheostats, see *Rheostats, Speed ad-*
  justing and starting.
  characteristics, c o m p o u n d-
    wound, d.c. motor......... 44
  d.c. motors, series, shunt, com-
    pound.................. 34
    shunt motors............. 42
    illustration............. 40
  series and compound-wound
    motors, graphic compari-
    son.................... 46
  control, a.c., polyphase, induc-
    tion motor by adjusting
    frequency............ 258
    by adjusting primary
      voltage............... 254
    by changing number of
      secondary phases.... 261
      poles................. 256
    with double primary..... 255
    motors.................. 252
    by adjusting resistance of
      secondary circuit...... 252
    cascade induction motor   257
    compound d.c. motors....... 78
    primary, a.c., polyphase, in-
      duction motor............ 255
    secondary, a.c. motor....... 253
    shunt d.c. motors........... 77
  d.c. motors proportional to vol-
    tage................ 34
    variation................. 35
    series motor, no-load........ 38
  formulas, motors.............. 148
  frequency and number of poles,
    a.c. generator, relation
    between, formulas..... 164
    synchronous induction
      motor................ 201
  motor, definition.............. 35
  normal, d.c. generator operating
    below.................... 14
  regulation, a.c. induction motor,
    slip.................... 202
  commutating-pole, shunt, d.c.
    motor.................... 41
    definition.................. 35
    d.c. motors, effect of commuta-
      ting poles............... 46
    how expressed............. 35
    single-phase a.c. induction
      motor, phase-splitting-start-
      ing..................... 210
  regulators, armature control.... 93
    operation.................. 94
  test, d.c. shunt motor......... 152
  -torque characteristics of series
    d.c. motor............... 37
    graphs, secondary speed-con-
      trol a.c., induction motor... 253
    turbo alternators............. 162
    variation, motor, definition.... 35
    with load d.c. series-wound
      motors................. 76
Speeds, different, voltage regulation
  of d.c. generator............ 12
Squirrel-cage induction motors, see
  Motors, a.c., induction,
  squirrel-cage.
  starting windings, a.c. synchro-
    nous motor................ 233
Stand, portable, graphic instruments. 297
Starters, automatic, a.c. motors, con-
  nections................... 260

Starters, float-control, a.c. pump motors connecting............ 261
  pressure-regulator-control, d.c.
    motor, connecting......... 102
  connections, wound motor a.c.
    induction rotor.............. 241
  motor, automatic, principle..... 83
  multi-switch, d.c. motors....... 84
    starting d.c. motor.......... 85
  self-contained, wound rotor a.c.
    induction motors............ 241
Starting, a.c., induction wound rotor
    motor.................... 242
    methods.................... 240
  and speed adjusting rheostats,
    see *Rheostats, starting and*
    speed adjusting.
  arrangement, three-phase coil-
    wound rotor a.c. motor....... 243
  compensators for induction mo-
    tors, a.c., see *Compensators,*
    starting.
  current, a.c. motors........... 200
    single-phase, a.c. induction
      motor, phase-splitting-start-
      ing..................... 210
    squirrel-cage induction a.c.
      motors, with different im-
      pressed voltages using com-
      pensator starter........... 246
  devices for a.c. motors........ 239
  panels, d.c. motors........... 75
  rheostat, see *Rheostat, starting.*
  single-phase a.c. induction motor,
    split-phase method.......... 207
  small a.c. induction motor, by
    throwing on line............ 240
  switch troubles, a.c., wound-
    rotor motors................ 265
  synchronous a.c. motor........ 231
  three-phase, squirrel-cage a.c.
    induction motors, delta-star
    method.................... 251
  torque, a.c. motors........... 200
  torques, squirrel-cage induction
    a.c. motors, with different im-
    pressed voltages using com-
    pensator starter............ 246
Stator a.c., or armature turbo generator, illustration.............. 161
  or primary winding, a.c. induc-
    tion motor................. 191
Steam engine, overload capacity.... 33
  turbine, operates at high speeds. 162
Surging, a.c. generators........... 186
Switchboard connections, three-wire
  d.c. generators.............. 58
Switchboards, synchronous a.c. motor 232
  diagram, generators operating in
    parallel.................... 184
Switch, centrifugal, single-phase induction motor.............. 209
  control, float, a.c. single-phase
    motor.................... 261
  float....................... 101
  knife, for shunting out ammeter 294
  starting, troubles, a.c. wound-
    rotor motors................ 265
  tank....................... 101
Switches, field-discharge........... 102
  and resistors for automatic-
    ally discharging field cir-
    cuits, a.c. generators...... 171
  field relay.................. 88
  not placed in circuits connecting
    collector rings to balance coils. 29

Sychronizing, a.c. generators requirements...................... 178
connections, more than two three
phase generators............ 180
dark or light, comparison....... 181
definition..................... 178
lamps......................... 181
single-phase circuit with lamps,
principle.................. 178
with lamps, circuits for......... 179
Synchronous condensers, see *Condensers a.c. synchronous*....... 229
impedance test, a.c. generator... 276
motors, see *Motors a.c., synchronous.*
Synchroscopes.................. 182

T

Tank switch..................... 101
Telephone receiver detector used with
inducer....................... 135
Temperature, ambient, definition.. 166
d.c., generator effected by speed
changes.................... 14
rise, maximum, a.c. generators.. 166
test, a.c., three-phase induction
motor.................... 286
d.c. shunt motor or generator,
loading back method...... 152
large three phase, a.c. generator or synchronous motor.. 278
three-phase a.c. generator or
synchronous motor....... 279
Terminal, exploring, and test lamp,
convenient arrangement........ 136
Test, a.c., three-phase motor, determination of input by voltmeter
and ammeter method....... 280
armature, "bar to bar"........ 138
short-circuits............... 138
excitation or magnetization, a.c.
generator.................... 276
external characteristic of shunt
d.c. generator.............. 154
input, a.c., three-phase motor,
a c c u r a t e "watt-
meter" method....... 28
method where neutral
motor is brought out.. 285
"one-wattmeter-and-Y-
box" method........ 284
"one-wattmeter" method 283
polyphase-wattmeter
method.............. 282
motor power, graphic instruments for recording....... 295
insulation resistance, a.c. generators....................... 277
load and speed, d.c. shunt motor 152
three-phase, a.c. generator... 277
lug, with open hole............ 293
magnetization-graph, d.c. motor
or generator, how conducted.. 151
motor-drive power............. 288
motors, portable, workable arrangements................ 290
of power required to drive machine, procedure............. 291
open armature circuits........ 137
polarity, field................. 64
practical determination of torque
required to drive or start a load 299
synchronous-impedance, a.c.gen-
erator..................... 276
temperature, a.c., three-phase
induction motor........... 286

Test, temperature, d.c. shunt motor
or generator, loading back
method................... 152
large three-phase, a.c. generator or synchronous motor.. 278
three-phase a.c. generator or
synchronous a.c. motor.... 279
to determine horse-power output
and torque, a.c. motors.... 278
power required to drive a load. 289
lamp and exploring terminal,
convenient arrangement...... 136
Testing a.c. generators and motors.. 276
armatures where only a.c. or low-
voltage cells are available.. 132
with high-voltage a.c......... 132
d.c. generators and motors...... 148
lug, "forked"................. 294
motor, connections............ 292
losses..................... 289
Three-phase generator, see *Generator,
a.c. single-phase.*
Three-wire generators, see *Generators,
d.c., three wire.*
Torque, a.c., motors test to determine 278
d.c. motors, effect of field, conductors and current on....... 34
formulas, motors.............. 148
low, starting a.c., induction
motors..................... 265
motor, function............... 101
prony brake concept, basis for.. 149
pull-out a.c. induction motor... 200
required for belt drive, determination with a spring balance..................... 299
to drive or start a load, practical test determination.... 299
single-phase a.c. induction motor,
phase-splitting-starting...... 210
speed, graphs, secondary speed-
control a.c., induction motor.. 253
starting, a.c. motors........... 200
single-phase a.c. induction
motor developes no, when
its rotor is not revolving... 207
squirrel-cage induction a.c.
motors, with different impressed voltages using compensator starter........... 246
when a.c. synchronous motor
starts but fails to develop
sufficient, procedure........ 235
Troubles, a.c. generators and motors. 263
bearing, a.c. generators and
motors.................. 263
induction motors.......... 265
motors and generators....... 143
synchronous a.c. motors...... 238
field, a.c. synchronous motor... 235
starting switch, a.c., wound-rotor
motors.................... 265
synchronous a.c. motor, summary..................... 234
Truing commutator with file........ 118
Turbo generator, see *Generator, a.c.
turbo.*
Two-phase generator, see *Generator,
a.c. single-phase.*

U

Universal motor, a.c., single-phase.. 225

V

Ventilation, turbo alternators..... 162

318 *INDEX*

Vertical waterwheel generator, a.c.,
  construction.................... 163
Voltage, a.c. motor operation, effect
  of changes.................. 196
  computation single.phase a.c.
    motor.................... 226
  two-phase motor a.c......... 205
  current, efficiency or power
    factor, a.c., three-phase
    generator, horse-power
    required, computation. 176
  generator, horse-power re-
    quired to drive, com-
    putation............. 172
  power factor, kilowatt output,
    a.c. generator, computation. 176
  drop, due to contact resistance,
    increased if fit of brushes or
    commutator is poor........ 125
  impressed, d.c. motor, to com-
    pute...................... 48
  or current, a.c., single-phase gen-
    erator, kilovolt-amperes out-
    put, computation.......... 174
  three-phase generator, kilo-
    volt-amperes output, com-
    putation.................. 174
  power-factor, efficiency horse-
    power current, computation of,
    three-phase motor.......... 204
  regulation, definition........... 1
  d.c. generator operating at
    different speeds........... 12
  shunt-wound d.c., generators... 8
  terminal, increase due to over-
    compounding............... 13

Voltages and frequencies, different,
  a.c., polyphase induction motor performance graph....... 259
Voltages unbalanced, a.c., induction
  motors, effects.. 270
Voltmeter, high-resistance, insulation resistance measured with.... 155

W

Wagner repulsion-starting-and-induction-running a.c. motor...... 222
Water-cooled machinery, standard
  temperature ratings............. 30
Waterwheel generator, vertical a.c.,
  construction.................... 163
Wattmeters, graphic ammeters used
  instead......................... 296
Winding, commutating poles........ 20
  faults, a.c., induction motors...... 268
  stator or primary, a.c. induction
    motor....................... 191
Windings, armature, d.c., flying
    grounds, short-circuits and
    open circuits............... 140
  commutating-pole, determining
    polarities.................. 66
  cumulative-and-differential-com-
    pound, for d.c. machines..... 14
  danger of overheating when dry-
    ing......................... 68
  differential-and-cumulative-com-
    pound, for d.c. machines..... 14
  field, on d.c. generator frames,
    direction of, illustration...... 15
Wound-rotor a.c. motors, see *Motors,
  a.c., wound-rotor.*